POPULATION
STATISTICS
AND THEIR
COMPILATION

POPULATION STATISTICS
AND
THEIR COMPILATION

Revised Edition

BY

HUGH H. WOLFENDEN

Fellow of the Institute of Actuaries, Great Britain
Fellow of the Society of Actuaries
Fellow of the Royal Statistical Society

WITH AN APPENDIX ON

Some Theory in the Sampling
of Human Populations

BY

W. EDWARDS DEMING, Ph.D.

PUBLISHED FOR THE SOCIETY OF ACTUARIES
BY
THE UNIVERSITY OF CHICAGO PRESS
1954

THE UNIVERSITY OF CHICAGO PRESS, CHICAGO 37
Cambridge University Press, London, N.W. 1, England
The University of Toronto Press, Toronto 5, Canada

FOREWORD

The first edition of this book, by the same author, was published by the Actuarial Society of America in 1925. In preparing this second edition the author has changed the text materially by bringing historical and other data up to date, by thorough revision throughout, and by many additions to the text which embody a number of developments, especially recent ones. The value of the work has thereby been increased substantially.

The Society of Actuaries, as successor to the Actuarial Society of America, appreciates the opportunity to publish this book. Reflecting the author's long and intensive study in the field of population statistics, this book has the added value of his wide practical experience in that field. This volume should be of great assistance to students who wish to acquire a mastery of both the elementary and advanced aspects of this subject. We believe that it will be consulted by demographers outside the actuarial profession as well as by actuaries.

The Society gratefully acknowledges the author's devotion to his profession in contributing so much of his time and effort to this publication.

JOHN R. LARUS, *President*
Society of Actuaries

PREFACE

A considerable number of major developments have occurred in the theoretical and practical problems involved in the compilation of population statistics since this book was first published under its present title, as "Actuarial Study No. 3," by the Actuarial Society of America in 1925. This new edition accordingly has been re-written and enlarged throughout, in order to incorporate the necessary descriptions and references covering that new material.

In Section II the history of census-taking has been dealt with more fully in the light of various papers which have appeared since 1925, and the details concerning modern censuses have been brought up to date. Similarly the discussion of registrations of births, deaths, and marriages in Section III includes recent contributions. Section IV, on the reliability of census and registration statistics and the nature of the errors therein, also now gives data which have become available for various countries since publication of the first edition, and the extent of under-enumeration and under-registration is considered. In Section V emphasis is given to the importance of preliminary adjustments for errors of age under some circumstances, and the treatment of population estimates includes an examination of the elusive problem of projections.

Section VI, dealing with the mathematical relationships between births, deaths, and populations, and the resulting formulae for the rates of mortality, now includes formula (18a) devised by Moriyama and Greville, and has been enlarged with additional explanations and proofs. This latter material has been brought in to emphasize the importance of the device by which the assumptions of uniform distributions can be stated in terms of probabilities, and to direct attention more effectively to the very easy and rapid manner in which the mortality formulae based on the uniformity assumptions can be reached by the use of a simple Lemma—both of which methods were first stated in my paper in T.A.S.A., XXIV, 126, from which the explanations have been taken.

Some further history has been included in Section VII on the construction of mortality tables, and the latest methods used in Great Britain and the United States have been added to the descriptions previously given. In this chapter the construction of population tables is discussed, necessarily, in the light of the fact that it also involves inherently the problem of "graduation"—the two processes of construction and graduation being practically inseparable in such work, in contrast with their almost distinct

vii

nature in the actuarial problem of preparing tables from the records of insured lives. The errors in population data are so varied, and their correction
demands at many stages the use of methods of such special types, that it
is not possible for a student to comprehend the questions which are posed
in these procedures unless the graduation principles are studied carefully
and are well understood. The graphic method, curve fitting, tangential
and osculatory interpolation, and linear compounding coefficients which
minimize the mean square error in a specified order of differences are
therefore all described with details which it is hoped will be sufficient to
enable the student to grasp the underlying principles and so equip himself
with the means of choosing appropriate methods under any practical
conditions he may meet.

Formulae recently suggested have been incorporated in Section VIII
on the construction of abridged life tables, and slight amplifications
have been made in Section IX on the methods of comparing the mortalities of different communities. A new chapter on the forecasting of mortality rates has been included as Section X. The discussions of mortality by
cause of death in Section XI, occupational mortality in Section XII, and
the use of census and registration data in the compilation of statistics relating to marriages, births, orphanhood, unemployment, etc., in Section
XIII, have been enlarged.

In this edition a new Section XIV dealing with the modern theory of
reproductivity has been inserted, with the object of explaining the principles and limitations of gross and net reproduction rates and the inherent
rate of natural increase. The final Section XV on sickness data now includes references to recent standard diagnosis and classification codes.

In the belief that students are assisted materially when methods are
identified by the names of their originators, the Table of Contents has
been compiled in more detailed form than in the first edition (thus in
effect eliminating the necessity for an index also) with the appropriate
names attached to original and important contributions.

Throughout these enlargements of the original edition, special attention has been paid to the needs of actuarial and other students as those
needs have been revealed during a long experience of lecturing on this
subject to students at the Actuarial Society and elsewhere. If a student is
to be considered well informed, it is not sufficient for him to assume, for
example, that some particular formula, however great its supposed authority may be, can be applied in any practical circumstances without a
careful examination of rival methods. Furthermore, the underlying principles and genesis of each process must be fully understood. Without

such knowledge, a student cannot assess the conditions proper for each method's application, and—even more importantly—he will not be aware of the circumstances in which it should not be used. The rapid and undiscriminating presentation of so-called routine methods thus can never constitute good or adequate education; any attempt to "teach" a subject such as this in capsule form, or in a prescribed and curtailed number of pages or hours, can produce only insufficient preparation full of pitfalls waiting to engulf the uninformed. Hard work and concentrated thinking —both of which take time and effort—will always be essential in the handling of technical procedures which naturally demand knowledge, judgment, and experience in their practical applications.

In conformity with this objective of maintaining thoroughness in our educational programs, references are given in the appropriate places to my companion volume on "The Fundamental Principles of Mathematical Statistics (with Special Reference to the Requirements of Actuaries and Vital Statisticians, and An Outline of a Course in Graduation)," which was published by the Macmillan Company of Canada for the Actuarial Society of America, New York (now the Society of Actuaries, Chicago), in 1942. In that volume readers will find explanations of many portions of the underlying mathematical theories which are too extensive for restatement here. As was remarked in the Preface to that book, history is not ignored—for it is, in my belief, "essential to the proper understanding of any subject to absorb the history of the mental processes which have guided its development." Detailed references also are given in both these volumes, so that students and research workers may be able, without frustrations, to find original and more elaborate sources on difficult or challenging points which inevitably arise in the minds of all enquiring readers in subjects of this kind.

The entirely new Appendix on Sampling has been written on my invitation by Dr. W. Edwards Deming. His acknowledged pre-eminence in that field made it especially appropriate that he should be the one to prepare a condensed statement of the theory for inclusion in this volume. My thanks in full measure are due to him for his cordial assistance.

Dr. Thomas N. E. Greville, F.S.A., has collaborated most generously and effectively in the preparation of material for this book dealing with those aspects of population statistics on which he has written so many original and valuable papers. Mr. Robert J. Myers, F.S.A., similarly has made notable contributions on several matters, and, like Dr. Greville, has made a critical reading of almost the whole of the completed manuscript. Dr. Deming's Appendix, to which earlier reference has been made, was prepared in the same co-operative spirit. And the final arrangements for publication have been assisted most significantly by Mr. Wilmer A. Jenkins, F.S.A. (as Chairman of a Special Committee of the Society of Actuaries, which included also Messrs. E. W. Marshall, A. Pedoe, R. G. Stagg, and J. S. Thompson). To all of these collaborators I wish to record my appreciation for their interest and invaluable help.

HUGH H. WOLFENDEN

TABLE OF CONTENTS

xi

APPENDIX

SOME THEORY IN THE SAMPLING OF HUMAN POPULATIONS

By W. Edwards Deming, Ph.D.

SECTION

1. The Reasons for Sampling

2. Uses of Sample Surveys

3. Some of the Uses of Sampling in Connection with Censuses of Population

4. Definitions: Frame, Sampling Unit, Probability Sample, Estimate, Standard Error, Bias, Population, Sample Design

5. The Aim of Sample Design

6. Random Variables; Random Numbers; The Mean of the Universe (μ), and Its Variance (σ^2), Standard Deviation (σ), and Coefficient of Variation (γ)

REFERENCES AND ABBREVIATIONS

The references throughout the text to "The Fundamental Principles of Mathematical Statistics" are to the companion volume by Hugh H. Wolfenden, published by the Macmillan Company of Canada, Toronto, for the Actuarial Society of America—now the Society of Actuaries, 208 South La Salle Street, Chicago—entitled *The Fundamental Principles of Mathematical Statistics (with Special Reference to the Requirements of Actuaries and Vital Statisticians, and An Outline of a Course in Graduation)*.

The following abbreviations are used:

J.I.A. . . . . . . Journal of the Institute of Actuaries (Great Britain).
T.F.A. . . . . . . Transactions of the Faculty of Actuaries (Scotland).
T.A.S.A. . . . . . Transactions of the Actuarial Society of America.
R.A.I.A. . . . . . Record of the American Institute of Actuaries.
T.S.A. . . . . . . Transactions of the Society of Actuaries.
J.R.S.S. . . . . . Journal of the Royal Statistical Society (Great Britain).
J.A.S.A. . . . . . Journal of the American Statistical Association.

I

INTRODUCTORY

1. The statistical or collective study of human life, or, as it is called, the science of Demography, may be considered as including the following subdivisions (see "Vital Statistics," by G. C. Whipple):

(1) Genealogy, which deals with individual ancestries and personal records.

(2) Human Eugenics, which investigates heredity from a scientific standpoint and is to a large extent the application of statistical method to genealogy.

(3) The Census, that is, the collection of physical, social, political, religious, and educational facts concerning population, usually by the method of governmental enumeration.

(4) The Registration of vital facts, such as those concerning birth, marriage, divorce, sickness, and death, usually under governmental direction and by use of individual records.

(5) Vital Statistics, i.e., the application of statistical methods to the study of these facts.

(6) Biometrics, which includes anthropometric studies of human growth, stature, strength, etc.

(7) Pathometrics, or statistical pathology, which includes the detailed study of diseases and their relations to the human body. These facts are obtained largely in hospitals, by health department laboratories, and by life insurance companies.

The following study will be devoted entirely to (3), (4), and (5) above.

VALUE OF STUDY OF VITAL STATISTICS

2. The Census is a national inventory, and is required primarily for the adjustment of representation in legislative bodies. The information gathered is also of great value to commerce and industry, and in many of the administrative problems of governments. Registrations of births, marriages, and deaths are essential as a means of preserving evidence of personal status, in order to establish the individual's identity, age, citizenship, and marital condition for the proper determination of the various rights and obligations which arise in connection with life insurance, pension plans, social security, employment, passports, military service,

1

public assistance, etc., and in the settlement of estates and inheritances. Moreover, when taken in conjunction with the census tabulations, they are of great statistical importance in many social investigations and enterprises undertaken by governmental or private agencies on both national and local bases, and they frequently provide invaluable material for the guidance of public health authorities as well as for the construction by actuaries of mortality and other tables based on statistics of the general population.

3. The desirability of a comprehensive system of social statistics is well stated in the following quotations which are given in a booklet "The Story of the Census, 1790–1916," published by the United States Census Bureau. In a speech delivered so long ago as 1869, in connection with a bill to provide for the taking of the Ninth Census of the United States, President James A. Garfield said:

"The developments of statistics are causing history to be rewritten. Till recently, the historian studied nations in the aggregate, and gave us only the story of princes, dynasties, sieges, and battles. Of the people themselves—the great social body, with life, growth, forces, elements, and laws of its own—he told us nothing. Now, statistical inquiry leads him into hovels, homes, workshops, mines, fields, prisons, hospitals, and all other places where human nature displays its weakness and its strength. In these explorations he discovers the seeds of national growth and decay, and thus becomes the prophet of his generation.

"The chief instrument of American statistics is the census, which should accomplish a twofold object. It should serve the country, by making a full and accurate exhibit of the elements of national life and strength; and it should serve the science of statistics by so exhibiting general results that they may be compared with similar data obtained by other nations. The census is indispensable to modern statesmanship."

A slightly different phase is referred to by John Cummings (J.A.S.A., XIII, 605):

"It is true of every sort of social change, whether of progress or decline, that the steps are imperceptible to the unaided vision of those who, as legislators or administrators, in the face of existing conditions of infinite complexity in their origin and interdependence, mold public policy. To determine the direction and extent of these changes requires the survey of a long period of time. It requires accurate measurements which embrace the full detail of social phenomena, and it is the proper function of a great statistical laboratory, by assembling the data of social phenomena, to make this survey, and by so doing to extend the scope and power of vision of those who are at any given time directing the trend of social forces. In the records of such a laboratory the growth of a nation is epitomized and in its current work the imperceptible changes which are taking place are accurately determined."

4. The principal types of information which are of value in most countries from these points of view are: The number of people, and their distribution by residence, with the numbers classified as urban and rural and the degree of concentration; age, sex, marital condition, and data respecting fertility; occupation, industry in which employed, and class of worker; color or race (i.e., white, Negro, Indian, Chinese, Japanese, etc.); years of schooling and/or highest grade of school completed; country of birth; year of immigration and citizenship of the foreign-born; nativity of parents; mother tongue and ability to speak English; religion; mode of housing; employment status and earnings; status under Social Security legislation; and birth-rates, marriage-rates, death-rates, rates of widowhood, probabilities of issue, statistics of dependency and orphanhood, and rates of unemployment.

5. The collection of the statistics under these various headings is effected either by "enumeration" or "registration." Enumeration is the process used in census-taking, when authorized officers called "enumerators," charged with the collection of the desired information, personally visit the individuals (or other units) to be enumerated. In the case of Registration—such as that of births, deaths, and marriages—the desired facts are reported to designated officers, commonly called "registrars," in accordance with prescribed regulations. The method of enumeration lends itself only to periodical and relatively infrequent enquiries, while registration is designed to secure a continuous record of events.

THE CENSUS

HISTORY OF CENSUS-TAKING

6. The idea of counting the number of people in a country is, of course, a very ancient one. Sir George H. Knibbs, late Commonwealth Statistician of Australia, gives the following interesting account of early census-taking:* "Though the practice of census-taking, in some form or other, is probably as old as any form of civilization, the institution now known as the Census may be said, in so far as its scope and application are concerned, to have been evolved only during the 19th century. We at least know that in Babylonia statistical inquiries were carried out as far back as 3800 or perhaps even 4500 B.C., whilst in China enumerations of the people took place certainly as early as about 3000 B.C., and in Egypt in about 2500 B.C. It is not without interest to note that the first Biblical account of an enumeration of the people is that referred to in the Book of Exodus (Exodus, xxx, 12), where it is stated that Moses was directed to number the Children of Israel and to levy a poll tax, the assigned date of this being 1491 B.C. There are several other Biblical references to Censuses (Numbers, i, 1–3, and 47–49; Numbers, iii, 14, etc., and 14, 34, etc.; 1 Chronicles, xxiii, 3, etc.; 2 Chronicles, ii, 17; 2 Samuel, xxiv, 1–9; Ezra, ii, 1–61; Nehemiah, vii, 6–69). The most notable of all these is, perhaps, that carried out in 1017 B.C. by the Hebrew King David. Strange as it may appear today, there is good authority for believing that the Biblical account of the Divine wrath (1 Chronicles, xxvii, 24; see also 1 Chronicles, xxi, 1–6), resulting from the action of David in carrying out this enumeration of the Israelites, gave rise to the idea that the act of Census-taking was in all cases a religious offence, and consequently had the effect of delaying the adoption of the Census in England for many years. A form of Census, taken every quinquennium for fiscal and military purposes, was a regular Roman institution, and lasted from about 435 B.C. until the sacking of Rome (A.D. 410). After the latter date . . . various works of a statistical nature, notably the Breviary of Charlemagne (A.D. 808) and the Domesday Book of William the Conqueror (A.D. 1086), were compiled in Europe during the Middle Ages. . . ." These early records of the Middle

* See "The First Commonwealth Census, 3rd April, 1911—Notes by G. H. Knibbs," and the exhaustive "Historical Review of Census Development" on pp. 1–6, Vol. I, 1911 Census of Australia.

Ages, while of course not census enumerations in the modern sense, are, as P. Granville Edge has observed ("Vital Registration in Europe," J.R.S.S., XCI [1928], 348), of considerable scientific interest and importance; and in addition to the Domesday Book he cites "the poll-tax returns of the 14th century in England, the Dutch tax registers of the 14th century, the 'État des Subsides' of 1328 enumerating the numbers of 'feux' or hearths in the territories of Philip VI of France, the 'Dénombrement de la Prévosté et Chastellanie de Pontoise' made in 1332 in order to ascertain the dowry of Queen Jeanne, the enumerations made for purposes of administration in certain German cities during the Middle Ages, and at the end of the 17th century the French records of the 'Intendants des Provinces.'"

The earliest statistical enquiries in Babylonia, China, and Egypt, to which Knibbs refers, appear to have been based on partial enumerations only, covering heads of families, taxpayers, males (citizens and slaves), or men of military age, and were undertaken, like those among the Biblical Hebrews, in Rome, and in other similar enumerations conducted in Greece, specifically for taxation and military purposes. The European records of the Middle Ages were likewise incomplete, although surveys of hearths, tax registers, and lists of citizens became more frequent, and some authorities suggest that a complete population count was taken in Nürenberg in 1449.

Beloch and Italian investigators have drawn attention to the remarkable series of population records, compiled usually by the parish priests and reported to the government, for the various states of Italy and Sicily in the 16th, 17th, and 18th centuries—some of them complete censuses for each sex separately, and even by age groups 18–50 and over 50 for males—which repose in 1,416 volumes in the archives of Naples and elsewhere. In Spain, also, as is pointed out by A. B. Wolfe ("Population Censuses before 1790," J.A.S.A., XXVII [1932], 357), "we have for the 16th century richer statistical material than for any other country in Europe with the exception of Italy," although there was still no reliable enumeration of the whole population. For France, Edge (*loc. cit.*) has emphasized the fact that "distinguished administrators and men of science had persistently advocated regular census enumerations probably earlier than in other European countries"; the practical results, however, were fragmentary.

Knibbs, an eminent authority, has stated (*loc. cit.*) that, following the partial and irregular recordings of the Middle Ages, "the credit for the revival of systematic enumeration belongs to the Canadian Province of Quebec, or La Nouvelle France as it was then called, [where] a census was taken in 1666"—doubtless under the stimulus of the French administrators who, as already remarked, had developed in France a consciousness of the importance of the problem; and "at a somewhat later date censuses were also taken in Nova Scotia (then Acadia) and Newfoundland." A description of those censuses may be found in the American Statistical Association's Memorial Volume "The History of Statistics—Their Development and Progress in Many Countries" (collected and edited by John Koren), and photographs of two of the original sheets of the 1666 census are given in Vol. I, Summary, of the Seventh Census of Canada, 1931 (Dominion Bureau of Statistics, Ottawa). Early censuses were also taken in the American Colonies (see "A Century of Population Growth," U.S. Bureau of the Census, 1909). Wolfe, however, in his carefully documented paper already mentioned, contends that "for no region on earth have we as old or as complete a series of censuses as we have for Sicily"—the first having been made in 1501, followed by three more in the 16th, six in the 17th, and four in the 18th centuries—and that in almost all the states of Italy "censuses of population in the true sense of the word had been undertaken by the end of the 15th century"; accordingly he concludes that these enumerations in Sicily and the Italian states, "extending over so long a period, and including at so early a time enumerations of whole populations, [are] sufficient to disprove once for all that Canada, the United States, or some of the American Colonies were the first to take complete censuses of population" (*op. cit.*, pp. 363 and 365). The shades of interpretation involved in the questions of priority raised by these conflicting claims are difficult, and need not be investigated here; they can be left for closer examination by those historically-minded persons who may have the opportunity to explore the original documents listed in the extensive bibliographies given in the papers to which reference has been made.

In Europe the first modern census was that of Sweden in 1749; but it was not until the United States commenced to take a periodical decennial census in 1790, and Great Britain instituted the same practice in 1801, that the census can be said to have attained its present position as a regular governmental procedure.

DATES OF VARIOUS NATIONAL POPULATION CENSUSES

7. The following table* shows certain particulars, as nearly as they can be stated definitely, of the national censuses of a number of the more im-

* Based mainly on the papers of G. H. Ryan (J.I.A., XXXVI, 329) and C. H. Wickens (J.I.A., XLIII, 1), the Statesman's Year-Book, the U.S. Census Bureau's 1943 publication "General Censuses and Vital Statistics in the Americas," the "Handbook of Latin American Population Data" (Office of Inter-American Affairs, Washington), the Census Library Project's 1948 volume "National Censuses and Vital

Country	Usual Inter-censal Period	Date of Most Recent Enumeration	Dates of Last Three Previous Enumerations	Present Custom Established
North America:				
Canada[1]	10[1]	June 1, 1951	1941, 1931, 1921	1871
Mexico	10	June 6, 1950	1940, 1930, 1921	. . . .
United States	10	Apr. 1, 1950	1940, 1930, 1920	1790
Central America:				
Costa Rica	. . . .	May 22, 1950	1927	. . . .
Cuba	. . . .	July 25, 1943	1931, 1919, 1907	. . . .
Dominican Republic	irregular	Aug. 6, 1950	1935, 1920	. . . .
El Salvador	irregular	June 13, 1950	1930, 1901	. . . .
Guatemala	. . . .	Apr. 18, 1950	1940, 1921, 1893	. . . .
Honduras	5	June 18, 1950	1945, 1940, 1935	. . . .
Nicaragua	. . . .	Apr. 15, 1950	1940, 1920, 1906[2]	. . . .
Panama	10	Dec. 10, 1950	1940, 1930, 1920	. . . .
South America:				
Argentina	. . . .	1947	. . . .	
Bolivia	. . . .	Sept. 5, 1950	1900	
Brazil	. . . .	July 1, 1950	1940, 1920, 1900	. . . .
Chile	10	Apr. 24, 1952	1940, 1930, 1920	1854
Colombia	10	1951	1938, 1928,[2] 1918	. . . .
Peru	. . . .	June 9, 1940	1879	
Uruguay	irregular	Oct. 12, 1908	1900	
Venezuela	irregular	Nov. 26, 1950	1941, 1936, 1926	
Europe:				
Austria	irregular	June 1, 1951	1939, 1934, 1923	1880
Belgium[3]	10	Dec. 31, 1947	1930, 1920, 1910	1880
Bulgaria	irregular	Dec. 31, 1946	1934, 1926, 1920	. . . .
Czechoslovakia	irregular	Mar. 1, 1950	1930, 1921, 1910	. . . .
Denmark	5	Nov. 7, 1950	1945, 1940, 1935	. . . .
Eire[4]	10	Apr. 8, 1951	1946, 1936, 1926	1921
England and Wales, and Scotland[5]	10	Apr. 8, 1951	1931, 1921, 1911	1801
Finland	10	Dec. 31, 1950	1940, 1930, 1920	. . . .
France[6]	5	Mar. 10, 1946	1936, 1931, 1926	1831
Germany	irregular	Sept. 1950	1946, 1939, 1933	1866
Greece[7]	irregular	Apr. 7, 1951	1940, 1928, 1920	. . . .
Hungary	irregular	Jan. 1, 1949	1941, 1930, 1920	. . . .
Iceland	10	Dec. 1, 1950	1940, 1930, 1920	. . . .
Italy[8]	10	Nov. 4, 1951	1936, 1931, 1921	1861
Netherlands[9]	10	May 31, 1947	1930, 1920, 1909	1889
Northern Ireland[10]	10	Apr. 8, 1951	1937, 1926	1925

[1] A decennial census is made for the whole country, and a census of Manitoba, Saskatchewan, and Alberta is also taken quinquennially by the Dominion Government (see par. 13).

[2] Incomplete.

[3] Census every ten years, 1846–76.

[4] Prior to 1922, a census was taken for Ireland as a whole decennially from 1821 to 1911—the first census having been taken in 1813. In 1941, also, a registration was carried out for the issuance of ration books, from which population statistics and life tables were published.

[5] Power to take the census quinquennially was conferred by the Census Act, 1920 (see par. 14). On September 29, 1939, a national registration for the issuance of ration books was carried out on census lines, from which statistics of the population were published.

[6] First census in 1801, second in 1806, third in 1821, and fourth in 1831; because of the Franco-Prussian War the 1871 census was deferred until 1872; no censuses in 1916 or 1941 on account of the European Wars.

[7] Censuses in 1836, 1879, 1889, 1896; annual enumerations to 1845.

[8] No census in 1891.

[9] Censuses decennially 1830–69 on varying dates.

[10] Prior to 1922, a census was taken for Ireland as a whole decennially from 1821 to 1911—the first census having been taken in 1813. Statistics of the population on September 29, 1939, were published from the returns obtained by the Food Control authorities for rationing purposes.

Country	Usual Intercensal Period	Date of Most Recent Enumeration	Dates of Last Three Previous Enumerations	Present Custom Established
Europe—Continued:				
Norway............	10	Dec. 1, 1950	1946, 1930, 1920	....
Poland............	irregular	Dec. 15, 1950	1946, 1931, 1921	....
Portugal..........	10	Dec. 15, 1950	1940, 1930, 1920	....
Rumania..........	irregular	Jan. 25, 1948	1941, 1930, 1913	....
Russia (U.S.S.R.)[11]..	irregular	Jan. 17, 1939	1926, 1920, 1897	....
Spain.............	10	Dec. 31, 1950	1940, 1930, 1920	....
Sweden[12]..........	5	Dec. 31, 1950	1945, 1940, 1935	1860
Switzerland[13].......	10	Dec. 1, 1950	1941, 1930, 1920	1880
Yugoslavia.........	irregular	Mar. 15, 1948	1931, 1921, 1910	....
Asia:				
Burma............	10	Mar. 5, 1941	1931, 1921, 1911	....
China[14]............	....	....	....	....
India.............	10	Mar. 1, 1951	1941, 1931, 1921	1881
Japan[15]............	irregular	Oct. 1, 1950	1946, 1945, 1944	....
Korea (Republic)...	5	May 1, 1949	1940, 1935, 1930	....
Malaya............	10	Sept. 23, 1947	1931, 1921, 1911	....
Netherlands East Indies (U.S. of Indonesia)............	....	Oct. 7, 1930	1920	....
Palestine (Israel)....	....	Nov. 8, 1948	1931, 1922	....
Africa:				
Egypt............	10	Mar. 27, 1947	1937, 1927, 1917	1897
Union of South Africa[16].............	5	May 9, 1951	1946, 1941, 1936	1911
Australasia:				
Australia[17].........	irregular	June 30, 1947	1933, 1921, 1911	1911
New Zealand[18]......	5	Apr. 17, 1951	1945, 1936, 1926	1881

[11] First complete census in 1897. A census taken in 1937 was stated officially to be unscientific and inaccurate; the schedules were destroyed and a new census ordered.

[12] First census 1749; triennially (with three omissions) to 1775, quinquennially to 1860, and thence decennially; quinquennially now; "enumeration" annually.

[13] Census in 1888 instead of 1890.

[14] Formal censuses made only three times in Chinese history (in 1910, 1912, and 1928); all, however, were faulty. Recently a census has been ordered as of June 30, 1953.

[15] First actual enumeration in 1913.

[16] The 1931 and 1941 censuses covered the European population only. Censuses were made in 1904 in each of the four Colonies which were incorporated as the Union in 1910.

[17] Prior to federation of the Australian States, each was responsible for its own census, the earliest of which was that of New South Wales in 1828.

[18] First census in 1858; irregularly to 1881. The quinquennial census due in 1931 was abandoned as an economy measure.

Statistics in Europe, 1918–1939; An Annotated Bibliography" and the "1940–1948 Supplement" thereto, "Population Index" (quarterly publication of the Population Association of America), and the valuable series of Statistical Handbooks of the League of Nations (published by the Health Organization of the League, and comprising 14 volumes for The Netherlands, Belgium, England and Wales, Spain, Austria, the Scandinavian Countries and the Baltic Republics, Portugal, Czechoslovakia, France, Hungary, Ireland, Switzerland, Scotland, and Canada). Reference should be made to these sources and the current publications of the various census offices for details, and for data respecting countries not included in this table.

portant countries. The regularity which previously had been established in the census procedures of Great Britain and many of the European countries was interrupted by the War. Registrations of the population for the purpose of issuing ration books were undertaken in several countries during the War, but they are not shown in this table which is intended to give a record of actual censuses only. The irregularities in the census dates of many of the Latin-American countries are likewise due partly to unsettled political conditions.

GENERAL PRINCIPLES OF CENSUS-TAKING

8. At an International Statistical Congress in St. Petersburg in 1872 (see J.R.S.S., XXXV [1872], 431–57, and Dudfield, J.I.A., XXXV, 342) an attempt was made to establish some degree of uniformity, which was believed to be desirable, in the conduct of the census in the various countries. Representatives were sent from the chief European nations and their dependencies, and from the United States. The most important decisions and recommendations of the Congress were as follows:

(1) To avoid misunderstanding and wrong use of terms, it is necessary to recognize:

(a) The *de facto* or present population—i.e., the whole number present in the place where and at the moment when the census is taken.

(b) The population of habitual residence, or "domiciliated" population (usually called the *de jure* population)—i.e., the population whose habitual residence is in the place where the census is taken (includes those temporarily absent and excludes those who are only temporarily present).

(c) The legal population—i.e., persons whose legal residence is in the place where the census is taken and who are registered there if legal registration is required.

(2) A general Census should include the names of the population (i.e., should be "*nominal*").

(3) As far as possible the census should be taken in one day, or at least be reported to a fixed day and an appointed hour.

(4) A Census should be taken at least every ten years, and in years ending in 0.

(5) The "essential" information comprises:

(a) Names and given names, (b) Sex, (c) Age, (d) Relationship to head of family, (e) Civil or conjugal state, (f) Profession or occupation, (g) Religion, (h) Language spoken, (i) Knowledge of reading and writing, (j) Origin (extraction), place of birth, nationality, (k) Usual residence and nature of sojourn at place of registration, (l) Blindness, deafness, muteness, idiocy, and mental aberrations. [The desirability of including these details of infirmities is now seriously questioned—see par. 27 here.]

All other information is optional.

(6) Where the degree of popular intelligence permits, and especially in large cities, age should be stated by year and month of birth. When the age is expressed in years, it should be age last birthday; for infants—in completed months.

The desirability of attaining the greatest practicable degree of uniformity in the census procedures of the different countries has been emphasized again recently by the proposal, made in 1943 by the Chairman (A. Arca Parró, then National Director of Statistics in Peru) of the Committee on Demographic Statistics of the Inter-American Statistical Institute, for a hemispheral population census by all the 22 American nations in 1950, which would observe the following minimum standards (see "Estadística," Journal of the Inter-American Statistical Institute, No. 9, 1945, p. 11):

(1) Each census should be taken in 1950, or before June, 1951, at the latest; (2) the census organization of each nation should be centralized with a high degree of autonomy, thereby guaranteeing a permanent staff of qualified technicians; (3) those nations which lack adequate maps for census enumerations should prepare them; (4) each census should be publicized, and the efficiency of the organization checked, by making pre-census counts, or a trial census; (5) the census should be taken by the "canvasser" system (see par. 10 of this Study) with adequately instructed enumerators, and should be completed in the shortest possible time; (6) all definitions in the schedules should be clear and concise, and to facilitate international comparisons the questions concerning age, place of birth, education, occupation, industry, economic position, and relationship to head of family should be uniform in all the countries; (7) recommended international nomenclatures (such as the League of Nations' classification for the gainfully occupied population) should be used when available; (8) where census omissions are supplied by estimation, both the enumerated and calculated populations should be given; and (9) the results should be published within a definite time limit—national results having priority over those for minor political divisions.

"De Facto" and "De Jure" Methods

9. In addition to the preceding suggestions it was resolved at the 1872 International Statistical Congress that the enumerations should be "de facto" and not "de jure," on account of the greater simplicity of the former

method. This recommendation, however, was not in harmony with the opinions of the U.S. representatives, who gave the following reasons for their views (see publications of 43rd Congress, 1st session, House Exec. Doc. No. 289, Serial No. 1615):

(*a*) The "de jure" population is the permanent population, which is what is desired; and

(*b*) Exact facts relating to those habitual residents can readily and correctly be obtained, whereas it is difficult to so treat the floating population.

(*c*) Under the "de facto" method persons actually traveling are indexed with difficulty; and

(*d*) It would result in erroneous and unjust information concerning certain communities which might be temporarily inflated or depleted at the time of the census.

The greater theoretical defensibility of the "de jure" method, as a result of its attempt to obtain the true geographical distribution of the population, is now widely recognized. In considering the plans for the 1921 censuses of the United Kingdom the Royal Statistical Society urged that, although, "in order to preserve the continuity of our national statistics, the 'de facto' population should be obtained, whatever other methods of tabulation are added, it is desirable that a 'de jure' tabulation should also be made, and the Census authorities should also be asked to consider whether the schedule could be so amended as to provide, in case of visitors, a statement of their usual place of residence. By this method the number of visitors (i.e. those persons who have a more permanent residence elsewhere) could be subtracted in the records of the district where enumerated, and transferred to the district where they usually resided. . . . The 'de facto' enumeration gives only an instantaneous picture of the population where it chances to be on a selected Sunday night, so that travellers, visitors . . . and people away for the week-end are counted in districts where they have no permanent residence. The fact that in fixing the date of the Census a night is chosen on which it is presumed that the minimum number of persons will be away from their own homes shows that the aim of those responsible for the 'de facto' censuses in the past has been to approximate them as nearly as possible to 'de jure' enumerations. The latter therefore have been tacitly acknowledged to form the ideal method of presenting the Census results, though practical considerations of accuracy and convenience might render that ideal difficult or impossible of attainment. . . . For all such questions as the apportionment of electoral areas, municipal status, equalization of rates, housing and so forth the 'de jure' population is evidently the appropriate measure, and the 'de facto' is only tolerable as a substitute in so far as it approximates to the 'de jure' . . ." (see Report on the Census, J.R.S.S., LXXXIII, 134).

The censuses of the United States and Canada, accordingly, are made on the "de jure" basis, and the most recent censuses of Costa Rica, Cuba, Mexico, and Nicaragua were also "de jure" (see R. Luna Vegas, "Métodos de los Censos de Población de las Naciones Americanas," Estadística, III, No. 9 for March, 1945). The "de facto" system, however, was used in Great Britain until 1931, when the Royal Statistical Society's recommended change was adopted by including also a question as to usual residence; and it has been followed extensively in Europe and in Latin-American countries (Bolivia, Columbia, Chile, El Salvador, Guatemala, Honduras, Panama, Peru, and Venezuela—see R. Luna Vegas, *loc. cit.*). Many countries (e.g., France, Belgium, Germany, Norway, Italy, Spain, Portugal, and Brazil) now present their data for both "de facto" and "de jure" populations.

"Householder" and "Canvasser" Methods

10. The problem of "de facto" or "de jure" enumeration, however, is intimately connected with the question as to who is primarily responsible for filling in the particulars on the forms. In Europe and most parts of the British Commonwealth (except Canada and India) the general practice is to employ a method which may be called the *Householder* method, by which "the occupier of each dwelling is held responsible for furnishing a written record of the desired particulars relative to the inmates of the dwelling occupied by him" (see Wickens, J.I.A., XLIII, 34); while in the United States, Canada, and India the *Canvasser* system is usually employed, whereby the enumerators themselves elicit the desired information by direct enquiry. Neither the system of "de facto" and "householder" enumeration, nor the American combination of "de jure" and "canvasser" methods, however, is entirely satisfactory. With the "de facto–householder" system the actual count of population for the whole country is probably fairly accurate, since no adjustments have to be made to the population which was in fact within the enumeration district on the census day; but the approximately true geographical distribution is not obtained, and it is stated on pp. 13–14 of the "General Report (with Appendices) of the Census of England and Wales, 1911" (Cmd. 8491) that "the transfer to the householder of the duty of record can be regarded as advantageous, if at all, only provided that the scope of the census enquiry is to be severely restricted," because "the census schedule is an elaborate and in the nature of things a difficult form to fill in, and the average house-

holder is a person without much clerical or literary training, and quite un-accustomed to the formidable form with which he is confronted." Under the American "de jure–canvasser" system, on the other hand, "the de-termination of the 'usual place of abode' is admittedly one of the greatest difficulties of the enumerators, who are instructed to count persons temporarily absent from their districts but not to enumerate persons temporarily present 'unless it is practically certain that they would not be enumerated anywhere else.' Particularly therefore in the case of men—who are more likely than women to be away from home—there is danger of considerable error by unintentional omission or duplication . . . and the employment of 'de jure' populations in the calculation of rates of mortality renders the difficult question of the distribution of non-resident and institutional deaths to their usual residences a matter of great im-portance, for otherwise the deaths and the populations from which they arise will not correspond."* The "canvasser" method, however, notwith-standing its higher cost and its dependence on the efficiency of the enumerators, is justified by the more elaborate enquiries which can be made when the information, as in that system, is obtained directly by officials who are familiar with the requirements of the schedule, and by the fact that it secures more reliable information from colored and foreign-born populations among whom the percentage of illiteracy is generally high.

Much consideration has been given by census authorities to the defects of the above systems, and the steps which might be taken to improve them. Thus in the United States the expense and possible inefficiency of the enumerators under the "canvasser" system is recognized, and at the 1910 census the "householder" method was tried experimentally for a small section of the population—but, probably because no penalty was provided in case of failure to fill in the schedule, only a small number were completed and the results were not satisfactory.† In Great Britain, while the shortcomings of the "householder" system are admitted officially (see, for example, the General Report on the 1911 Census, pp. 11–14), and the adoption of the "canvasser" method was urged by the 1921 Census Com-mittee of the Royal Statistical Society (see J.R.S.S., LXXXIII, 135), it was then suggested that the American "canvasser" system has the dis-advantage that "the compilation of the schedules occupies a considerable time, two weeks to one month we understand, during which appreciable

* See paper by H. H. Wolfenden, "Observations on the Methods and Publications of the United States Census Bureau," T.A.S.A., XVIII, 260, and par. 50 here.
† *Ibid.*

movement of population must take place."* A modified combination of the "de facto" and "canvasser" methods was consequently then commended, on the lines of the system employed in India—in which the enumerators visit every house prior to a fixed census day and obtain the necessary information "for every person habitually living in the house, and when the census day comes round he revisits the house, inquires who have slept there the previous night, strikes out the entries of any absentees and has to record on the busy day itself the facts only with regard to newcomers, who must form but a small proportion of the total population" (*op. cit.*, Cmd. 8491).

Date of Census, and Intercensal Period

11. Just as in the case of the above matters, considerable discussion and diversity of practice have arisen from some of the other recommendations of the 1872 Congress. The dates on which the various censuses are taken are by no means uniform. This, however, is a question which is necessarily affected by local conditions, because it is clear that any census should be made at a time when disturbances of population on account of general and special holidays, fairs, religious festivals, etc., are at a minimum. Again it has frequently been urged by authorities of high standing that a census should always be taken at least once every five years. This is obviously desirable not only for legislative and general economic purposes but also to facilitate the computation of reliable rates of births, deaths, and marriages, because, especially in countries which experience large waves of immigration, it is very difficult to estimate populations over a ten-year period. Greater familiarity with the importance of the census, and closer attention to accuracy in supplying the

---

* This objection, however, is of course dealt with carefully in the American system. In the 1940 U.S. census, for example, "special provision was made for the enumeration of transients. . . . As the census enumeration is carried on over a period of several weeks, transients may be missed by the enumerator if they move during the enumeration period. In order to avoid this contingency, April 8 was set aside as the day when the usual places of residence of transients in all cities would be visited by enumerators. . . . Absent family schedules and non-resident schedules were used more extensively than in previous censuses, and were mailed directly to Washington for allocation to the proper enumeration districts. A card for new occupants was left in all vacant dwelling units to insure the enumeration of persons moving during the census period. The use of these supplemental forms was aimed directly at securing a more complete count of transient population than in previous censuses. It has been necessary to check these various forms against the names on the population schedules to avoid duplicate enumeration. It is evident that a good enumeration of transients has been secured" (Annual Report of the Secretary of Commerce, 1940, p. 41).

information, would also attend more frequent enumeration. Prior to the interruptions caused by the War, the custom of taking a quinquennial census was actually established in several countries, notably Denmark, France, Germany (though with considerable latitude in its application), Honduras, Sweden, the Union of South Africa, and New Zealand. In Great Britain authority to take such a census was conferred by the Census Act of 1920 (see par. 14), and for more than fifty years the Royal Statistical Society (see its "Memorandum Regarding a Quinquennial Census," J.R.S.S., XCVIII [1935], 523) has steadily advocated, though hitherto without success, the taking of a population census every five years. In Canada the custom of taking a quinquennial census in the western prairie Provinces has now been established for some time (see par. 13).

Several other methods have also been put forward on various occasions with the object of securing reliable population data more often than decennially or even quinquennially. A restricted quinquennial enumeration by the usual methods, or a postal enumeration, might be made, or automatic registration of voters might be extended "to embrace all householders, who might in certain years at least be required to state the age and sex of each member of the household" (see *op. cit.*, Cmd. 8491, p. 14, and "The Census Methods of the Future" by E. Dana Durand, J.A.S.A., XIII). During the War, national registrations, for the issuance of ration books and other war purposes, were made in the United Kingdom (see United Kingdom, National Register: Statistics of Population on 29th September, 1939, by Sex, Age, and Marital Condition; H.M. Stationery Office, 1944) and several other countries. In the United States the Bureau of the Census has devised a plan for an annual sample census of population and agriculture (see Philip M. Hauser's paper on a "Proposed Annual Sample Census of Population," J.A.S.A., XXXVII [1942], 81); and in 1943 a new national sampling procedure was placed in operation to secure monthly estimates of the numbers by age and sex of agricultural and non-agricultural workers, non-workers, and the unemployed. The development of sampling techniques in census work has also led to the suggestion in England that the "continuous enumeration" of consecutive representative samples might be undertaken (see J. P. Mandeville, "Improvements in Methods of Census and Survey Analysis," J.R.S.S., CIX [1946], 111, and discussion thereon by H. O. Hartley, pp. 126–27). Most nations, however, so far have preferred the decennial census as the foundation of their systems for enumerating population.

The United States Population Census*

12. The first decennial census of the United States was made in 1790, and the most recent as of April 1, 1950, in accordance with Article I, section 3, of the Constitution, which is, in part, as follows:

"The actual enumeration shall be made within three years after the first meeting of the Congress of the United States and within every subsequent term of ten years, in such manner as they shall by law direct."

The census of 1890 was the first which covered the areas now forming the 48 States and the District of Columbia.

Until 1900 (inclusive) the Census Office established for the taking of each decennial census and the compilation and publication of its results had been a temporary institution, going practically out of existence at the conclusion of its work. On July 1, 1902, however, under authority of an Act of Congress passed in March of that year, the Census Office became a permanent branch of the Department of the Interior under the name "Bureau of the Census"; later it was transferred to the Department of Commerce and Labor, and in 1913 to the Department of Commerce. The establishment of this permanent bureau effected great improvements in the personnel of the Census Office, and resulted in better and more systematic organization throughout. The ultimate result has been a great broadening of the scope of the Bureau's investigations. It has been stated by the Registrar-General of England and Wales (General Report, Census of England and Wales, 1911, p. 13) that the United States "produces a more elaborate census, probably, than any other country"; and it will prove beneficial for the reader to familiarize himself with the contents of the most recent census reports and the manner in which the facts are presented.

At each census until that of 1930 inclusive, all the items covered by the enquiry were recorded on the population census schedules for every

* See also the paper thereon by H. H. Wolfenden, T.A.S.A., XVIII, 260, and discussion by J. S. Thompson; and, for more detailed information, "The Story of the Census" already mentioned, "The History and Growth of the U.S. Census" by C. D. Wright and W. C. Hunt (Washington, Senate Doc. No. 194, 56th Congress, 1st Session), and "The Bureau of the Census; Its History, Activities, and Organization" by W. Stull Holt. It should also be noted that in the individual States many censuses have been taken on various dates between the national decennial censuses; they are mainly intended, however, for purposes of State legislative apportionment, and they are not generally used for statistical analyses on account of lack of uniformity in dates and details (see the 1948 publication of the Census Library Project—sponsored by the U.S. Bureau of the Census and the Library of Congress—on "State Censuses; An Annotated Bibliography of Censuses of Population Taken after the Year 1790 by States and Territories of the United States").

individual in the country. In the 1940 census,* however, a sampling procedure was employed for the first time for certain items of a subsidiary character (concerning nativity of parents, mother tongue, veterans, Social Security status, occupational shifts, and fertility), by asking "Supplementary Questions" only for a 5% sample which was obtained by completing those questions for two marked lines out of forty on each of the two identical sides of the population schedule.

In the 1950 census† the schedule was changed considerably—the back for the first time being wholly occupied by housing items so that the "population schedule" of earlier censuses became in 1950 the schedule for the census of "population and housing." The main personal questions which were asked in respect of every individual enumerated were name, relationship to head of household, race, sex, age last birthday (except for infants under one year of age, for whom month of birth was required), marital status, state or country of birth, and whether naturalized if foreign-born; and, for persons 14 years and over, eight more questions covered employment and unemployment in the previous week, and occupation, industry, and class of worker. The sampling also was widened by asking additional questions for persons whose names fell on six sample lines of the thirty-line schedule, and still further questions for each person on the last of the six sample lines. The additional questions in respect of every name on the six sample lines (giving a 20% sample) concerned migration, nativity of parents, highest grade of school attended, and school attendance since February 1, and for those aged 14 and over other queries were included as to present unemployment and work last year, income in 1949, and military service. The further questions which were asked on the last sample line (for a $3\frac{1}{3}$% sample) concerned marriage, number of children ever born (excluding stillbirths), and in some cases the individual's kind of work and industry in his last job. An auxiliary "individual census report" was used for the enumeration of persons who were away from their usual places of abode, in order to provide a check upon their proper entry on a regular population schedule where they lived. An "infant card" also was used to record information for every infant born in January, February, or March of 1950—the questions including the date of birth of the infant, sex, the ages last birthday of the father and

---

* For that census the many complex procedures involved in the compilation of the schedules and auxiliary forms by the field enumerators, and in their subsequent editing, coding, and tabulation by the office staffs, were tested in advance by a trial census, which was taken as of August 14, 1939, for two counties in Indiana.

† The 1950 census methods were tested in advance by three full-scale trial censuses for certain localities which were made in 1948 and 1949, and by a further "pretest" on a small scale in 1949.

mother, the father's occupation and industry, and the order of birth of the child (i.e., whether the 1st, 2nd, etc., child excluding stillbirths).

The Censuses of Canada

13. As stated in par. 6, the first census in Canada was taken in 1666 in the Province of Quebec (then called La Nouvelle France), and is often claimed to be the first real census of modern times. "Still earlier records of settlement at Port Royal (1605) and Quebec (1608) are extant; but the census of 1666 was a systematic 'nominal' enumeration of the people (i.e., a record of each individual by name), taken on the 'de jure' principle, on a fixed date, showing age, sex, occupation, and conjugal and family condition. It is, therefore, clearly a census in the modern sense, and not a mere report of settlement, like its precursors" (see the First Annual Report of the Dominion Statistician: "The Dominion Bureau of Statistics, Its Origin, Purpose, and Organization," 1919, and the 1921 Census Reports). After the British conquest in 1763, censuses of Upper and Lower Canada, Nova Scotia, and New Brunswick "continued to be taken at frequent though irregular intervals"; and in 1847 an Act was passed providing, inter alia, for a decennial census, under which censuses were taken in 1851 and 1861. After Confederation a census under a special Act was taken in 1871, and thereafter a decennial census has been made for the whole Dominion as required by the Census and Statistics Act of 1879. Quinquennial censuses for the rapidly-growing North-West Territories and Manitoba were inaugurated in 1885 and 1886, were repeated for Manitoba in 1896, and were extended by the Census and Statistics Act of 1905 to cover Saskatchewan and Alberta as well as Manitoba. This Act of 1905, also, made the Census Office for the first time a permanent Bureau, which was enlarged by the Statistics Act, 1918, into the present general statistical office called the Dominion Bureau of Statistics.

The usual census for the whole country was taken as of June 1, 1951; the latest quinquennial census, covering Manitoba, Saskatchewan, and Alberta (but not British Columbia or the North-West Territories), was made in 1946.

The 39-column population schedule used in the 1941 Dominion census was of the same general type as the 34-column schedule of the 1940 U.S. census, with naturally some variations in arrangement and in its bilingual (English and French) wording, and with the addition of questions on years of immigration and naturalization, ability to speak English and/or French, and religion.

At the 1951 census the questions, which followed the same general pattern, were reduced to 29. The replies were recorded directly on individual cards (about seven inches square printed on both sides) called "mark sense documents"—the enumerators marking the data on designated oval spaces with ink which will carry an electric current. The mark sense documents were next "read" by a specially designed "document punch," equipped with brushes which pass over the document in such a way that when the brushes come to an ink mark an electrical current is completed and a hole is punched automatically in a punch card correspondingly placed. An electronic statistical machine was then used to edit these punched cards (by rejecting for examination cards showing certain inconsistencies), and as the principal equipment for making the final tabulations. These mechanized processes were decentralized in five regional statistical offices across the country, from which the verified punched cards were shipped to Ottawa for tabulation.

In order to test the many innovations thus introduced in the 1951 procedures, two trial censuses were taken in 1949—the first in Ottawa, and a second larger one in seven centers across Canada.

The Censuses of the United Kingdom and Eire

14. The censuses of (1) England and Wales, (2) Scotland,* and (3) Northern Ireland (which now together constitute the United Kingdom) and (4) Eire (the Irish Free State) have always been under the control of separate authorities, although the organizational methods and the forms of the reports have generally exhibited considerable uniformity. Until the passing of the Census Act of 1920 each decennial census (see par. 7) was provided for by special legislation—England and Wales and

---

* In Scotland, Sir John Sinclair's first "Statistical Account of Scotland" which was started in 1791 and completed in seven years, and the "Second Statistical Account" which was prepared on the same lines by the Society for the Sons and Daughters of the Clergy of the Church of Scotland between 1834 and 1845, are noteworthy as being unique enquiries into the "way of life" as well as the merely statistical characteristics of the population. They were not censuses, of course—they were based on elaborate questionnaires which were sent to every parish minister covering "the state of the country, for the purpose of ascertaining the quantum of happiness enjoyed by its inhabitants and the means of its further improvement"; J. G. Kyd (the Registrar-General for Scotland) has stated, however, that from these investigations Scotland "has a more precise knowledge of the way of life of her people in bygone days than any other country of the world." The data for a "Third Statistical Account" are now being compiled with the assistance of the Nuffield Foundation and the four Scottish Universities; the main object will be (in Kyd's words again) "to describe not merely the physical facts, the social conditions and industries, but to show how the people *live*, and what they think about religion, their work and their lesiure. . . . The promoters of this Third Account feel that unless the local condition and the view of the local people are known, the problems which life places before those who are planning for the future will be difficult to measure and therefore hard to solve."

Scotland generally being dealt with by one Act, and Ireland by another (cf. J.I.A., XXXV, 365); and the census organization was reconstituted for each occasion. That Act, however, which applies only to England and Wales and Scotland, or any area therein, is permanent in its operation, and marks a great advance in its provision that future censuses shall be taken at intervals of not less than five years by authority of an Order-in-Council made under the Act.

Details of the development of the English census will be found in J.I.A., XXV, 83 ("Some Account of the Census, from 1801–1881," by A. F. Burridge), J.I.A., XXXVI, 329 ("The Case for Census Reform" by G. H. Ryan), J.I.A., LII, 341 ("The Census of 1921; Some Remarks on Tabulation" by F. A. A. Menzler), and the General Report, 1911 Census of England and Wales (pp. 2 and 25). The Householder's Schedule (cf. par. 10) may be found in the official reports, and that of 1921 in Newsholme's "Vital Statistics"; and a useful comparison of the 1911 and 1921 schedules is given in J.I.A., LII, 345.

Under the Government of Ireland Act, 1920, and the establishment of the Irish Free State (Saorstat Eireann) by the Treaty of December 6, 1921, Ireland has been split into Eire (as it is now called, i.e., the Irish Free State) and Northern Ireland. The statistical activities of the Free State were centralized in 1923 in the Department of Industry and Commerce; The Census Act (Northern Ireland) of 1925 established the separate powers and duties of the Registrar-General for Northern Ireland. The usual decennial census for Ireland as a whole was not taken in 1921 (see footnotes 4 and 10 of the table in par. 7); a census was therefore made in both Northern Ireland and the Irish Free State as of April 18, 1926.

Censuses of Other Countries

15. Full details of the development and recent practices of the censuses of other countries, which need not be described here, may be found in the chapters on "Censuses of Modern Times" and "Census-taking in Australia" in Vol. I, 1911 Census of Australia (G. H. Knibbs, Commonwealth Statistician), in Koren's "History of Statistics," in C. H. Wickens' paper of J.I.A., XLIII, 30, and in the various references given in par. 6 and the footnote at the commencement of par. 7 of this Study.

III

THE REGISTRATION OF BIRTHS, DEATHS, AND MARRIAGES

16. As already stated, the complete statistical utilization of census results depends largely upon their ultimate employment in conjunction with properly collected annual returns of births, deaths, and marriages— for only by that means can the extent and character of the progress of nations and communities be measured. Statistics of migration, also, should be included in the category of essential facts, because with complete records in all these particulars it would be possible to determine not only the numbers of the people as enumerated by the census but also their birth, death, marriage, and migration rates, so that the population at any time could be estimated with reasonable accuracy. At the present time, however, records of migration are very incomplete in most countries (see also par. 57).

HISTORY OF REGISTRATION SYSTEMS

17. Records of baptisms, burials, and weddings have naturally been kept by the officiating clergy from early times. In Europe (according to Edge, *op. cit.*, "Vital Registration in Europe," J.R.S.S., XCI, 354) the maintenance of such records appears to have been originated in Spain by the Archbishop of Toledo in 1497; and Edge draws attention to the further interesting fact that "when Pizarro . . . conquered Peru [in 1535] he found . . . the admirable system of registration in use among the Peruvians, which was so efficient in operation as scarcely to have its counterpart in the history of any semi-civilized community." In Britain the recording of these events by the clergy was made compulsory in 1538 by order of Thomas Cromwell, Vicar-General under Henry VIII. Edge has also commented that "in 1563 the Council of Trent made the keeping of registers of births and marriages a law of the Catholic Church, and no doubt this order led to the introduction of such registers among the Catholic communities of the various European States." In the Canadian Province of Quebec, moreover, the Catholic records have been maintained since 1621, and thus appear to constitute "the longest unbroken series of records of baptisms, marriages, and burials in the world" (see R. R. Kuczynski's "Birth Registration and Birth Statistics in Canada" and the review thereof in T.A.S.A., XXXII, 280).

Independently of the ecclesiastical records, tabulations of deaths, called

"Weekly Bills of Mortality," were compiled certainly in 1592–94 during the first plague in London, and probably as early as 1532 (see J.I.A., III, 248, and Raymond Pearl's "Medical Biometry and Statistics," pp. 32–35) —the information thus recorded being "procured by persons called 'searchers,' and arranged, printed, and distributed for weekly, quarterly, and yearly periods by the Company of Parish Clerks of London, at whose hall they were supposed to remain" (J.I.A., III, 249). In Ireland, the "Dublin Bills of Mortality" were compiled similarly between about 1658 and 1772. These old records are important historically because, amongst other reasons, they provided the foundations for the "Observations upon the Bills . . ." published by Graunt in 1661 and Petty in 1683 which fore-shadowed the modern mortality table.*

The tabulation of such records by governmental agencies, and their extension to include all births, deaths, and marriages as distinguished from baptisms, burials, and weddings, however, has been attended by considerable difficulty, and even opposition (see, for example, J.I.A., XXV, 84). In its pamphlet of March, 1941, entitled the "Model Vital Statistics Act" (for which see par. 22 herein), the U.S. Bureau of the Census has noted, with references to other authorities also, that "as early as 1639 the judicial courts of the Massachusetts Bay Company issued orders and decrees for the reporting of births, deaths, and marriages, not as incidents of canon law, but as matters of 'evidence whereupon the verdict and judgment did passe.' Massachusetts was thus the first political unit on this continent to create by judicial order an administrative-legal technique for the protection of rights by preserving evidence thereof. The State imposed upon informed citizens the duty of recording with the government all births, deaths, and marriages occurring in the community, and conferred upon the recorded occurrence of these social facts the character of competent evidence." Kuczynski has accordingly remarked

---

* See also par. 82 here; the League of Nations Statistical Handbook No. 11 on Ireland, by Greenwood and Edge; J.I.A., III, 248; J.I.A., V, 198; and J.I.A., XIX, 174. In 1661 Captain John Graunt published the "Natural and Political Observations upon the Bills of Mortality" of London, which in the field of medical statistics is widely regarded as a classic. In 1683 and 1686 Sir William Petty compiled his "Observations" and "Further Observations" upon the Dublin Bills. Much controversy has surrounded the authorship of Graunt's work—Lord Lansdowne, in his "Petty Papers," holding that Petty was the author. Greenwood, however, in his contribution on "Graunt and Petty; A Re-statement" in J.R.S.S., XCVI, 76, and his recent (1948) "Medical Statistics from Graunt to Farr" (for a review of which see J.I.A., LXXV, 146), strongly refutes this interpretation. A further examination by D. V. Glass ("Graunt's Life Table," J.I.A., LXXVI, 60) of the arithmetical techniques apparently used respectively by Graunt and Petty also "lends additional support to the view of Professor Greenwood, that Graunt's life table was really constructed by Graunt and not by Petty."

(J.A.S.A., VII, 1) that Massachusetts "was the first State in the Christian world which recorded births, deaths, and marriages by government officers." The records, however, were not maintained (see also "Vital Statistics" by J. W. Trask, Supplement No. 12 to the U.S. Public Health Reports, 1914, for details of the Massachusetts laws, and for a copy of the order of Thomas Cromwell previously mentioned). The same authority has also pointed out (in his "Birth Registration and Birth Statistics in Canada," *op. cit.*) that the Act of 1826 in Quebec, providing for the preparation of returns of baptisms, marriages, and burials by the Clerks of the Civil Courts in order to ascertain the annual increase of the population of the Province, for presentation to the Governor and the Legislature, "constitutes the first start of vital statistics in North America."

These early efforts, however, being localized in Massachusetts and Quebec, were not national in scope. It is therefore generally claimed that credit for the longest continuous series of national vital statistics is to be accorded to Sweden, for there data are available since 1748.

Because efficient central administration is obviously an essential element in maintaining comprehensive records and statistics, an important landmark was the establishment of the office of the Registrar-General of England and Wales by Act of Parliament in 1836. This was followed in North America by the passage of the first State registration law by Massachusetts in 1842 (see "The Federal Registration Service of the United States" by Dr. C. L. Wilbur—U.S. Census Bureau, 1916). Under the provisions of these enactments, however, registration was voluntary. It was not made compulsory in Britain until the Births and Deaths Registration Act of 1874, and in America even later.*

Registration in the United States

18. The development of birth, death, and marriage registration in the United States has been slow and often difficult, principally because such registration is entirely within the control of the various States, with the result that no central authority has been armed with the power to obtain the enactment of efficient laws.† It has consequently been necessary,

* On account of the difficulty of enforcing continuous registration, attempts were made in the United States at each census from 1850 to 1900 to collect mortality statistics by the insertion in the census schedule of questions relating to those who had died in the year immediately preceding the census, and a similar practice was followed in Canada. The results, however, were extremely unreliable, as the method depends so largely upon the existence and memories of the relatives of decedents. This practice, therefore, has now been abandoned in both countries.

† The Census Bureau's March, 1941, publication on the "Model Vital Statistics Act" (cf. pars. 17 and 22 herein) records a number of Court decisions, together with the

through many years of agitation, to convince the various authorities of the desirability of inter-state co-operation as well as of efficient registration within each State. This educational campaign was originally conducted mainly by the American Public Health Association (which includes the majority of the foremost sanitary and registration authorities of the United States and Canada), the American Medical Association, the American Bar Association, and the Life Insurance Association of America (which, under its former name as the Association of Life Insurance Presidents, issued numerous pamphlets dealing with the question); the American Statistical Association and the Actuarial Society of America have taken their share in urging and helping to guide improvements (cf. T.A.S.A., XVIII, 271); and amongst Government organizations the Public Health Service, the Children's Bureau, and particularly, of course, the Bureau of the Census have led the activities, with more recent assistance also from the Social Security Administration.

19. A *"Registration Area for Deaths"* was established by the Census Office in 1880. For this area, which comprises those states and cities in which at least 90 per cent of the deaths are properly recorded, transcripts of the death records are forwarded to the Census Bureau for tabulation and subsequent analysis. In 1880 only Massachusetts, New Jersey, and the District of Columbia were included, representing 17 per cent of the population of the country; in 1890 and 1900 the other New England States and Michigan were admitted at various times. These transcripts until 1900 were only obtained decennially; since 1900, however, annual compilations have been made. The registration area, moreover, has been extended gradually until finally all the States were included by the admission of Texas in 1933.*

20. A similar *"Registration Area for Births,"* comprising states and cities in which registration of births is at least 90 per cent complete, was not established until 1915, and then comprised only 10 States and the

---

following statement: "Vital statistics have been considered almost exclusively to be a State responsibility. They are regarded as a necessary part of the public health functions of the State and, in legal theory, as an outgrowth of the police power of the State. This has been well established and judicially accepted, though only two State constitutions [those of Texas and Washington] refer expressly to the subject. The Federal Government has no express constitutional power to enact vital statistics legislation of a national scope."

* In the "Physicians' Handbook on Birth and Death Registration" (Bureau of the Census, 1939, p. 26), a complete table is given which shows, for each State and the District of Columbia, and separately for deaths and births, the years in which the first registration law was enacted, the records on file became complete, and admission to the registration area occurred.

District of Columbia. It expanded rapidly, however, and (like the area for deaths) was completed by the admission of Texas in 1933.

21. The compilation of *marriage and divorce* statistics was approached for many years by the utilization of certain State reports and through information obtained by the U.S. Census Bureau from the records kept at the State Capitols or the county courts. The data on which reports were published covered only the 20-year periods 1867–86 and 1887–1906, then the single year 1916, and finally each of the years from 1922 to 1932 (when the annual reports were discontinued because of the economy program of 1933)—estimates for the missing years from 1907 to 1915 and from 1917 to 1921 being given in the 1926 report. The information thus made available was seriously inadequate, moreover, by reason of varying degrees of incomplete coverage, and the absence of important tabulations such as those by age, color or race, residence, and occupation. In 1940 plans were made by the Bureau of the Census for the separate creation of partial marriage and divorce registration areas (covering 27 of the States for marriages, and 14 for divorces), which would operate through transcripts of adequate data from the original records in the same manner by which the Bureau has gradually organized the collation of the birth and death statistics. These plans, which in 1946 became the responsibility of the National Office of Vital Statistics (see par. 22 here), have not yet materialized fully; at present the only data published cover the total number of occurrences on the basis of voluntary information supplied by county clerks and other officials. A recent (1953) discussion of the problems involved is given in H. Carter's paper "Improving National Marriage and Divorce Statistics," J.A.S.A., XLVIII, 453.

22. Because the attainment of nation-wide registration has thus been a problem of inter-state co-operation and the standardization of divergent regulations, the American Public Health Association in 1895 suggested a model State Bill, which was subsequently developed with the assistance of various non-governmental organizations until in 1907 it was sponsored by the Bureau of the Census for submission to the States as the Model Vital Statistics Law (see also T.A.S.A., XVIII, 271–73, and the pamphlets of Dr. Trask and Dr. Wilbur noted in par. 17 for a copy of this Model Law). Its promulgation exercised great influence, and its principles were eventually adopted in every State. Since, however, it dealt only with the registration of births and deaths, and because its legal theory and specific provisions had become inadequate despite several revisions, the Bureau of the Census in 1938, after exhaustive study and co-operation with numerous agencies, initiated the recommendation to the States of a *Uniform Vital Statistics Act* covering marriages and divorces as well as births

and deaths, recognizing stillbirths as a separate statistical entity (in place of the previous practice of recording a stillbirth by the simultaneous completion of a birth and a death certificate), and providing for delayed and amended registrations. It embodied the legal principle of preservation of evidence in its descriptive title as an "Act to secure complete data pertaining to births, deaths, stillbirths, marriages, divorces, and annulments of marriage, to authorize and regulate the use of vital statistics records as evidence, [and] to authorize the (State Board of Health) to make regulations for the enforcement of this Act." For the specific purposes of the law, and "in order to delimit approximately the scope within which vital statistics shall operate as a governmental function" (as distinct from the wider interpretation given in par. 1 of this Study), this Act also, for the first time, has "attempted a definition of vital statistics" as comprising "the registration, preparation, transcription, collection, compilation, and preservation of data pertaining to the dynamics of the population, in particular, data pertaining to births, deaths, marital status, and the data and facts incidental thereto" (see the Census Bureau's March, 1941, publication entitled "Model Vital Statistics Act").

On July 16, 1946, the Division of Vital Statistics of the Bureau of the Census, Department of Commerce, was transferred to the Federal Security Agency, and the Federal Security Administrator assigned the vital statistics functions to the Office of the Surgeon General in the U.S. Public Health Service. The former Vital Statistics Division of the Bureau of the Census, thus transferred, is now known as the National Office of Vital Statistics (in the Bureau of State Services of the Public Health Service).

The standard live-birth and death certificates which constitute the foundation of the system are shown on the pages following. The standard certificate of stillbirth, which need not be shown here, is similar to that for live-births with the addition of questions concerning history and cause.

REGISTRATION IN CANADA

23. As in the United States, the main difficulty for many years in securing satisfactory reigstration in Canada was the fact that vital statistics are, by the British North America Act, under Provincial jurisdiction, as pertaining to "civil rights." The activities of the Dominion Government have therefore been restricted to those of a co-ordinating agency, by virtue of the powers conferred by the Census and Statistics Act of 1879 which provided that the Minister of Agriculture should "collect, abstract, and tabulate . . . vital statistics," and might also arrange for "the transmission of such information as is required, by schedules prepared by the Census Office," from any Province or territory where "any system is

PHS-796(VS)
REV. 4-48
FEDERAL SECURITY AGENCY
PUBLIC HEALTH SERVICE

(1949 Revision of Standard Certificate)

CERTIFICATE OF LIVE BIRTH

Form approved.
Budget Bureau No. 68-R374.

STATE OF _____

BIRTH NO. _____

1. PLACE OF BIRTH a. COUNTY	2. USUAL RESIDENCE OF MOTHER (Where does mother live?) a. STATE b. COUNTY
b. CITY (If outside corporate limits, write RURAL and give township) OR TOWN	c. CITY (If outside corporate limits, write RURAL and give township) OR TOWN
c. FULL NAME OF (If NOT in hospital or institution, give street address or location) HOSPITAL OR INSTITUTION	d. STREET ADDRESS (If rural, give location)

3. CHILD'S NAME (Type or print)	a. (First)	b. (Middle)	c. (Last)

4. SEX	5a. THIS BIRTH SINGLE ☐ TWIN ☐ TRIPLET ☐	5b. IF TWIN OR TRIPLET (This child born) 1ST ☐ 2ND ☐ 3RD ☐	6. DATE OF BIRTH (Month) (Day) (Year)

FATHER OF CHILD

7. FULL NAME	a. (First)	b. (Middle)	c. (Last)	8. COLOR OR RACE
9. AGE (At time of this birth) YEARS	10. BIRTHPLACE (State or foreign country)	11a. USUAL OCCUPATION	11b. KIND OF BUSINESS OR INDUSTRY	

MOTHER OF CHILD

12. FULL MAIDEN NAME	a. (First)	b. (Middle)	c. (Last)	13. COLOR OR RACE

14. AGE (At time of this birth) YEARS	15. BIRTHPLACE (State or foreign country)	16. CHILDREN PREVIOUSLY BORN TO THIS MOTHER (Do NOT include this child)		
17. INFORMANT		a. How many OTHER children are now living?	b. How many OTHER children were born alive but are now dead?	c. How many children were stillborn (born dead after 20 weeks pregnancy)?

I hereby certify that this child was born alive on the date stated above.	18a. SIGNATURE	18b. ATTENDANT AT BIRTH M. D. ☐ MIDWIFE ☐ OTHER ☐ (Specify)
	18c. ADDRESS	18d. DATE SIGNED

19. DATE REC'D BY LOCAL REG.	20. REGISTRAR'S SIGNATURE	21. DATE ON WHICH GIVEN NAME ADDED BY (Registrar)

FOR MEDICAL AND HEALTH USE ONLY
(This section MUST be filled out)

22a. LENGTH OF PREG-NANCY WEEKS	22b. WEIGHT AT BIRTH LBS. OZS.	23. LEGITIMATE YES ☐ NO ☐	

(SPACE FOR ADDITION OF MEDICAL AND HEALTH ITEMS BY INDIVIDUAL STATES)

(1949 Revision of Standard Certificate)
CERTIFICATE OF DEATH

Form approved.
Budget Bureau No. 68-R375.

BIRTH NO.   STATE OF   STATE FILE NO.

1. PLACE OF DEATH	2. USUAL RESIDENCE (Where deceased lived. If institution: residence before admission).
a. COUNTY	a. STATE b. COUNTY

1.b. CITY (If outside corporate limits, write RURAL and give township) OR TOWN   **c. LENGTH OF STAY** (in this place) | **2.c.** CITY (If outside corporate limits, write RURAL and give township) OR TOWN

1.d. FULL NAME OF HOSPITAL OR INSTITUTION (If not in hospital or institution, give street address or location) | **2.d.** STREET ADDRESS (If rural, give location)

3. NAME OF DECEASED (Type or Print)	a. (First)	b. (Middle)	c. (Last)	4. DATE OF DEATH (Month) (Day) (Year)

5. SEX	6. COLOR OR RACE	7. MARRIED, NEVER MARRIED, WIDOWED, DIVORCED (Specify)	8. DATE OF BIRTH	9. AGE (In years last birthday)	IF UNDER 1 YEAR Months	Days	IF UNDER 24 HRS. Hours	Min.

10a. USUAL OCCUPATION (Give kind of work done during most of working life, even if retired)	10b. KIND OF BUSINESS OR INDUSTRY	11. BIRTHPLACE (State or foreign country)	12. CITIZEN OF WHAT COUNTRY?

13. FATHER'S NAME	14. MOTHER'S MAIDEN NAME

15. WAS DECEASED EVER IN U.S. ARMED FORCES? (Yes, no, or unknown) (If yes, give war or dates of service)	16. SOCIAL SECURITY NO.	17. INFORMANT

MEDICAL CERTIFICATION

18. CAUSE OF DEATH Enter only one cause per line for (a), (b), and (c)		INTERVAL BETWEEN ONSET AND DEATH
*This does not mean the mode of dying, such as heart failure, asthenia, etc. It means the disease, injury, or complication which caused death.	I. DISEASE OR CONDITION DIRECTLY LEADING TO DEATH* (a) ___	
	ANTECEDENT CAUSES Morbid conditions, if any, giving rise to the above cause (a) stating the underlying cause last. DUE TO (b) ___	
	DUE TO (c) ___	
	II. OTHER SIGNIFICANT CONDITIONS Conditions contributing to the death but not related to the disease or condition causing death.	

19a. DATE OF OPERATION	19b. MAJOR FINDINGS OF OPERATION	20. AUTOPSY? YES ☐ NO ☐

21a. ACCIDENT SUICIDE HOMICIDE (Specify)	21b. PLACE OF INJURY (e.g., in or about home, farm, factory, street, office bldg., etc.)	21c. (CITY, TOWN, OR TOWNSHIP) (COUNTY) (STATE)

21d. TIME OF INJURY (Month) (Day) (Year) (Hour) ___ m.	21e. INJURY OCCURRED WHILE AT ☐ WORK NOT WHILE ☐ AT WORK	21f. HOW DID INJURY OCCUR?

22. I hereby certify that I attended the deceased from _____, 19___, to _____, 19___, that I last saw the deceased alive on _____, 19___, and that death occurred at _____ m., from the causes and on the date stated above.

23a. SIGNATURE	(Degree or title)	23b. ADDRESS	23c. DATE SIGNED

24a. BURIAL, CREMATION, REMOVAL (Specify)	24b. DATE	24c. NAME OF CEMETERY OR CREMATORY	24d. LOCATION (City, town, or county) (State)

DATE REC'D BY LOCAL REG.	REGISTRAR'S SIGNATURE	25. FUNERAL DIRECTOR ADDRESS

PHS-798(VS) REV. 4-48   FEDERAL SECURITY AGENCY   U. S. GOVERNMENT PRINTING OFFICE   16—55457-2
PUBLIC HEALTH SERVICE

established or any plan exists for collecting . . . vital statistics." Accordingly, in 1882 an Order-in-Council was passed empowering the Minister to collect "mortuary statistics" from certain cities and towns of 25,000 persons or over; and these were published annually until 1891, when they were abandoned on the gradual organization of the Provincial systems. Census enumerations of deaths were also made at each decennial census to 1911 inclusive.

In 1918, however, under authority of the Statistics Act, 1918, the Dominion Bureau of Statistics called a Conference on Vital Statistics (at which the Actuarial Society of America was represented, on invitation, by a committee); and it was then decided to cease the attempt to collect mortality statistics on the census schedule, and a scheme of Dominion and Provincial co-operation was approved. This plan provided for the admission of any Province which should enact legislation in conformity with a "Model Act" and which should "furnish satisfactory evidence that it received returns of at least 90 per cent of all marriages, births, and deaths" —the Dominion Bureau undertaking the tabulation of transcriptions (microfilms now being used) of the Provincial registrations (see Report of Conference on Vital Statistics, 1918; First Annual Report of the Dominion Statistician, 1919; and the first three [1921 to 1923] of the Annual Reports on Vital Statistics—all prepared by the Dominion Bureau of Statistics). A carefully detailed historical account of the situations both before and after the establishment of the registration plan which followed the 1918 Conference on Vital Statistics is available in Kuczynski's "Birth Registration and Birth Statistics in Canada." The organization, which also resembles that of Australia, was thus placed upon a basis very similar to that of the United States except that the registration areas for births and deaths have not been different and marriages are included in the plan. As a result of this conference the whole country except Quebec and the Yukon and the North-West Territories—embracing 73 per cent of the total population—was admitted to the scheme in 1921. The standard certificates approved by the Dominion Bureau were adopted subsequently by Quebec in 1924, the North-West Territories in 1926, and the Yukon in 1929. Quebec finally entered the registration area as from January 1, 1926. In the annual reports of the Bureau the figures for the Yukon and North-West Territories are stated separately because they are not regarded as complete and are so small that they are not of material significance.

REGISTRATION IN THE UNITED KINGDOM AND EIRE

24. Centralized control of registration was established in England and Wales in 1837, through the creation of the General Register Office (under

the direction of the Registrar-General) by an Act in 1836. The legislation was amended some years later by the Births and Deaths Registration Act of 1874, which, in particular, placed the responsibility for registration of births upon the parents instead of on the local registrars (as in the Act of 1836). Through its compulsory features and strict enforcement, the 1874 Act secured very complete returns, and failure to register is now practically negligible (cf. par. 45). Effective civil registration commenced in Scotland in 1855, and in Ireland in 1864.

The data for England and Wales have been examined in a long series of "Annual Reports of the Registrar-General of Births, Deaths, and Marriages," which commenced in 1838 and in each year thereafter gave, in the form of "blue books," a thorough analysis of the statistics until the 83rd report of 1920. In 1921 a change in style was made, the reports until 1937 inclusive being published in three parts—Tables (Medical), Tables (Civil), and Text—under the title "The Registrar-General's Statistical Review." Since 1937, the Review has appeared irregularly in consequence of the disturbances due to the War. In commemoration of the centenary (1837–1937) of the General Register Office and the registration service in England and Wales, "The Story of the General Register Office and Its Origins from 1538 to 1937" was compiled by the Registrar-General and published in 1937.

The reports for Scotland and Ireland have always been prepared separately by their respective Registrars-General. Those for Scotland appeared regularly until 1938, were interrupted by the War, and subsequently have been brought up to date. The Irish reports have been issued for Eire (Saorstat Eireann) and Northern Ireland independently since 1922.

REGISTRATION IN OTHER COUNTRIES

25. Particulars of the registration systems of other countries, which need not be detailed here, may be found in Koren's "History of Statistics" previously mentioned, partially also in J.I.A., XLIII, 39, in P. G. Edge's paper on "Vital Registration in Europe" (J.R.S.S., XCI, 346), and in the Statistical Handbooks series of the League of Nations, the U.S. Census Bureau's "General Censuses and Vital Statistics in the Americas," and the Census Library Project's "National Censuses and Vital Statistics in Europe, 1918–1939" and the "1940–1948 Supplement" (cf. footnote to par. 7).

THE FUNDAMENTAL REQUIREMENTS FOR SATISFACTORY BIRTH AND DEATH REGISTRATION

26. In addition to a central registration office in full control, and the employment of efficient local registrars—which are the foundations upon

which the systems already described are organized—the further essential provisions for satisfactory birth and death registration are (1) immediate registration, and (2) the use of standard forms, upon which the entries must be made by qualified practitioners wherever possible, and again checked by the registration officials in order to secure uniformity of classification and nomenclature; while (3) the law must be rigidly enforced, and its observance must be checked by requiring a burial or removal permit in case of death.

These conditions, however, are not easily attained. The securing of immediate registration is largely dependent upon strict regulations, which must be accompanied by adequate penalties in case of non-compliance. The requirement of a burial or removal permit prior to interment gives an automatic check on death registration; but it is difficult to devise any similar check upon the observance of the birth registration laws, and this has contributed largely to the less effective registration of births which exists in many countries. Interested readers will find basic discussions of these regulations in the English "Report of the Select Committee of the House of Commons on Death Certification" in 1893, and for the United States in Dr. Wilbur's pamphlet, noted in par. 17.

IV

THE RELIABILITY OF CENSUS AND REGISTRATION STATISTICS, AND THE NATURE OF THE ERRORS THEREIN

The preceding paragraphs have dealt with the general question of the methods by which census and registration data may be secured, the organization which is necessary for their collection, and the diversities of classification which may arise through the difficulty of securing uniform entries by the officials charged with their collection. We may now consider the nature of the errors in the resulting statistics, and the manner in which they may be detected and minimized.*

ERRORS IN CENSUS STATISTICS

27. The principal sources of error in census statistics are (a) accidental or wilful misstatements by the individuals enumerated, (b) carelessness or lack of training on the part of the enumerators, (c) the difficulty of uniform classification, and (d) the possibility of the entries on the schedules being wrongly inserted, or of the census clerks misreading those entries, and other errors of tabulation. The questions on the schedule, and their columnar arrangement, must therefore be framed with a view to minimizing the danger of such inaccuracies.

The accidental misstatements in (a) are attributable either to ignorance on the part of the individuals concerned, or to the fact that frequently the information has to be obtained from other parties—such as some other member of the family, or a boarding-house or hotel keeper. Wilful misstatements are generally due to vanity, to a desire to appear as conforming to certain labor and immigration laws, and social conventions, or to resentment against the personal nature of some of the enquiries and suspicions of their motives. The fact that this last class of error may sometimes be of considerable importance still is illustrated by the abandonment (in conformity with the recommendations of the British Empire Statistical Conference, 1920, and of the Royal Statistical Society) of the questions relating to infirmities in the 1921 census of England and Wales on account largely of the unwillingness of the parties concerned to give the desired information. (See also Census of England and Wales, 1911, General Report, p. 232.)

* The methods of correcting or adjusting such errors in the statistics are discussed subsequently, in pars. 51–54.

28. The errors and uncertainties which arise from these various sources may affect most of the items of information on the census schedule to some extent, as may be seen from a perusal of the text reports on the censuses of such countries as England and Wales, and the United States. The most important of such difficulties with which actuarial students are concerned, however, are those relating to age; they are evidenced, generally, in four ways, viz.: (1) A deficiency in the number of infants reported at ages 0 and 1 last birthday; (2) a tendency for disproportionately large numbers to be enumerated at ages ending in 0 and 5, and at other ages ending in even rather than odd digits; (3) a natural inclination to overstate the age until the attainment of majority, and then to understate at adult ages, with some overstatement in advanced years; and (4) the return of the ages of some persons as "unknown." These types of inaccuracy will now be considered in detail. In so doing it is to be remembered that such errors may be masked or accentuated by past changes in the rates of birth, death, and migration, and due consideration must therefore be given to the possible influence of such changes in any particular case.

(1) The Deficiency in the Number of Infants

29. In those countries, such as England and Wales, where birth and death registrations are reliable and practically complete, the correctness of the populations enumerated by a census at the youngest ages may be checked by recalculation from the birth and death statistics, and the influence of migration at these early ages may generally be ignored. The following table, for example (taken, with additions, from Vol. VII, p. xliv, Census of England and Wales, 1911—Report on the Graduation of Ages, by George King) shows the results of such a comparison—the estimated populations being obtained by deducting the appropriate deaths from the births of previous calendar years, on the principle of formula (6), par. 64, of this Study:

	MALE POPULATION, AS AT 2ND APRIL, 1911			
AGE			Deficit by Census	
	Estimated	Enumerated		
			Actual	Percentage
0–1....	421,135	395,110	26,025	6.18
1–2....	400,988	374,109	26,879	6.70
2–3....	396,490	395,919	571	.14
3–4....	390,682	388,669	2,013	.52
4–5....	380,585	382,306	excess 1,721	excess .45

It will be seen from this table that there is a considerable deficit in the numbers enumerated at ages 0 and 1 last birthday, and that at ages 2 and over the populations are substantially correct. In view of this latter circumstance the deficit at ages 0 and 1 may also be shown by assuming the populations aged 2 and over as practically correct and adding thereto the appropriate deaths, in accordance with formula (5) of this Study.

These deficiencies at ages 0 and 1 were found again at the 1921 census of England and Wales, although then they had decreased to 2.93% and 2.59% (cf. T.A.S.A., XXIX, 330, and XLII, 79). The 1931 census, moreover, revealed even greater improvement, as may be seen from the following results of applying the method used by King for the 1911 table already shown (see Lewis-Faning, J.R.S.S., C, 68, and Wolfenden, T.A.S.A., XLII, 79):

| AGE | POPULATIONS (IN THOUSANDS) AS AT THE MIDDLE OF 1931 | | | |
| | Estimated | Enumer-ated | Deficit by Census | |
			Actual	Percentage
0–1....	605	599	6	.99
1–2....	599	589	10	1.67
2–3....	596	593	3	.50
3–4....	599	593	6	1.00
4–5....	611	611	0	0.00

In Northern Ireland similar deficiencies of 3.43%, 3.88%, and 2.26% at ages 0, 1, and 2 were shown in the census of 1926 (see p. xxxvii of the General Report thereon, and Wolfenden, *loc. cit*).

30. These deficiencies at ages 0 and 1 appear also in the United States and Canada, where they have frequently been pointed out (see A. A. Young's report on Ages at the 1900 U.S. Census, in Supplementary Analysis, 12th Census, p. 140; Prof. Glover's U.S. Life Tables 1890, etc., p. 342; U.S. Abridged Life Tables 1919–20, p. 9; R. Henderson, T.A.S.A., XXIII, 435; H. H. Wolfenden, T.A.S.A., XXIV, 132; and R. J. Myers, T.A.S.A., XLI, 396). On account of incomplete birth and death registration the method of exhibiting the deficiencies which has generally been employed in the U.S. reports is to express the number enumerated at each age under (say) 5 as a percentage of the total number enumerated under 5, on the theory that under normal conditions these percentages should decrease steadily. In the case of the 1911 English data of par. 29, for

example, they are 20.4, 19.3, 20.5, 20.1, and 19.7, indicating clearly a deficiency at age 1 (and suggesting also, though not so clearly as King's method, that the number enumerated in the first year is too small in relation to those at ages 2 and over). For U.S. data (see Myers, T.A.S.A., XLI, 396) the comparable percentages are 20.8, 18.6, 20.4, 20.3, and 19.9 at the 1910 census, and 19.1, 18.9, 20.3, 21.0, and 20.7 in 1930.

31. Two explanations of these anomalies at ages 0 to 1 have been put forward, namely, (*a*) that there is a tendency to omit young children altogether from the census, and (*b*) that there are considerable misstatements of age in the case of those children who are actually enumerated.

With regard to (*a*) it is suggested by George King (Supplement to the 75th Annual Report of the Registrar-General of England and Wales, Part I, p. 13—see also the similar remarks in the General Report on the 1921 Census of England and Wales, and Lewis-Faning, J.R.S.S., C, 68) that where, as in the data of par. 29, the populations enumerated at ages 2 and over practically agree with the numbers estimated from the birth and death returns, "the conclusion seems to be inevitable that a large number of infants under two years of age escape enumeration"; and this is undoubtedly so except to the extent that persistent overstatement of age (carried forward into the higher ages also) may explain a portion of the deficit.

King's conclusion is also supported by an investigation of the children born in Washington, D.C., in 1919 which was made by Miss Foudray in preparing the U.S. Abridged Life Tables, 1919–20. As there stated, "the census returns for the District and its death records were searched for the children born there in 1919, and a form letter was sent to the parents of those children whose names did not appear either in the census schedules of Jan. 1, 1920, or on the death records for the District for 1919. Between 500 and 600 answers to these enquiries were received, and they were used as a basis for estimating the status on Jan. 1, 1920, of the children whose names were missing from the schedules and about whom it was impossible to obtain definite information. Separate records were kept for white and Negro children, and the per cent of children whose names were missing from the census schedules, but who were actually living in the District on Jan. 1, 1920, was found to be much greater among Negroes than among whites. The constant per cent of infants whose names were missing was taken as 9 for whites and 25 for Negroes." The original statistics upon which these percentages were based were not given, however; and although they were assumed to be equally applicable in all other sections of the U.S. it is to be noted that they were derived only from the local data of Washington, D.C.

For the whole of the United States some calculations by Myers (T.A.S.A., XLI, 396–97), based on projections of corrected and estimated births of previous years (which had to be used instead of actual births, on account of the incompleteness of birth reporting in the U.S.), also indicated substantial deficiencies for whites and greater deficiencies for the colored population at both the 1920 and 1930 censuses.

These omissions may be due largely (as remarked in the 1921 census report of England and Wales) to "the possible and intelligible non-enumeration of . . . infants of whose births the registration details necessarily would not have been completed at any census date, and the natural reluctance of parents to state the true ages of children born within a short time of their marriage."

32. With regard to (*b*)—misstatements of age in the case of the children actually enumerated—it has been customary in the English census to require the ages of children under one year old to be stated in completed months, and at the 1921 census this method was extended to the higher ages which were asked for throughout in years and months. In the United States years and months (expressed as twelfths of a year) were required for children under 2 in the census of 1910, and in 1920 for children under 5. It was therefore thought at one time that this mode of age statement in months would be likely to eliminate most errors, especially when accompanied by the explicit instructions which are generally given to enumerators to be particularly careful in obtaining such ages (cf. 1911 Census of England and Wales, General Report, p. 86, and Vol. VII, pp. xxx and xliv). Two valuable investigations which have been made by Dr. J. C. Dunlop (then Registrar-General for Scotland), however, definitely show the existence of a marked tendency to overstate the ages of young children. Dr. Dunlop took a sample population, and the children enumerated therein were identified in the birth registers and their reported ages compared with their true ages. In the first study (J.R.S.S., LXXIX, 309) the sample comprised the children of Paisley and Haddington, Scotland, who were under 5 at the 1911 census; in the second (J.R.S.S., LXXXVI, 547) those under 6 in Paisley and East Lothian at the 1921 census were used. In the former case the census asked for the age in months only for children under 1—subsequent ages being given in completed years; the 1921 census required the age in years and months throughout. In both studies slightly over 83% of the enumerated children were successfully identified in the birth registers—the untraceable balance being attributed largely to migration (see also J.R.S.S., LXXXVI, 568). The detailed comparisons of the true and reported ages of the children actually traced were shown thus:

TRUE AGE LAST BIRTHDAY IN YEARS	AGE LAST BIRTHDAY AS STATED IN CENSUS RETURNS						
	0	1	2	3	4	5	Total
	Census of 1911						
0.................	2,626	142	7	3	2	Not	2,780
1.................	13	2,304	229	2	0	included	2,548
2.................	2	13	2,176	231	5	in	2,427
3.................	4	8	25	2,051	168	1911	2,256
4.................	1	6	7	30	1,926	study	1,970
Total 0–4.........	2,646	2,473	2,444	2,317	2,101	....	11,981
	Census of 1921						
0.................	2,626	76	1	2	1	....	2,706
1.................	19	2,717	66	4	1	....	2,807
2.................	1	9	1,711	86	5	2	1,814
3.................	1	3	6	1,702	59	1	1,772
4.................	1	....	1	15	1,826	56	1,899
5.................	....	....	2	1	11	1,753	1,767
Total 0–5.........	2,648	2,805	1,787	1,810	1,903	1,812	12,765

The fact that these statistics demonstrate a persistent tendency to overstate the age may be seen clearly from the table on page 38 epitomizing the results.* It is to be noted, of course, that the enquiry analyzes only the correctness of the ages of those children who were enumerated, and so does not touch upon the other question of actual omissions from the schedules.†

While Dr. Dunlop's investigations show that the ages of children under 1 are not correctly obtained merely by the process of asking for the age in years and months, that form of question does appear to have secured in 1921 more accurate results at ages over 1 than the previous method of requiring such ages only in completed years. It therefore seems that the

* The figures in the last two columns of that table differ slightly from those given originally by Dr. Dunlop in J.R.S.S., LXXXVI, 555, in order to correct the errors therein pointed out by H. H. Wolfenden in T.A.S.A., XLII, 81.

† See also H. H. Wolfenden and J. S. Thompson, T.A.S.A., XXIV, 132 and 163; and compare Sir A. W. Watson's and Dr. Stevenson's remarks in J.R.S.S., LXXXIII, 437 and 443 on the similar features which are shown by the statements as to duration of marriages at the census, and Dr. Dunlop's analogous investigation of marriage durations in J.R.S.S., LXXVIII, 35. A further discussion of Dunlop's data is given by D. V. Glass in Population Studies, V, 77.

form of the age query has an appreciable influence on the accuracy of the stated ages (see also the last sentence of par. 34(*d*) here). This suggestion is also made in the 1911 English census reports (General Report, p. 86, and Vol. VII, p. xxxi), and is further borne out by A. A. Young's previously mentioned report on ages at the 12th U.S. census. Dr. Young there applied the percentage test to the data of a number of countries where the ages are obtained in years or years and months, and also to other countries where they are derived from a direct statement of the date of birth,

	1921					1911				
		Errors					Errors			
AGE	Number Reported	Over-statement		Under-statement		Number Reported	Over-statement		Under-statement	
		Actual	Per Cent	Actual	Per Cent		Actual	Per Cent	Actual	Per Cent
0.....	2,706	80	2.96	......	......	2,780	154	5.54	......	......
1.....	2,807	71	2.53	19	0.68	2,548	231	9.07	13	0.51
2.....	1,812	91	5.02	10	0.55	2,427	236	9.72	15	0.62
3.....	1,771	59	3.33	10	0.56	2,256	168	7.45	37	1.64
4.....	1,843	......	......	17	0.92	1,970	......	......	44	2.23
0–4...	10,939	301	2.75	56	0.51	11,981	789	6.59	109	0.91

and it was found that the deficiency at age 1 was clearly shown in the former case, but that when the date of birth was used the deficiency in a number of cases did not appear and the percentages showed a normal decrease throughout. Similar comparisons are also given by W. B. Bailey in Vol. I, p. 294, of the 13th U.S. Census Reports, together with the percentage of illiteracy in each country; but another suggestion is there made that "probably illiteracy is responsible for most of the anomalies shown and that the form of age enquiry does not materially affect the results."

Analysis of a small sample from the General Report on the New Zealand census of 1921, in which the comparisons of the stated and true ages were carried out beyond as well as below age 5, also showed tendencies closely comparable with those of Dunlop's 1921 material. For males and females separately the tabulations at ages 0–5 are shown in the table on page 39 (as stated, after correction, by H. H. Wolfenden in T.A.S.A., XLII, 81–82):

TRUE AGE LAST BIRTHDAY	AGES LAST BIRTHDAY AS STATED IN THE CENSUS RETURNS						
	0	1	2	3	4	5	Total
			Males				
0........	63						63
1........		62	4	1			67
2........			58	3			61
3........				57	1		58
4........					63	4	67
5........						56	56
Total 0–5...	63	62	62	61	64	60	372
			Females				
0........	61						61
1........		64	3				67
2........			59	1			60
3........			1	60	2		63
4........					60	4	64
5........						56	56
Total 0–5...	61	64	63	61	62	60	371

Comparison with Dunlop's 1911 and 1921 data already given at ages 0–4 then shows the following results (as given by Wolfenden, *loc. cit.*), in which the similarity of the 1921 percentages for both sexes together is notable:

Data	Percentage Overstated	Percentage Understated
(1) Dunlop (Scotland), 1911.................	6.59	.91
(2) Dunlop (Scotland), 1921.................	2.75	.51
(3) New Zealand, 1921, Males and Females.....	2.41	.16
(4) New Zealand, 1921, Males...............	2.88	.00
(5) New Zealand, 1921, Females.............	1.93	.32

(2) "Heaping" at Ages Ending in 0 and 5, and at Other Ages Ending in Even Digits

33. The actual age constitution of a population on any particular date may be depicted conveniently by means of a diagram, in which the numbers at each age or age-group may be represented either by points joined

by straight lines, or more clearly by rectangles as in the U.S. reports. The contour of such a diagram would be perfectly smooth in the case of a theoretical life-table population—in which there are no migrations, and the births and deaths are absolutely uniform; but in the actual populations enumerated by a census the outline of the diagram will be irregular,

DIAGRAM I

AGE AND SEX DISTRIBUTION OF NATIVE WHITES OF NATIVE
PARENTAGE IN AGE GROUPS; U.S. 1910

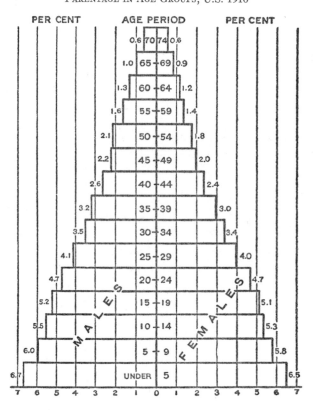

on account of migrations, varying birth and death rates, and misstatements of age. The irregularities produced by migration will, of course, only be traceable to that cause when the migration has occurred in sufficient quantity to affect markedly the outline at several consecutive ages; changes in the birth and death rates will generally be difficult to analyze in their effect on the general shape of the diagram; but misstatements of age will be shown clearly by projections and depressions at individual ages.

The accompanying diagrams illustrate these principles. The first two (taken from Vol. I of the 1910 U.S. Census Reports)* show the age and sex constitutions in age groups only—the diagram for native whites of native parentage being a normal triangular shape, and that for foreign-

DIAGRAM II

AGE AND SEX DISTRIBUTION OF FOREIGN-BORN WHITES IN AGE
GROUPS; U.S. 1910

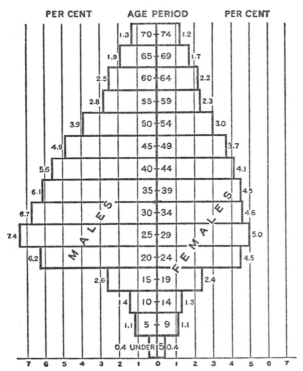

born whites clearly showing the distortion of the triangle produced by immigration at adult ages. The third (from Young's report)† gives the distribution by single years for the whole U.S. population in 1900, and clearly indicates that disproportionately large numbers were returned at

* More elaborate diagrams exhibiting similar characteristics in the 1940 U.S. population may be found on p. xi of Part 1 (United States Summary) of Vol. IV of the Reports on the 1940 Population Census.

† A similar diagram for the 1930 and 1940 U.S. populations appears on p. ix of the publication referred to in the preceding footnote.

DIAGRAM III

AGE AND SEX DISTRIBUTION OF WHOLE POPULATION BY SINGLE YEARS; U.S. 1900

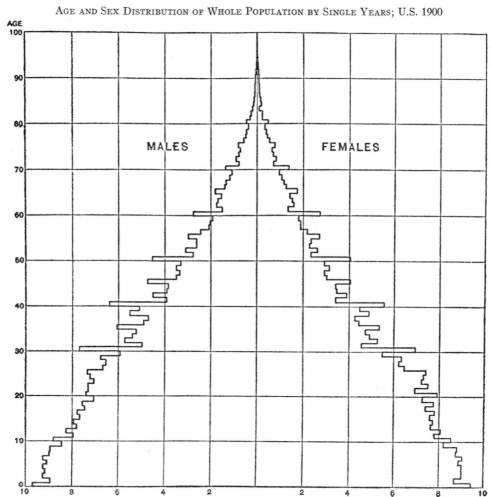

age 21, at higher ages ending in 0 and 5, and to a lesser degree at those ending in 2 and 8—which, in the absence of any evidence that migration or varying birth and death rates could produce such marked and isolated irregularities, must be attributed to misstatements of age.

34. (*a*) This concentration on particular ages has been analyzed numerically in a number of ways. The well-known tendency to return ages ending in 0 and 5 has been indicated in the U.S. reports by comparing "the number of persons between 23 and 62 years whose ages are returned as multiples of 5 with one-fifth of the total number from 23 to 62 years," on the theory that if there were no concentration on multiples of 5 these two figures would be "about equal"—the limits 23 and 62 being selected as covering the period in which such concentration is most marked. When expressed as a percentage this "Index of Concentration" gave the following results in 1910 (13th Census Report, Vol. I, p. 291):*

CLASS OF POPULATION	INDEX OF CONCENTRATION—PER CENT THAT NUMBER REPORTED AS MULTIPLES OF 5 FORMS OF ONE-FIFTH OF TOTAL NUMBER AGED 23 TO 62 YEARS INCLUSIVE		
	Male	Female	Total
Native White, Native Parentage	111.4	112.7	112.1
Native White, Foreign or Mixed Parentage	110.5	114.0	112.3
Foreign-born White	130.6	127.7	129.3
Colored	152.5	154.2	153.3
Total	120.0	120.2	120.1

(*b*) The same principle was used more comprehensively in the following table given by T. G. Ackland in J.I.A., XLVII, 319, which shows the numbers recorded at each digit of age out of a total of 1,000 at all ages in each of six Provinces of India at the census of 1911, and the order (in parentheses) in which the several digits were recorded (see page 44). The preference for 0 and 5 in this comparatively illiterate population is very marked, with even digits following in the order 2, 8, 6, 4, and thereafter the odd digits appearing in the order 3, 7, 1, and 9. (It must be noted, however—as emphasized in the next paragraph, and as shown also

---

* References to the reports of the U.S. census of 1910 are made here and elsewhere in this Study despite the lapse of time, because the descriptive text and analyses presented in those volumes were particularly complete and valuable. The 1920, 1930, and 1940 reports were published with generally much less analytical text. These later reports, however, are of course also recorded whenever necessary as additional sources of information.

by L. S. Vaidyanathan's Actuarial Report on the 1931 census of India, pp. 128–30—that the last position occupied by digit 9 results from the manner in which the count was taken for Ackland's table, and is consequently fictitious.) This same order of preference was found by H. G. W. Meikle in the 1921 census of India (see review in T.A.S.A., XXVII, 467). At the next census of 1931 Vaidyanathan's Report (cf. T.A.S.A., XXXVI, 138) showed that the digit selection was again the same except that the

PROVINCES	DIGIT OF AGE RECORDED IN CENSUS:									
	0	1	2	3	4	5	6	7	8	9
	Numbers (per 1,000) Recorded in Respect of Each Digit of Age									
Bengal....	253	43	121	56	64	187	76	57	106	37
	(1)	(9)	(3)	(8)	(6)	(2)	(5)	(7)	(4)	(10)
Bombay...	292	43	110	56	60	215	66	47	78	33
	(1)	(9)	(3)	(7)	(6)	(2)	(5)	(8)	(4)	(10)
Burma....	187	76	106	98	78	142	85	80	84	64
	(1)	(9)	(3)	(4)	(8)	(2)	(5)	(7)	(6)	(10)
Madras....	264	48	113	64	73	171	89	48	90	40
	(1)	(9)	(3)	(7)	(6)	(2)	(5)	(8)	(4)	(10)
Punjab....	279	44	110	55	67	198	78	49	84	36
	(1)	(9)	(3)	(7)	(6)	(2)	(5)	(8)	(4)	(10)
United Provinces	294	47	113	45	65	186	83	43	91	33
	(1)	(7)	(3)	(8)	(6)	(2)	(5)	(9)	(4)	(10)
Totals.....	1,569	301	673	374	407	1,099	477	324	533	243
Mean values......	262	50	112	62	68	183	79	54	89	41
Order of record.....	(1)	(9)	(3)	(7)	(6)	(2)	(5)	(8)	(4)	(10)

order of the odd digits was 7, 3, 9, and 1. Meikle's and Vaidyanathan's reports both contain elaborate discussions of the psychology and characteristics of digit selection for a population in which the percentage of illiteracy is high (as evidenced, inter alia, by the marked preference for digit 5 in comparison with its later position in more literate populations).

The principle of the numerical illustrations shown in the preceding tables of this paragraph is to compare the numbers recorded at each digit with the total number at all digits for an extensive range of ages (such as from 23 to 62). Another similar method was used in J.I.A., XLVIII, 208, where the numbers at each digit were compared with the number at digit 9 instead of with the number at all digits. It must be noted particularly, however, as pointed out by George King (J.I.A., XLIX, 301), that these methods of dealing with digits at different ages conceal the fact that when the count is started from digit 0 the population at digit 0 is normally greater than at digit 1, and that similarly the number at digit 1 is normally greater than at digit 2, and so on, with the consequence that some excess of population will appear at digit 0 in comparison with 1, and so on up to digit 9, without any selection of digits whatever. This natural excess of digits 0, 1, . . . , 8 over digit 9 when the count is started from 0 is there shown to range from a ratio of 1.196 to 1.022 even for the H^M (Text Book) Table which, being a graduated life-table population, should not show any digit preference; and these ratios will be varied when the count is started from some other digit. This natural excess of some digits over others, and its dependence upon the digit from which the count starts, must therefore be borne in mind in using these methods.

(c) The assumption underlying method (a)—that the number at a particular age x would be about one-fifth of the total population enumerated at ages $x - 2$ to $x + 2$—and the corresponding assumption of method (b), implicitly suppose that the populations decrease with age in arithmetical progression, that is, in a straight line with a constant first difference. Under normal conditions, however, the population curve has a significant second difference, and the assumption of arithmetical progression consequently introduces a slight error. In the Reports on the 1901 and 1911 censuses of England and Wales, therefore, the concentration at ages ending in 0 was estimated by redistributing the proportionate populations per 1,000 enumerated at ages $10x - 2$ to $10x + 2$ only, on the assumption of a second difference curve with the three constants chosen to reproduce the group total and the numbers at the extreme ages $10x - 2$ and $10x + 2$ (and so that the total of the three values in the middle is also unchanged).* The results were shown for English subdivisions and for a number of foreign countries, in tables of which the following is a sample (see 1911 Census Reports, Vol. VII, p. xxviii):

* The preliminary redistributions applied by Greville in the U.S. Life Tables and Actuarial Tables, 1939–41, for certain Negro populations and deaths (as explained in par. 52 of this Study) produce exactly the same numerical results as this method of par. 34(c). In both procedures, moreover, it should be noted that five values are in fact adjusted so that the two end values are unchanged and the three in the middle are redistributed subject to their total remaining the same.

AGE	PROPORTIONS PER 1,000 IN EACH 5-YEAR GROUP, OF WHICH THE CENTRAL AGE ($10x$) IS		
	$10x = 40$		
	Enumerated	Calculated	Difference
	England and Wales, Males		
$10x-2$......	222	222	....
$10x-1$......	198	204.5	$-$ 6.5
$10x$........	222	193.5	$+28.5$
$10x+1$......	167	189	-22.0
$10x+2$......	191	191	....

These tables show that generally the excess at the round number is drawn considerably more from the age above than from the age below (see also par. 53). It is to be noted that this method measures the concentration at each separate decennial point by using five ages only, and thus practically eliminates the objection as to the natural excess of certain digits. A disadvantage, however, is that the age ending in 8, which usually shows an excessive population, is included in the group and is assumed to be one of the correct values from which the adjusted numbers are computed.

(*d*) In order to eliminate this last objection and broaden the method, an improved technique (which was applied to the 1911 as well as the 1921 data) was introduced in the General Report on the 1921 Census of England and Wales (p. 73). Instead of using each 5-year group separately (as in the illustrative table for $10x = 40$ of the preceding paragraph) and adjusting its five values by a second degree curve reproducing the group total and the two end values, the populations for the entire range of ages from 23 to 72 were aggregated in ten groups according to the units digit in the age—so that those enumerated at 23, 33, 43, 53, and 63 formed the first group, those at 24, 34, etc., the second group, and so on—and then (after reduction to a total of 10,000 for comparative purposes) a second degree curve was fitted by least squares. The table on page 47 illustrates the method.

The results showed the order of digit selection as 0, 8, 2, 5 (4, 6|3) 9, 7, 1 for males and 0, 8, 2 (4, 5, 3|6) 9, 7, 1 for females at the 1911 census, and 0, 8, 2 (3, 9|5, 4, 6) 7, 1 for males (as in the following table) and 0, 8, 2 (3, 4, 5|9) 6, 7, 1 for females in 1921, where the bar marks the point of change from selection of digits to avoidance, and the parentheses enclose those digits for which the difference between the actual and graduated numbers is less than 1% of the graduated (see H. H. Wolfenden, T.A.S.A., XXIX, 329). Analysis of the figures, moreover, emphasized again that the persistent preference for 0 is almost entirely at the expense of the next higher age (as remarked earlier), and that the other principal disturbance involves digits 7 and 8 in which "the movement may be more fairly associated with an avoidance of the digit 7 than with any special respect for ages ending in 8." (Similar features appear in the 1931 census, for which the General Report was not published until 1950 on account of delays due

AGES ENDING IN	PROPORTIONATE POPULATION		DIFFERENCE	
	Actual	Graduated	Amount	Per Cent of Graduated
Males, 1921				
3	1,083	1,074	+ 9	+ .8
4	1,064	1,068	− 4	− .4
5	1,056	1,057	− 1	− .1
6	1,038	1,044	− 6	− .6
7	1,002	1,026	−24	−2.3
8	1,020	1,005	+15	+1.5
9	982	979	+ 3	+ .3
0	998	950	+48	+5.1
1	868	917	−49	−5.3
2	889	880	+ 9	+1.0
Total. . . .	10,000	10,000	±84	± .84

to the War.) It was further pointed out that in Britain the other digits showed "no consistent and significant disagreement between the crude and graduated figures and it may be inferred, therefore, that statements at these ages are fairly accurate on the whole." In comparison with the marked preference for 5 in more illiterate populations, the data indicated that feature to be of small importance in the literate population of Britain, while the selection of even digits was slight. The adoption in 1921 of the age query in years and months (instead of age last birthday), and increasing familiarity with the forms and objectives of the census, appear to have been major influences in reducing digit misstatements in 1921 to less than half for males and less than two-thirds for females of those in the census of 1911 (see the 1921 General Report, p. 75).

35. (*a*) The preceding methods of examining the ungraduated enumerated populations are intended to show the concentration at particular

ages. A general measure of these inaccuracies at all ages may be obtained from the ungraduated populations by means of a "Coefficient of Error" which was employed by A. A. Young in the Report on Ages at the 1900 U.S. Census, and was also used at the 1910 census under the name of the "Test of 'Minus Differences' " (see Supplementary Analysis, 12th Census, p. 135, and Vol. I, 13th Census, p. 292). By this method it is assumed that in a true series of normal enumerated populations the number at each age would be less than at the preceding age, so that $P_x^z - P_{x+1}^z$ would be positive throughout and there would be no "minus differences."* The sum of all these differences regardless of sign from age 0 to (say) age 99 would then equal the total decrease from age 0 to 99. When the enumerations are affected by errors, however, there will be some "minus differences" at ages affected by those errors, and the total decrease from age 0 to 99 will now be given by the sum of all the differences regardless of sign (as in the true series) less twice the sum of the "minus differences." This sum of the "minus differences" may therefore be regarded as "a measure of the inaccuracy of the reported ages," and should be expressed as a percentage of the corresponding populations. The following are some of the results for certain sections of the U.S. population:

"Coefficients of Error"—Percentages That Sum of "Minus Differences" Forms of Populations Aged 0–99

CLASS	1910		1900		1890	
	Male	Female	Male	Female	Male	Female
Native White of Native Parentage................	3.0	3.4	1.6	1.6	5.9	6.2
Native White of Foreign or Mixed Parentage.......	2.8	3.5	1.4	1.4	4.4	4.9
Colored................	10.6	11.5	9.7	11.2	13.2	15.7

(*b*) Another general measure of the inaccuracies caused by digit selection has been developed more recently by R. J. Myers ("Errors and Bias in the Reporting of Ages in Census Data," T.A.S.A., XLI, 402 and 411). In order to eliminate the inherent bias which results from starting the count always from some particular digit, Myers' procedure uses a "blended" count starting at each of the ten digits in turn and then averaging the

---

* This assumption is not permissible in the case of populations markedly affected by migration, such as the foreign-born whites of Diagram II, par. 33; and the method therefore cannot be applied in such cases. It may be noted that the differences here used are the first differences of P_x^z taken negatively, P_x^z being defined as in par. 64 of this Study.

results. This method (as he demonstrated for the H^M [Text Book] Table for which King had shown the natural excesses over digit 9 ranging from 19.6% for digit 0 to 2.2% for digit 8 when the count is started from 0—see par. 34(*b*) here) removes the bias completely.

The extent of the concentration or deficiency for each digit, as measured by this blended method, is shown by Myers as a percentage; and an "Index of Preference" is then taken as the sum, regardless of sign, of the deviations of these percentages from 10% (for if no digit selection were present, all the percentages would be 10%, and the index would be 0). The method was applied in Myers' paper to the U.S. populations from 1880 to 1930, and was extended by Greville to the 1940 census (see "United States Life Tables and Actuarial Tables, 1939–1941," p. 121) with the following results:

"INDEX OF PREFERENCE" IN UNITED STATES
POPULATIONS, 1880–1940

Census	Index of Preference	Census	Index of Preference
1880	20.8	1940	
1890	15.6	Total Population	6.0
1900	9.4	White Males	4.2
1910	11.2	White Females	5.6
1920	9.0	Non-white Males	16.2
1930	8.6	Non-white Females . . .	18.2

Greville's analyses accompanying these figures (which may be compared with those reached by Young's Coefficient of Error as shown in this paragraph) draw attention to the generally sustained improvement over the entire period, to the favorable index for 1900 which emerged in consequence of age and date of birth (instead of age alone) being asked for in that census (see also T.A.S.A., XVIII, 265, and par. 42 here), and to the high indices for non-whites. The influences of increasing familiarity with the objectives of the census, the form of the age query, and the degree of literacy are also shown by the low indices for the total population of England and Wales, which in 1911, 1921, and 1931 were only 4.4, 2.4, and 1.6 respectively (see Myers, *loc. cit.*, 403–4, and compare the conclusions stated in par. 34(*d*) here).

36. The object of all the preceding methods is to obtain from the ungraduated data an approximate estimate of the errors which they contain. The true test, however, would of course be to compare the number actually enumerated at each age with the correct number which should have been enumerated; and it has therefore been suggested that a close

estimate will be given by graduating the enumerated populations, assuming that these graduated numbers are correct, and examining the differences between the graduated and ungraduated figures. This method, however, is open to the objection that no graduated series can properly be assumed to be a representation of the numbers which should have been recorded, in the sense that the differences between it and the ungraduated series are only misstatements of age; furthermore, different methods of graduation vary greatly in their smoothing power, and hence may produce very different estimates of errors. The extent to which such estimates are attributable to migrations rather than to misstatements of age will also be difficult to measure. For quantitative comparisons the results must of course be expressed as percentages or ratios of the graduated populations to which they relate.

The method may sometimes be used with caution, however, so long as the population curve has not been seriously disturbed by migration, and if a method of graduation is adopted which is designed to eliminate only the minor roughnesses which cannot be explained as the effects of migration. Dr. Dunlop, for example, in J.R.S.S., LXXXVI, 550 et seq., estimated the errors in the age returns at the Scottish censuses of 1871, 1911, and 1921 by adjusting the ungraduated populations between ages 17 and 93 by osculatory interpolation—the resulting deviations per thousand at each age being shown in tables of the following form:

ERRORS PER THOUSAND IN RETURNS OF AGE—
CENSUS 1921, SCOTLAND, MALES

Tens Digit of Age	Unit Digit of Age									
	0	1	2	3	4	5	6	7	8	9
10......								−18	+28	+16
20......	+ 4	+ 49	− 8	−36	−25	−28	− 6	−10	+26	+ 6
30......	+ 59	− 45	+14	−19	−17	− 2	+19	−42	+14	+18
40......	+ 55	− 25	+30	−31	−40	+19	−16	−34	+50	+ 3
50......	+ 73	− 74	+18	−34	+ 2	−17	+41	−24	+18	−21
60......	+107	− 71	−12	−32	− 5	+68	−15	−77	+18	+23
70......	+ 36	− 85	+70	−23	−34	+ 5	+48	+21	−20	−74
80......	+ 60	− 76	−11	−41	+70	+15	−55	−36	+39	−23
90......	+ 94	−168	+22							

The excess at ages ending in 0 and 8, and the disinclination to use those ending in 1, 3, and 7, is apparent.

In consolidating such results the actual enumerated populations at the same digit of age are sometimes merely added and compared with the corresponding graduated populations, as in the following table given by G. H. Knibbs in his "Mathematical Theory of Population" (Appendix A, 1911 Census of Australia), p. 111, which again shows a marked tendency to report ages ending in 0, 5, 6, and 8, and avoidance of digits 1, 3, 7, and 9:

RATIO OF NUMBER RECORDED TO ADJUSTED NUMBER, CENSUSES 1891, 1901, 1911, AUSTRALIA, MALES

YEAR OF CENSUS	UNIT FIGURE IN AGE LAST BIRTHDAY									
	0	1	2	3	4	5	6	7	8	9
1891....	1.1388	.9167	1.0088	.9545	.9969	1.0366	1.0207	.9513	1.0055	.9532
1901....	1.1044	.9369	1.0072	.9677	.9809	1.0343	1.0134	.9636	1.0144	.9667
1911....	1.0485	.9956	.9944	.9787	.9990	1.0085	1.0097	.9691	1.0191	.9695

This method of consolidation gives, for each digit, slightly greater weight to the earlier ages, since normally their populations are larger than at the later ages. In any case where this may be a disturbing factor the populations may be equalized at each age, in order to give the same weight to the earlier and later ages. This was done by George King in J.I.A., XLIX, 317 (and 302), as is shown in columns (2) and (3) of the following table there given:

ENGLAND AND WALES, MALES, AGES 10–89: TOTAL DEVIATION AT EACH DIGIT OF AGE PER 100,000 OF GRADUATED POPULATION OF EACH AGE, AND THE CORRESPONDING ENUMERATED POPULATIONS

Digit of Age (1)	Total Deviation (2)	Corresponding Enumerated Population (3)
0........	70,989	870,989
1........	−61,618	738,382
2........	7,513	807,513
3........	−25,060	774,940
4........	− 4,743	795,257
5........	2,496	802,496
6........	1,246	801,246
7........	−27,094	772,906
8........	25,584	825,584
9........	− 736	799,264

In now presenting in ratio form the conclusions to which these figures lead we may either take for each digit the ratio of the enumerated population in column (3) to the corresponding graduated population, which is 800,000 in each case, or we may use the ratio of the enumerated population at each digit to the enumerated population at some particular digit—such as digit 9 as used by King. The relative results for the different digits are the same by these two methods, for the reference in the second method to digit 9 (say) in each case merely multiplies the ratios of the first method by the constant factor (800,000) ÷ (799,264). It is to be noted, however, that in King's method the ratio 1.000 for digit 9 does not indicate correctness at that digit (as would be concluded if such a ratio appeared in the first method here, or in Knibbs' table), and that the measure of inaccuracy at digit 9 and at each of the other digits should strictly be obtained from King's ratios by multiplying by the factor (799,264) ÷ (800,000).* The measures so obtained (for comparison with Knibbs' Australian results), and King's ratios to digit 9, are as follows:

ENGLAND AND WALES, MALES, 1911, AGES 10–89

Digit of Age......	0	1	2	3	4	5	6	7	8	9
Ratio of Recorded to Graduated Number, on basis of 100,000 Graduated at each Age...........	1.0887	.9230	1.0094	.9687	.9941	1.0031	1.0016	.9661	1.0320	.9991
Ratios to Digit 9, as shown by Mr. King...........	1.090	.924	1.010	.970	.995	1.004	1.003	.967	1.033	1.000

The order of digit selection here is 0, 8 (2, 5, 6|9, 4) 3, 7, 1 for males.

The corresponding order for females was 0, 8, 2 (4, 5, 6)|9, 3, 7, 1, as given in T.A.S.A., XXIX, 329. The numerical results shown in this table on the basis of equally weighted graduated populations are extremely close to those obtained for the same data by Myers' blended method of par. 35(*b*)—see T.A.S.A., XLI, 414–15.

The graduated results, by age and sex, of a 1% sample of the 1951 population of Great Britain have recently been published in Part II of the "Census of Great Britain; One per cent. Sample Tables" (1952).

37. All the preceding indications of misstatements of age are derived from populations as actually enumerated—the numbers which should have been returned at each age being merely estimated therefrom. The

* Digit 9 was used by King only in order to compare the method of this paragraph with that of J.I.A., XLVIII, 208 (par. 34(*b*) of this Study). He indicates clearly the disadvantages of this selection of a particular digit.

misstatements so shown are therefore only approximate. It is of course not practicable to obtain complete statistics of actual misstatements, since it would be necessary to secure corrected statements from all those who had originally given their ages incorrectly. It may be noted, however, that at the Australian census of 1911 (G. H. Knibbs, *loc. cit.*, pp. 112–16), 7,000 admissions of misstatement (mostly from women) were obtained as a sample, the actual amount of error being given in 1,660 cases; and the results were analyzed according to correct age and amount of misstatement. Although the number of cases was small, and the proportion which the 7,000 admissions bore to the total number of misstatements in the census was unknown, the results are interesting as giving some indication of the form of the curves of actual misstatement, and as showing that 94.64% of the aggregate cases of misstatements were understatements and only 5.36% were overstatements (see also par. 53 here).

Another approach to the problem, by which the actual misstatements are traced precisely, is of course the extension to all ages of the method used by Dr. Dunlop for children under 5 or 6 as described in par. 32 here. This was done in the General Report on the 1921 Census of New Zealand, where for 2,219 individuals (1,111 males and 1,108 females) the ages stated (as of last birthday) in the census returns were actually checked with the birth registration records.*

(3) *Inclination To Overstate the Age until Majority, Then To Understate, and Afterwards To Overstate at Advanced Ages*

38. In addition to the tendency to select particular digits, an inclination is often manifested in census statistics to overstate the age slightly until attainment of age 21 (with concentration on that age, particularly by men—see, for example, Myers' analysis in T.A.S.A., XLI, 397–98), then to understate at adult ages, and afterwards to overstate at the advanced ages. These errors were called "major deliberate errors" by King, in order to distinguish them from the errors of digit selection which he named "minor deliberate errors."

The nature of these "major deliberate errors" may vary considerably according to the laws and social customs under which the people live. The regulations governing school attendance, and child labor laws, may invite overstatement at the juvenile ages arising from a desire to report an age which will allow freedom from such enactments; in most countries the

* In analyzing this material, it is to be noted that the detailed tables on pp. 93–94 of the General Report are correct, but that a slight discrepancy appears in the summarized table at the middle of p. 96. The error is pointed out in H. H. Wolfenden's discussion in T.A.S.A., XLII, 81, where these New Zealand statistics are also shown for ages 0 to 5 in Dr. Dunlop's tabular form (see par. 32 of this Study).

attainment of marriageable age and of majority is often a supposed objective; and in countries such as India these influences are further complicated by superstition and religious customs (see J.I.A., XXV, 242, and XLVII, 401–2). At the adult ages deliberate understatement has long been suspected, especially among women. The widespread introduction of pension and social security legislation covering the older ages, such as 65 and beyond, has produced in some communities a marked overstatement at those ages. In the final age groups, moreover, considerable overstatements are often found, which usually are attributed to a desire to share in the greater consideration and esteem which attach to extreme old age.

39. The precise measurement of these errors, however, is often difficult, and their explanation frequently necessitates an attempt to apportion the relative influences of various involved causes. Moreover, when there is a significant irregularity at several consecutive ages in the contour of the age diagram which might be explained by one of the causes enumerated in par. 38, it can often be argued that the irregularity might be due to migrations, and in the absence (generally) of complete and reliable migration statistics it is sometimes difficult to establish or disprove that argument.

The suspicion of considerable major deliberate errors at adult ages is usually supported by the fact that in England and Wales, for example, the females aged 20–24 (and sometimes over the wider range of ages 19 to 28) at each census since 1851 have always largely exceeded the numbers who could have survived from those enumerated at the previous census, and the same feature has been noticed in the United States (see J.I.A., XLIX, 99–101 and 341, the General Report on the 1910 U.S. Census, p. 296, and the General Report on the 1921 Census of England and Wales, p. 80). This peculiarity, also, is sometimes associated with an apparent deficiency in the numbers recorded at ages above 24 (and especially, in the 1921 census of England and Wales, at the age group 34 to 38) in comparison with the survivors expected from the previous census. It has therefore been suggested that the excess at ages 20–24 (or 19–28) in conjunction with the deficiency at higher ages points to large deliberate understatements of age; and it is held by those who favor this view that only a portion of the anomalies can be satisfactorily explained as being due to migration (see J.I.A., XLIX, 100, 333, 337, and 341, the General Report, 1921 Census of England and Wales, p. 80, and V. P. A. Derrick's analyses in J.I.A., LVIII, 117).

At the 1911 census of England and Wales, however, King contended that this alleged understatement of age "does not exist to any great extent, and that the apparent excess in the populations enumerated at the younger ages must be due to some other cause, and the only other cause that occurs to me is migration." His argument was based on the theory that if the ratio $P_{x+1}^z \div P_x^z$ for the enumerated populations shows marked irregularities, then (a) if these irregularities are due to deliberate and extensive misstatements of age (unaccompanied by corresponding misstatements in the death records), there would be similar contortions in the curves of m_x and the resulting life-table populations $L_{x+1} \div L_x$, while (b) if they are due to migrations, so that the enumerated populations "are real, and the deaths recorded correspond to them," then m_x and $L_{x+1} \div L_x$ would be smooth—as was actually found to be the case (see J.I.A., XLIX, 303–7, and discussion pp. 328, 333, 341–42, 348, and 350). The assumption that discrepancies between the enumerated populations and the survivors expected from the preceding census may be ascribed to migration was also used in preparing the Austrian National Life Tables, 1901–10 (J.I.A., LIII, 216). The suspicion that "major deliberate errors" do exist at the younger adult ages, however, is hardly yet satisfactorily disproved.

40. The disturbances which have been noted in certain census data in the neighborhood of the ages covered by the introduction of pension legislation have been considered, to give two instances, in connection with the 1921 census of England and Wales and the 1940 census of the United States.

In the British data, comparisons by age-groups of the enumerated 1921 populations with the survivors expected from the previous census suggested that the enumerated populations of both sexes were deficient before and in excess after age 64. These calculations have been interpreted "as indicating that a number of persons of both sexes tend hereabouts to give their ages as somewhat in excess of their true value, leading to an overstatement of population." It was remarked, however, that this inference is not conclusive, because although "the discrepancies from age 64 upwards could be attributed to a series of overstatements of population at each census . . . they could equally be ascribed to a series of understatements diminishing with advancing age and terminating at about age 70; and since the period from 70 onwards is that covered by the Old Age Pension Scheme under which grantees are required to produce evidence of their ages, an explanation which is consistent with the assumption that the population at ages over 70 is approximately correct appears to be preferable to one which assumes that very large overstatements have occurred" (see the General Report, 1921 Census of England and Wales, p. 80).

In the analyses of the U.S. census of 1940, similarly, the enumerated populations were deficient at ages 55 to 64, and in excess at ages 65 and over, in comparison with the survivors expected from the previous census; and it was again suggested that "the enactment of old-age insurance and old-age assistance legislation during the decade may have led to some overstatement of age in 1940 by persons actually 55 to 64 years old," although "it is also possible that persons in this age range may have understated their ages in 1930" (see p. 3, Part 1, Vol. IV, 1940 Census). The disturbances were so marked in the Negro data that special preliminary redistributions of those populations (and deaths) between 55 and 69 were made in the preparation of the life tables (see T. N. E. Greville, "United States Life Tables and Actuarial Tables," 1939–41, p. 110, and pars. 47 and 52 here).

41. The tendency to overstatement at the most advanced ages is usually revealed by an examination of the statistics of centenarians. Careful investigations of those who so report themselves are often made by census authorities in Europe, and sometimes also in the United States; and it is frequently found that the stated ages are either difficult to substantiate or are definitely exaggerated. The largest numbers claiming to be 100 years of age or over are generally found in populations which show high percentages of illiteracy, as may be seen from the tables on pp. 143–44, Supplementary Analysis, 12th U.S. Census, and p. 295, Vol. I, 1910 U.S. Census. In the U.S. census of 1940, also, it was again observed that "the returns exaggerate the number of centenarians, particularly among non-whites" (Vol. IV, 3).

42. As in the case of inaccuracies in the reported ages of young children, two factors may be suggested as the causes of these erroneous statements of age, namely, (1) the form of the age query, and (2) illiteracy.

With regard to the age query, the International Statistical Congress of 1872 recommended that "where the degree of popular intelligence permits, age should be asked for by year and month of birth." This form of question, or the even more exact method of recording the year, month, and day of birth, as recommended by the Royal Statistical Society's Census Committee (J.R.S.S., LXXXIII, 138), is used in many European countries, and it has the undoubted advantages that an approximate reply to it is not easy, that it asks for a date which does not change, and that it does not instantly reveal the age to curious enquirers. The census authorities in the United States, however, have generally asked for the age last birthday. Exceptions to this practice were the use of the nearest age at the 1890 census, and the double question of date of birth and age last birthday in 1900, which was discarded subsequently because it was then considered that the combination of these two queries was rendered valueless by the practice of many enumerators of computing the date of birth from the age given (see J.A.S.A., XII, 110; Young's contrary opinion, *loc. cit.*, p. 360, and Supplementary Analysis, 12th Census, p. 130; and the favorable indices for 1900 quoted in par. 35 here). In Great Britain the age last birthday was used until 1921, when a new method was introduced which asked for the age in years and months, on the ground

Country	Date of Census	Index of Concentration on Multiples of 5, between Years of Age 23–62 Inclusive	Per Cent of Illiteracy
1. Countries Where Age Inquiry Called for "Year of Birth"			
Belgium............	1900	100	18.6
Germany..	1900	102	....
France............	1901	106	14.1
Austria............	1900	111	22.6
Hungary..........	1900	133	40.9
Bulgaria..........	1905	245	65.5
2. Countries Where Age Inquiry Called for "Age Last Birthday"			
United States.......	1910	120	7.7
England and Wales..	1901	100	....
Sweden...........	1900	101	....
Netherlands.......	1899	102	....
Spain.............	1900	139	58.7
Russia............	1897	182	72.3
Argentina.........	1895	189	54.4
Brazil............	1890	196	85.2

NOTE.—The illiteracy is variously expressed as a percentage of the population over 10, or 15, or some intermediate age, according to the form of the available reports. The percentages for Argentina and Brazil are based on populations over 6 and 0 respectively, and must therefore be used with caution in comparison with the percentages for other countries.

that this would necessitate more careful replies than a question as to age last birthday only, and because the authorities were not convinced of the superiority of the query as to date of birth (see also the last sentence of par. 34(*d*) here). In the 1931 census of India the nearest age was adopted instead of the age last birthday, because under the particular circumstances of the Indian population it was then suggested that "the ages which the enumerators either guess or accept as correct are recorded without any consideration as to whether they are ages next birthday or last birthday, and they may therefore be assumed to be the ages at the nearest birthday" (see the review of H. G. W. Meikle's 1921 Report in T.A.S.A., XXVII, 470); for the 1941 census, however, Vaidyanathan recommended (see his Actuarial Report on the census of 1931, p. 136) the use of completed years and months which, as in Great Britain, was held to be preferable because it forces attention to the question and to some extent at least discourages a careless reply.

Although a considerable body of evidence thus exists which indicates that the accuracy of the reported ages is partially dependent on the form of the age query, it is also true that high concentration on quinquennial ages is associated with a high percentage of illiteracy. This may be inferred from the data of pars. 32 and 34(*b*) here, and is also shown by the statistics in the table on page 57 (from Vol. I, 1910 U.S. Census, p. 292).

(4) Persons of Unknown Age

43. An indication of the number of persons whose ages are returned at a census as "unknown" is given by the following table from the General Report, 1911 Census of England and Wales, p. 88:

Country, and Date of Census	Total Enumerated Population	Number of Ages Not Stated
England and Wales, 1911.....	36,070,492	13,167
Belgium, 1901..............	6,693,548	8
Denmark, 1901.............	2,449,540	6,090
France, 1901..............	38,450,788	116,772
Holland, 1910.............	5,858,175	84
Italy, 1901................	32,475,253	1,442
Prussia, 1900..............	34,472,509	6,741
Spain, 1901...............	18,618,086	20,698
United States, 1910.........	91,972,266	169,055

These returns of "unknown" age may be due to (1) the method of collecting the data, (2) illiteracy, or (3) the form of the age query. The influence of the method of enumeration is shown by a greater proportion of males than females of unknown age, which results from the fact that men are more likely than women to be away from home, and that consequently the information concerning men is more frequently supplied by third parties who are ignorant of the true age. The effect of illiteracy is indicated by the higher percentages of unknown ages which are often found in the more illiterate population groups (see, for example, the classification by population groups of the 169,055 persons of unknown ages in the preceding table, and the comparable analysis of illiteracy, on pp. 295 and 1187 of Vol. I, 1910 U.S. Census Reports). With regard to the age query, it is probable that when date of birth is asked for there may be a greater tendency to state "unknown" than when the age last birthday is requested—for in the latter case an approximate age rather than the reply "unknown" will more frequently be given without hesitation. In the United States censuses since 1910 the enumerators have been instructed to state the approximate age rather than return the age as unknown; and although this will reduce the numbers whose ages are returned as completely unknown, it nevertheless undoubtedly tends to increase the concentration on multiples of 5.

In the United States census of 1940, the "age unknown" category was eliminated entirely from the published tables by a method developed by W. E. Deming (see W. E. Deming, "The Elimination of Unknown Ages in the 1940 Population Census," Bureau of the Census). Where the age shown on the census schedule was unstated, partially stated, inconsistent, or illegible, a "master indicator" correlated the defective age with other information available on the schedule such as marital status, highest grade of school completed, employment status, ages of other members in the family, etc., and so supplied an estimated age. The system develops estimated ages consistent with the other information at a fraction of the cost formerly expended in entering unknown age classifications in the numerous published tables. The method was also adopted, with slight modifications, in the Canadian census of 1941.

(5) Under-enumeration

44. Except with respect to the data for very young children (as already discussed in pars. 30–32), little information is available concerning the extent of any actual incompleteness of enumeration in census returns. The possibility of such under-enumeration is recognized and discussed, for example, in the United States Life Tables and Actuarial Tables, 1939–41 (pp. 1, 101, and 102).* In those tables, however—just as in the data of

---

* Two recent analyses of the U.S. Selective Service data (by D. O. Price in the American Sociological Review of February, 1947, and R. J. Myers in the same journal for June, 1948) have raised the suspicion that significant under-enumeration at the census may exist in some groups, although it is recognized, on the other hand, that the anomalies discussed in those papers may result rather from over-registration in the selective service figures.

In order to estimate the extent of error in the 1950 U.S. population census, the Bureau of the Census has made an intensive small-scale sample check, through highly trained special enumerators, of approximately 22,000 households in a sample of areas, with the object of discovering any people who were missed in the census, any who should not have been but actually were enumerated, and such duplicate enumerations as those at both permanent and temporary residences. The survey was also used to check the accuracy of various items, such as age, birthplace, occupation, industry, etc.,

other countries where the censuses are taken through a carefully organized system—it is believed that in general the unreported cases constitute only a small and negligible percentage of the totals involved. Ordinarily, therefore, no attempt is made to introduce any direct adjustments for under-enumeration at the census, beyond those which are inherent in the other types of correction discussed in pars. 27–49 here.

Errors in Registration Statistics

45. In Great Britain (see par. 24) and some European countries, in which systems providing for compulsory registration of births, deaths, and marriages have existed under centralized control for many decades, the returns are reliable and complete, so that usually they can be accepted without any correction for possible under-registration. In "A Note on the Under-registration of Births in Britain in the Nineteenth Century" (Population Studies, V, 70), for example, D. V. Glass has concluded, by the indirect method of estimating the populations at ages under 5 from the statistics of births and deaths (cf. pars. 64 and 92 here) and then comparing the results with the actual census enumerations, that birth registration appears to have been complete in England and Wales since the census year 1881, and in Scotland since 1861.

In the United States and Canada, however, where nation-wide birth and death registration systems have been operating for a comparatively short time and the transcripts are derived from areas in which registration is believed to be only 90% or more complete (see pars. 18–23), it is obvious that the statistics of both births and deaths may be affected by under-registrations of significant amounts. Until recently little was known of the actual extent of these omissions, although their importance as a source of error was of course fully realized.

(1) Under-registration of Births

46. With respect to *under-registration of births*, direct investigations were accordingly undertaken in connection with the 1931 and 1941 censuses of Canada, and the 1940 census of the United States, with a view to obtaining some measure of the extent of the omissions.

In Canada, a sample of 26,205 children under one year of age was taken

---

which had been given at the census in properly enumerated cases—the checks including subsequent matching with the independent records available in birth certificates, previous censuses, social security data, etc. M. H. Hansen (The American Statistician, VI, 7) has reported that the preliminary results indicate "a net omission from the census of between 1% and $1\frac{1}{2}\%$ of the population; this is the difference between total omissions of a little more than 2%, and duplications or other over-enumerations of less than 1%."

for the nine Provinces from the records of the 1931 census, and the files were searched for their birth registrations. Of these children who were thus actually enumerated at the census, 88% were matched with their birth registrations—the total unmatched percentage of 12% being composed of Provincial percentages varying from 20% for Prince Edward Island and Nova Scotia to 6% for Quebec. These unmatched percentages, however, are partly attributable to misspelled names, children having been adopted, illegitimate children who could not be traced, immigrant children erroneously reported as born in Canada, and clerical errors by the matching staffs. For these reasons it was concluded that the real deficiency in the birth registrations was not more than half the percentage unmatched (see pp. 231–34, Vol. XII, Monographs, Census of Canada, 1931), which thus would be approximately 6% for the whole country. At the census of 1941, the census data and birth records were again matched for a number of districts, with resulting estimates of under-registration amounting to 3% for the 1931–41 census period and 2.5% for 1936–41 (see 1941 Census of Canada, Monograph No. 1; and comments by D. V. Glass in Population Studies, V, 88). This figure doubtless has improved in the last few years as a result of the introduction of cash "family allowances," which naturally have caused parents to make sure that births are duly registered.

In the United States census of 1940, special cards were prepared for all the enumerated infants who were under 4 months of age on April 1, 1940 (the census date). These cards were then matched against copies of the birth certificates for all births reported as having occurred between December 1, 1939, and April 1, 1940; furthermore, copies of all the death certificates of infants born in the 4-month period were matched with the birth certificates. By this means the under-registration of births was indicated to be about 8%—the components of this over-all percentage varying for whites from 20.4% in Arkansas to 1% or less in Connecticut, Minnesota, New Jersey, and New York, and for non-whites over a wider range (in which the highest figure, 59.7%, was for New Mexico). Other tabulations based on a sample with a more detailed racial classification for the United States as a whole showed under-registration of 6% for whites, 18.1% for Negroes, and 24.9% for other races (see R. D. Grove, "Studies in Completeness of Birth Registration," Vital Statistics Reports, Vol. 17, No. 18; I. M. Moriyama and T. N. E. Greville, "Effect of Changing Birth Rates upon Infant Mortality Rates," Vital Statistics Special Reports, Vol. 19, No. 21; and T. N. E. Greville, "U.S. Life Tables and Actuarial Tables, 1939–1941," p. 103). Improvement in these figures was anticipated as a result (among other reasons) of the increasing proportion of births which now occur in institutions. This improvement has been confirmed by a second nation-wide test (see "Birth Registration Completeness, U.S., 1950" by S. Shapiro and J. Schachter—Public Health Reports, LXVII, No. 6), which was made by comparing the birth records with the infant cards of the 1950 census (see par. 12 here).

In making tests of this kind, the estimated percentage of under-registration is based on the number of infants enumerated in the census and not on the total infant population. Usually it is found that non-registration and non-enumeration are correlated, so that the proportion of births not registered is greater among those infants not enumerated in the census than among those enumerated. This means that the estimates of the extent of under-registration are somewhat too low. C. Chandrasekar and W. E. Deming ("On a Method of Estimating Birth and Death Rates and the Extent of Registration," J.A.S.A., XLIV, 101) accordingly have suggested (on the basis particularly of the somewhat intractable material of India) that the correlation between non-registration and non-enumeration may be regarded as due to a heterogeneity in the population with regard to certain characteristics which affect both types of reporting. The correlation can therefore be minimized by dividing the population into homogeneous groups, estimating the total births separately for each group, and then obtaining the grand total by addition. This suggestion undoubtedly is theoretically sound, although it may be difficult to apply successfully in practice because tabulations of the infant population by those characteristics which have most influence on the quality of reporting are sometimes difficult to obtain. The method has been applied to the 1940 birth registration tests in the United States, using data for small geographic areas in an effort to secure homogeneous groups; except in a few States, however, the results did not differ appreciably from those based on the assumption of zero correlation (see S. Shapiro, "Estimating Birth Registration Completeness," J.A.S.A., XLV, 264, and comments therein with respect to additional tests planned for 1950 and the possibility that the method here under discussion may have "an appreciable effect on measures of registration completeness only in those areas with a comparatively high degree of under-registration").

(2) Under-registration of Deaths

47. In connection with *under-registration of deaths*, as in the case of births, due weight must be given to the efficiency of the registration system. In the United States, for instance, registration in many of the southern and most of the western States was established much later than in the Northeast, and consequently is less well developed—especially in

the rural areas, and more particularly among Negroes in the South. Very little specific information is available, however, on the extent of such under-registration, and no adjustment was contemplated in any of the Census Bureau's life tables until the problem was examined carefully in the construction of the complete tables for 1939–41 (see U.S. Abridged Life Tables, 1930–39 (Preliminary), p. 1; U.S. Abridged Life Tables, 1939 (Urban and Rural), p. 5; and U.S. Life Tables and Actuarial Tables, 1939–41, pp. 1, 101, 102, and 103–6). In that examination it was pointed out, of course, that if the deaths and the census enumerations (as to which see par. 44 here) are both under-stated by the same percentage (which, however, would hardly be expected), the unadjusted data of both would produce correct mortality rates, but that under-reporting in the deaths to an extent greater or less than in the populations would result in deficient or excessive rates. Because information on this matter of relative incompleteness was "almost entirely lacking," the 1939–41 tables were again constructed without any direct adjustment for under-registration of deaths, although the data were handled throughout by various methods (discussed elsewhere in this Study) which were designed to minimize any effects of relative incompleteness in the deaths and populations. An elaborate analysis of the problem was made, however, for the first year of life, because "there is evidence that the proportion of infant deaths [under 1 year of age] not reported is sufficiently large to have an appreciable effect on life table values." Even there, the problem had to be approached indirectly, by examining the deaths per 1,000 births (corrected for incomplete birth registration), in each of seven sub-divisions of the first year of life for each State, in relation to the completeness of birth registration in the State; the figures so arranged showed anomalies which seemed to be explainable only on the theory that the deaths in that year "are affected by an incompleteness of reporting having, in general, the same geographical incidence as in the case of births"; and a numerical estimate was reached which suggested that white and non-white infant deaths were respectively about 94.5% and slightly less than 81% reported (see the 1939–41 Tables, p. 106).

(3) Stillbirths

48. The chief difficulties which occur in connection with the births actually registered arise from the designation of stillbirths. The definition and interpretation of the term "stillbirth," and its differentiation from "live birth" and from "premature birth," necessarily involve numerous points of uncertainty and controversy. Furthermore, the statistical methods adopted for the treatment of stillbirths obviously may have a

marked effect upon the resulting mortality rate shown by the first year of age.*

The procedures adopted in different countries have followed several patterns. The definitions, for instance, have described a stillbirth as a child who has not lived "any time whatever, no matter how brief, after birth" (in the United States, Canada, and Britain), or as one dying within the two days before registration whether death be before, during, or after birth (as in France, Belgium, and Holland); and the distinctions between premature births and stillbirths are not uniform. The methods of recording stillbirths† have also varied greatly—for although their registration has been compulsory in numerous European countries for many years, Great Britain did not adopt actual registration of stillbirths until 1927 (even though notification to the Medical Officer of Health had for a long time been one of the requirements). In the United States the practice until 1939 was to register each case as a birth and also as a death, and in such a manner that they could subsequently be excluded from the tabulation of "living" births and deaths; since 1939, however, stillbirths have been registered on a separate certificate as a distinct entity (cf. par. 22 here).

Under these circumstances the International Statistical Institute and the League of Nations recommended a definition, which is used in many countries, whereby a stillborn child means, in brief, one born after at least 28 weeks' pregnancy and without respiration occurring. The definition used in the United States, however, requires that only the 20th week of gestation has been reached. The unsatisfactory character of the general situation was summarized as recently as 1943 by F. E. Linder and R. D. Grove ("Vital Statistics Rates in the United States, 1900–1940," p. 57—U.S. Census Bureau) in the statement that "irrespective of the definition

---

* For example, under the practice adopted in many government reports of stating the so-called "infant mortality rate" as the ratio of the deaths of infants under 1 year of age to 1,000 live births during the same calendar year—an approximate method only, as will be evident from formulae (15)–(18a) and (21)–(23) of Section VI herein (see also par. 79, footnote)—the inclusion of stillbirths in the data of both births and deaths would increase that rate in New Zealand from 38.74 to 68.08 in 1927, while the system then used in France, Holland, and Belgium by which deaths within two days of birth were treated as stillbirths and excluded from the computations would have reduced the 38.74 to 27.40 (see "New Zealand—Infant Mortality Rates and Stillbirths" by Malcolm Fraser [Government Statistician], J.R.S.S., XCII, 429 and 431).

† For more detailed material see Newsholme's Vital Statistics, pp. 77–83; T.A.S.A., XIX, 139 and 141; the definitions of stillbirths, premature births (stillborn), and premature births (not stillborn) in the Rules of Statistical Practice of the Vital Statistics Section of the American Public Health Association (Annual Reports on Mortality Statistics, U.S. Census Bureau, 1907 et seq.); P. G. Edge, "Vital Registration in Europe," J.R.S.S., XCI, 360; and Fraser's paper mentioned in the preceding footnote.

which is applied, there is no doubt that the registration of stillbirths is very poor in almost every country."

(4) *Age at Death, Cause of Death, and Occupation*

49. The reported *ages at death*, like the ages returned at the census, frequently show a marked preference for the digits 0 and 5, and for even rather than odd digits. These features, however, do not always occur at the same ages as in the census figures, and usually they are not quite so prominent (except in the more backward communities). They have been analyzed on a number of occasions in the reports of the Registrars-General of England and Wales and of Scotland, by the methods already described in par. 34. In the U.S. Life Tables and Actuarial Tables, 1939–41, Greville made an examination of the white and non-white deaths of 1935—the most recent year for which they were available by single years of age—by Myers' method (see par. 35 here); the investigation confirmed the selection of 0 and 5 by whites and non-whites, indicated preference for 2, 4, and 8 by whites but not by non-whites, and showed less bias than in the census returns for the whites but greater bias among non-whites. It was also pointed out in the same volume (p. 111) that among Negroes the deaths (and also the populations) were so seriously misstated around age 65—presumably as a result of the establishment of the social security programs—that a special preliminary redistribution of the data was considered advisable between ages 55 and 70 (see also pars. 40 and 52 herein). The general similarity between the ages selected in the census returns and in the death records may often be seen from the fact that a series of death-rates calculated as ratios from the unadjusted death and census data is usually much smoother than either of the series of death or census returns alone.

The statements by the physician respecting the *cause of death* are affected by errors resulting from careless or incomplete certification—particularly failure to distinguish between the immediate and contributory causes in such a manner that effective statistical use of the certificates can be made. The registration authorities in Britain, the United States, and Canada have given much attention in recent years to the development of plans by which the physician in his medical certification shall state definitely the underlying cause to which, in his opinion, the death should be charged statistically. The difficulties in thus recording, and later tabulating, the data with regard to cause of death are considered in Section XI.

The records of the *usual occupation* and the *industry or business* of the father and mother on the birth (and stillbirth) certificates, and the similar questions on the death certificate, are of course important for statistical purposes in studies of fertility and mortality by type of work and economic status, and therefore should be handled as closely as possible in conformity with the occupational classifications adopted in the census tabulations. This, however, is rendered difficult by the fact that the statements of occupation on the death certificate are necessarily made by friends or relatives who may be unacquainted with the precise details or indifferent to their importance. The problems involved in dealing with the resulting errors are discussed in Section XII.

(5) *Deaths and Births of Non-residents*

50. A further question of considerable difficulty arises in connection with the *deaths and births of non-residents*, and the *children born of non-resident parents (or mothers)*. In order to determine accurate birth and death rates it is clear that the births and deaths which enter into the calculations should be those which correspond strictly to the census populations. That is to say, if in a particular locality the population actually enumerated by the census can be assumed to be the population normally "resident" in that locality, then the deaths registered therein of persons normally domiciled outside its boundaries (and enumerated elsewhere by the census) should be excluded, while the deaths occurring outside the locality, of "residents" who were enumerated within it by the census, should be included; and the births should be treated similarly. When the census aims to record each individual at his "usual place of residence" (his "usual place of abode"), as in the "de jure" method, the general principle would be to tabulate the births and deaths by the "usual place of residence" as that phrase is interpreted in the census instructions; but if the population is enumerated by the "de facto" method the distribution by residence is not usually as accurate, and special adjustments of the census populations may be necessary as a preliminary measure in order to obtain an approximate figure for the "resident" population which will correspond to such a tabulation of births and deaths according to their "usual residences" (see, for example, the Registrar-General's Statistical Review of England and Wales, 1921, Text, pp. 91–93).

In the United States, with its "de jure" censuses and the internal movements of its population which result from modern travel facilities and its numerous urban medical institutions, the allocation of non-resident deaths to their places of residence has been developed carefully by the Bureau of the Census in order to provide consistent death and census statistics for areas smaller than the country as a whole.* The general

* The first (1906) of the annual volumes on Mortality Statistics included a discussion of the problem; total deaths for cities and counties were published by residence

rules followed are that for births "the residence of the child is defined as the residence of the mother"; for decedents, those "who at the time of death had been living more than one year in a community are considered residents of that community even though some other place of residence is stated," those "in general hospitals, tuberculosis sanatoriums, etc., are reallocated to the place of residence," and those "in mental institutions or other institutions where the duration of stay is usually long are not re-allocated to the place of prior residence." The importance of the problem may be judged from the fact that in 1940, for the United States as a whole, 14.8 per cent of all deaths were non-residents, while for cities of 10,000 to 100,000 over 23 per cent of deaths were non-residents and 36.8 per cent of births were to non-resident mothers. It must be noted, how-ever, that of course such figures do not measure the net result of realloca-tion, because the non-resident births and deaths are reducible by the births and deaths of residents which occurred elsewhere. The general con-clusion has been reached in the United States that rates for individual States or groups of registration States, and even State figures for particu-lar age, sex, or race groups, based on "place of occurrence" data, would be changed only slightly if the tabulations were made by "place of resi-dence," but that care must be exercised in respect of cities, counties, or other units smaller than the State (see F. E. Linder and R. D. Grove, "Vital Statistics Rates in the United States, 1900–1940," pp. 15–18).

In Great Britain the deaths in institutions have been referred to the place of usual residence for many years. In 1911 a comprehensive plan was adopted by which all non-resident deaths, in institutions and else-where, are transferred as nearly as possible to the area of residence. Simi-lar rules are employed for the distribution of births according to the mother's residence. A new enquiry as to the usual residence, moreover, was included in the census of 1931, in order, amongst other objectives, to facilitate the determination of the "de jure" resident population notwith-standing the "de facto" basis of the British census system (see also par. 9 here).

The annual Canadian reports on Vital Statistics have presented all the tabulations by place of residence since 1944, with classification of the births by place of residence of the mother. Previously the data were shown by place of occurrence, although some special tabulations according to residence were made for several years prior to 1944.

---

in the volume for 1914, and subsequently for each year from 1918 to 1930; in 1935 more detailed tabulations were given for births as well as deaths; and since 1939 still more extensive data have been made available.

V

PRELIMINARY ADJUSTMENTS FOR ERRORS OF AGE IN CENSUS AND REGISTRATION STATISTICS; AND ESTIMATES OF POPULATIONS

Before taking up the main problem of the construction of mortality tables (Sections VI and VII) it will be well to consider two preliminary or independent adjustments which are sometimes required. The first of these concerns the elimination, so far as may be advisable in a special preliminary operation, of some of the worst of the disturbing effects of the errors of age considered in the preceding Section IV; the second is the problem of estimating the populations living at some time other than the census date.

(1) Preliminary Adjustments for Errors of Age

51. Of the various types of errors of age dealt with in Section IV, the numbers at "unknown" ages (par. 43), when they are stated as a separate category, are usually absorbed into the general body of data by being distributed in proportion to the populations of known ages.

52. The tendency to concentrate on certain digits of age, especially in extreme cases, is sometimes dealt with by a *preliminary redistribution*. One elementary instance of this has already been illustrated numerically in par. 34(*c*) for the special purposes there mentioned.

In the preparation of the Austrian National Life Tables discussed in J.I.A., LIII, 225, the populations and deaths were redistributed over the three ages comprising the age showing the concentration and one on each side of it, by taking the average of the three as the adjusted central value, and by correcting those on each side on the assumption that the error in each was proportional to the number observed and that the total of the three values should remain unaltered.

In the United States Life Tables and Actuarial Tables, 1939–41 (pp. 111–12), the marked disturbances in the Negro populations, and in the deaths, between ages 55 and 69 inclusive (to which references have been made in pars. 40 and 49 here) were dealt with by separate preliminary redistributions. The ratios of the Negro populations or deaths to the corresponding white populations or deaths were calculated for the six age groups 50 and over, 55 and over, . . . , and 75 and over, whence corrected ratios for 60 and over and for 65 and over were inserted in the series by interpolation from the other four values by Waring's* (Lagrange's)

* Edward Waring's priority as the discoverer (in 1779) of the interpolation formula to which Lagrange's name is usually attached was pointed out by T. N. E. Greville

68

formula, and then the adjusted values for the five quinquennial age-groups 50–54, . . . , 70–74 were obtained by differencing. This method, which gives exactly the same numerical results as the direct application of the method of par. 34(c) to the five quinquennial age-groups themselves, leaves unchanged the values at each end of the series of five age-groups between ages 50 and 74, and reproduces the total for the three in the middle (for ages 55 to 69) and also the total for the five between ages 50 and 74.

Another type of special adjustment, which may also be recorded here, was employed in presenting comparative life-table values for various countries in the United States Life Tables and Actuarial Tables, 1939–41 (p. 14 and footnote), in order to correct certain ungraduated rates of mortality for Mexico which were overstated at ages ending in 0 and 5 in consequence of a marked preference for those digits in recording the ages at death—the number of deaths in the life-table cohort at each quinquennial age, y, from 15 to 90 being determined by taking the total deaths at ages y to $y + 4$ as correct and then assuming the deaths at age y to be the same fraction of the total deaths at ages y to $y + 4$ as they were in a graduated life table for Mexico (prepared by Solórzano and Mortara).

Other examples occur in several actuarial reports dealing with the censuses of India. In J.I.A., XLVII, 320 (following the earlier reports of G. F. Hardy), T. G. Ackland made a rough adjustment of the abnormal concentration shown at ages ending in 0 and 5 in the Indian returns by the following method: The number returned at age group 0–4 was increased by one-half the number recorded at age 5; group 5–9 was adjusted by correspondingly deducting the number already transferred to group 0–4, and by adding one-half of the excess of the number at age 10 over the mean of the numbers at ages 9 and 11; group 10–14 was then adjusted by correspondingly deducting the one-half (already transferred to group 5–9) of the excess of the number at age 10 over the mean of the numbers at ages 9 and 11, and by adding one-half of the excess of the number at age 15 over the mean of those at 14 and 16; and the subsequent quinquennial groups were treated by the same method as group 10–14.*

A more elaborate procedure was evolved subsequently by H. G. W.

———

(with acknowledgment to W. E. Deming and D. C. Fraser) in the Annals of Mathematical Statistics, XV (1944), 218. A note on this priority, and on Waring's life and work, is given by H. H. Wolfenden in T.A.S.A., XLVI, 97–98.

* In the computation shown by Ackland on his p. 321, the second line of the formulae should be $\sum\limits_{0}^{4} u_{5n+t} - \frac{1}{4} (\Delta^2 u_{5n+4} - \Delta^2 u_{5n-1})$, with column (4) headed Δu_{5n-1}, Δu_{5n} and column (5) $\Delta^2 u_{5n-1}$.

Meikle in his actuarial report on "The Age Distribution and Rates of Mortality Deduced from the Indian Census Returns of 1921 and Previous Enumerations" (reviewed in T.A.S.A., XXVII, 467). Taking as an example the data

Year of Age Recorded	Number Reported at the Census
58–59	130
59–60	56
60–61	2,509
61–62	58
62–63	213
	2,966

which show the tremendous concentration on the age ending in 0, and treating the ages (which were intended to be as of age last birthday) as being more closely nearest ages (see par. 42 here) so that the whole 2,966 could be viewed preferably as lying between actual ages $57\frac{1}{2}$ to $62\frac{1}{2}$, Meikle supposed that in this range half of the 2,509 would be aged $57\frac{1}{2}$ to 60 and half aged 60 to $62\frac{1}{2}$; next assuming that $\frac{2.966}{5}$ would be aged $59\frac{1}{2}$ to $60\frac{1}{2}$, that $\frac{2.966}{5}(1 - q_{60})$ would represent approximately those between $60\frac{1}{2}$ and $61\frac{1}{2}$, and that $\frac{2.966}{5}(1 - 2q_{60})$ would be aged $61\frac{1}{2}$ to $62\frac{1}{2}$, and that similarly $\frac{2.966}{5}(1 + q_{60})$ would be between ages $58\frac{1}{2}$ and $59\frac{1}{2}$, and $\frac{2.966}{5}(1 + 2q_{60})$ between $57\frac{1}{2}$ and $58\frac{1}{2}$, and further taking half of the assumed $\frac{2.966}{5}$ aged $59\frac{1}{2}$ to $60\frac{1}{2}$ as being aged $59\frac{1}{2}$ to 60, he obtained the corrected total of the whole group under 60 as $\frac{2.966}{5}[\frac{1}{2} + (1 + q_{60}) + (1 + 2q_{60})] = 2,966(.5 + .6q_{60})$, and therefore $2,966(.5 + .6q_{60}) - (56 + 130)$ as representing the shortage at those ages.

Preliminary redistributions for errors of age, such as those just described, have usually been applied only when the disturbances are very marked. Their importance should not be under-estimated, however, because the digit misstatements of age with which they are intended to deal are, in fact, generally systematic and cyclical even in reliable material, so that the data uncorrected by preliminary redistributions are often affected by an inherent waviness which is difficult to handle satisfactorily by any subsequent graduation method (see also Wolfenden's remarks on the principle of preliminary redistributions in T.A.S.A., XLII, 85).

53. *Grouping.*—The more usual method of dealing with the concentration on particular ages is to group together the data for certain adjacent ages so that the total of each group may be assumed to be approximately correct—these group totals, instead of the values at individual ages, then being employed as the basic data. This principle requires that the age at which concentration occurs shall be in the same group with the ages from which that concentration is drawn. The selection of appropriate groups in

this manner would not be difficult if, for example, concentration at ages ending in 0 were the main feature; for then the groups 15–24, 25–34, etc. (which were used for many years in the treatment of the vital statistics of England and Wales, and are still employed in the reports of some countries) would be satisfactory so long as it could be assumed that the concentration was not drawn from ages more than four or five years from the decennial point. And where there is concentration on ages ending in 5 as well as in 0 the analogous quinquennial grouping would be 13–17, 18–22, etc., in which the main point of concentration is again central to each group. This quinquennial arrangement will be referred to as the "3–7" grouping.

Another grouping which is used extensively in census and death returns is that in which the quinquennial points are at the beginning of each group, as in 15–19, 20–24, etc., which may be called the "5–9" grouping. This method has been criticized because it assumes implicitly that the heaping at each age which is a multiple of 5 is drawn solely from the ages above and not at all from ages below. It has been justified, however, in the 73rd Annual Report of the Registrar-General of England and Wales (p. ix), and since then has been used for some of the death statistics in those reports, because it was found that "the heaping up of deaths at ages which are multiples of 10 is caused mainly by transfer from the next succeeding year of age in each case." Further support was provided by A. A. Young's analysis for ages 20–55 in the 1890 U.S. population and 20–65 in the 1900 enumeration (see "The Comparative Accuracy of Different Forms of Quinquennial Age Groups," J.A.S.A., VII, 27, and Supplementary Analysis, 12th Census, p. 138); by testing the regularity of progression of the group totals by the smoothness of the ratio

$$\frac{2G_x}{G_{x-5}+G_{x+5}}$$

where G_x is the group total for ages x to $x + 4$, he concluded that the "5–9" grouping (with the quinquennial year of concentration at the beginning) there produced totals which progressed more regularly than either the "3–7" grouping (with the year of concentration in the middle) or the "1–5" grouping (in which the quinquennial point of concentration is at the end). The "5–9" method was also preferred, after due examination, for the 1931 census data in England and Wales (see T.A.S.A., XXXVII, 248, and Myers' confirmation in T.A.S.A., XLI, 406), and in Scotland (see the Supplement to the 78th Annual Report of the Registrar-General for Scotland, Part I, Life Tables, p. 4). For the 1940 U.S. populations, moreover, the "5–9" grouping was the best for white males (see the

U.S. Life Tables and Actuarial Tables, 1939–41, p. 122, and note Greville's additional reasons stated in par. 54 here for adopting that method throughout).

Although one of the three quinquennial groupings just considered is generally adopted for convenience in presenting the unadjusted data of census and registration reports, it is clear that there are also two other quinquennial arrangements, namely, the "2–6" grouping (that is, 12–16, 17–21, etc.) and the "4–8" method (composed of ages 14–18, 19–23, etc.). The possible advantages of these groups were not considered in early investigations, because attention was then directed mainly to the importance of minimizing only the heapings at ages which are multiples of 5, and therefore naturally groupings were suggested in which the digits 5 and 0 were at the beginning (to deal with understatements), in the middle (for evenly distributed understatements and overstatements), or at the end (for overstatements). Now, however, it is recognized that marked concentration occurs also at even digits, and especially at digit 8 (see pars. 33 et seq.); and investigations have therefore been made to determine which of these five quinquennial methods of grouping will give the most satisfactory results in the light of the known tendency to concentrate on ages which are multiples of 2 as well as of 5.

54. (*i*) This question may be examined, firstly, by extending Young's ratio method of the preceding paragraph to the "2–6" and "4–8" groupings as well as to the others. This was done by J. W. Glover in the case of the 1910 populations and 1909–11 deaths of males in New York State— the regularity of the ratios for each method of grouping being tested by calculating the average difference between the ratios for groups including ages ending in 0 and for those including ages ending in 5 (see U.S. Life Tables, 1890, 1901, 1910, and 1901–10, p. 362). The results confirmed Young's conclusion as to the superiority of the "5–9" method over the "1–5" and "3–7" groupings, but showed also that the "2–6" and "4–8" methods are practically as good.

(*ii*) Another test used by George King in examining the data of the 1911 English census (see his Report on the Graduation of Ages in Vol. VII, p. xl), and more exhaustively by P. C. H. Papps for the data between ages 30 and 40 of the U.S. registration states in 1900 ("Effect of Grouping in Graduation by Osculatory Interpolation," J.A.S.A., XVI, 190), was to calculate the values at individual ages by osculatory interpolation on the basis of each of the five possible groupings, and to consider the most satisfactory grouping to be that which gives the best interpolated results. As a criterion of "best" Papps employed the third differences of the interpolated values, and also the deviations of the interpolated values for each mode of grouping from the average of the results of the various groupings. Glover (*loc. cit.*) also applied the same principle to the 1910 New York State data, and used two further tests, namely, the deviations between the actual and expected deaths, and the weighted squared deviations between the graduated and observed rates of mortality. As a result of these investigations King found the "5–9" grouping to be unsatisfactory, and pronounced in favor of the "4–8" method; Papps showed the "5–9" method to be inferior, and "3–7" in general the best—the "2–6" and "4–8" groupings also being good; and Glover discarded "1–5" and "5–9," but found that "the decision as to groups '2–6,' '3–7,' and '4–8' still remains a problem." In finally deciding, as did King, in favor of the "4–8" method Glover said: "As between these three groups it will be observed that groups '2–6' and '3–7' contain both the ages ending in the digits 0 and 8 in the same quinquennial age group, while the adjacent five-year groups contain the ages ending in the digit 5. This tends to exaggerate unduly alternate quinquennial age groups in these sets. With the group '4–8,' however, the ages ending in the digits 5 and 8 are in the same quinquennial group and the ages ending in the digit 0 are in the adjacent five-year groups. Since the exaggeration for ages which are multiples of 10 is undoubtedly greater than for ages which end in the digit 5, the group '4–8' would seem to furnish a better balanced grouping than the group '2–6' or '3–7.' " (For the populations of England and Wales in 1921, moreover, the "4–8" method was held [in the General Report and Appendices, for a review of which see T.A.S.A., XXIX, 330] to be superior for females, although "2–6" was preferred for males; in preparing English Life Table No. 9 therefrom Sir Alfred Watson adopted the "2–6" grouping as being advantageous for both sexes. The "2–6" method was also indicated by Myers' analysis [see T.A.S.A., XLI, 406, and par. 54(*iii*) here] as being slightly better than "4–8" for the U.S. Census data of 1910, 1920, and 1930.)

(*iii*) A third method proposed by R. J. Myers (and adopted by Greville in preparing the 1939–41 U.S. Life Tables) emerges immediately from his "blended" measure of digit preference as described in par. 35 (*b*) of this Study. Since the extent of the concentration or deficiency for each digit is shown therein as a percentage (so that every percentage would be 10% if no digit selection were present), it follows that the best grouping of five digits would be that for which the sum of their five percentages is closest to 50%. Myers thus showed the superiority of the "5–9" arrangement for the 1931 census of England and Wales, and of the "2–6" method for the U.S. census data of 1910, 1920, and 1930, as already noted (see T.A.S.A., XLI, 407); and by the same principle Greville found that for the 1940

U.S. populations the best groupings were "4–8" or "5–9" for whites and "4–8" for non-whites, while for the 1935 deaths "1–5" was indicated for whites and "2–6" for non-whites (see U.S. Life Tables and Actuarial Tables, 1939–41, pp. 121–22).

(*iv*) These grouping methods are generally applied to separate tabulations of populations and deaths, and the tests of digit concentration and most advantageous grouping are made for various reasons—for example, to examine the general character of the material, the efficiency of the enumerators and registrars, the effectiveness of the form of the age query, the extent of illiteracy, and the comparative accuracy of age reporting in urban, rural, and different racial communities. In such instances it is not usually necessary to maintain any special consistency in the analyses which thus are applied separately to the populations and deaths. However, when the separate groups of population and death data are to be used for the construction and graduation of mortality table ratios such as m_x or q_x, it becomes important to select groupings which will be consistent to the extent that they will not of themselves exaggerate, maintain, or produce waves in the m_x or q_x curves. Thus in preparing the 1926 life tables for Northern Ireland, quinquennial groupings showed waves in the q_x curve as a result of more pronounced heaping of deaths than of populations at digit 0, and in consequence a decennial "5–14" grouping was adopted (see the Registrar-General's Review of Vital Statistics of Northern Ireland and Life Tables, 1926, p. 53, and T.A.S.A., XLII, 84). In the 1939–41 U.S. life tables also, this desirability of using groups of populations and deaths which would minimize waviness in the q_x curve was discussed in the following words (see Greville, U.S. Life Tables and Actuarial Tables, 1939–1941, p. 121): "In computing rates of mortality, if the same grouping is to be used for both populations and deaths, it is of little avail to select the most effective grouping for populations if this grouping produces marked bias in the death figures, and vice versa; on the other hand, the correct mortality rates will be obtained, even with considerable error in both population and death statistics, if both are deficient or both excessive in the same proportion." The best grouping for the mortality rate calculations was therefore selected as that in which the smallest difference appeared between the best "blended" percentages for the populations and deaths as found by Myers' method of the preceding sub-par. (*iii*) here; for example, for white males the blended percentages by the five different groupings were

GROUPING	BLENDED PERCENTAGES FOR		
	Populations	Deaths	Difference
1–5......	49.5	50.1	.6
2–6......	50.4	50.8	.4
3–7......	49.6	50.6	1.0
4–8......	49.9	50.8	.9
5–9......	50.0	50.4	.4

from which the "5–9" grouping emerges as the best for computing mortality rates because the difference (with that for "2–6") is smallest and both the percentages themselves are better than for the "2–6" arrangement.

(*v*) All the methods considered in this and the preceding paragraphs are based on equal quinquennial or decennial groups throughout. Departures from this system of equal groups, however, have been examined carefully as a means of dealing with the intractable material of India. In his report on the 1921 Indian census (see pars. 34(*b*), 42, and 52 here, and T.A.S.A., XXVII, 470), H. G. W. Meikle discarded the "2–6" method which appeared to be desirable if equal quinquennial groups had been adopted, and recommended instead that for the census of 1931 a new system should be employed in which the groups (based on the assumption that the ages stated in the returns should be taken as really being nearest ages— see par. 42 here) should consist of "three and seven ages alternately, according as the middle age of each group is an odd or an even multiple of 5." The advantages of this proposal (which may be identified as a "4–6; 7–13" arrangement) were stated to lie in the simpler formulae (given in the report) for obtaining a regrouping of the figures according to the "5–9" method—as is sometimes desirable for comparisons with other data—and in the fact that it appeared to produce, in the particular case of India, a more reliable series of values of T_x for final graduation than the "2–6" method.

L. S. Vaidyanathan, however, in his report on the 1931 census expressed the view that actually "the numbers returned at each age would have been the same whether ages next birthday or last birthday or nearest birthday had been asked for"; consequently he investigated the results of Meikle's "4–6; 7–13" method in conjunction with his nearest birthday assumption, and also of another arrangement of unequal groups of four and six ages based on "3–6; 7–12" and the assumption that the ages recorded at the census were ages last birthday. After examining these two unequal grouping plans as well as all the five usual equal quinquennial arrangements, Vaidyanathan concluded that the "2–6" method of equal groups was the best of all for the particular errors encountered in the Indian returns.

The numerous investigations respecting the best methods of grouping which are recorded in the preceding paragraphs have been based on widely different data and have led to varying decisions. In all cases the conclusions reached were simply those which appeared, on statistical and general grounds, to be acceptable for the particular material at hand. No general rules, therefore, can be laid down (cf. H. H. Wolfenden's remarks, T.A.S.A., XLII, 83–85).

(2) *Estimates of Populations*

55. As stated in pars. 7 and 11, censuses are not generally taken on December 31 or January 1, while birth and death statistics are usually tabulated by calendar years. It is therefore frequently necessary, before undertaking the construction of a mortality table from such data, to relate the populations as well as the births and deaths to the beginnings or ends of calendar years. A similar problem is encountered by vital statisticians, independently of the construction of mortality tables, in the preparation of annual reports on vital statistics which necessitate the calculation, for a variety of purposes and areas, of estimated populations for each year since the last census; and such calculations have often been extended to the prediction of the populations which may be expected to exist many years from the present time. The term *intercensal population* may be applied to a population figure calculated for a date anywhere between two dates for which the actual census returns are available; while a *postcensal population* is one computed for a date subsequent to that of the last census.

56. Another type of estimated population, namely, the average or *mean population*, is also required sometimes when a table is constructed to represent the mortality which has prevailed during a calendar year, or during a series of calendar years between two censuses (see par. 85). This "mean population," in respect of a certain community for a given period, may be interpreted as the equivalent of the number of such periods of life which were actually lived by the members of the community during that period. "Thus the statement that a mean population of a given town for a certain month was 1,000,000 should mean that during the month 1,000,000 months of human life had been experienced in the town" (C. H. Wickens, J.I.A., XLIII, 67); and in the usual case of one year being

considered as a unit the expression "years of life" is consequently often used to denote the mean population multiplied by the number of years to which that mean population relates. Such a mean population may be expressed very conveniently in terms of the intercensal populations by the integral calculus; for if the intercensal population at any time t since the last census is, say, P_t when one year is taken as a unit, the mean population for, say, a 10-year period will be

$$\frac{1}{10}\int_0^{10} P_t\, dt,$$

or if the entire ten years are taken as the unit the equivalent expression would be

$$\int_0^1 P_t'\, dt$$

in which P_t' is the population at time t with ten years as the unit.

57. The most obvious method of computing intercensal, postcensal, and mean populations for the whole of a country is the *statistical method*, by which a continuous statistical record of the movement of population is maintained, and the total population at any date is the Number at Preceding Census + (Births + Immigrants) − (Deaths + Emigrants). This method has been used for many years in Sweden (where the estimates have been remarkably accurate) and in a number of other European countries; Australia and New Zealand have employed it for a long time; and it has been adopted in Great Britain, and in the United States since the birth and death registration areas were extended to cover the entire country. The greatest difficulty in its application is the incompleteness of the statistics of migration, and especially of emigration; for although many countries record particulars of immigrants with reasonable accuracy by personal examination at the place of entry, the departures from a country are not always supervised, so that many emigrants escape notice altogether and can only be traced imperfectly if they are reported as immigrants into another country. On this account it is sometimes assumed, where birth and death registrations are reliable, that any discrepancy between a census population predicted by this method and the actual census figure is attributable to "unrecorded departures," and that consequently the recorded departures should be increased in the appropriate ratio (cf. Wickens, J.I.A., XLIII, 61, and J. S. Thompson, T.A.S.A., XIX, 260). In applying the method for estimating the population of the United States, the birth and death statistics are corrected by the Bureau of the Census for under-registration (see the Bureau's "Estimated Population in Continental United States, by Age, Color, and Sex,

1940–1942," Population Special Reports, 1944). A recent discussion of several aspects of the problems involved may be found in a paper by J. S. Siegel and C. H. Hamilton on "Some Considerations in the Use of the Residual Method of Estimating Net Migration" (J.A.S.A., XLVII, 475).

In determining a mean population by this method the integral as in par. 56 would be computed from the yearly (or half-yearly, quarterly, or monthly) intercensal populations either by a formula of approximate integration, or by the less accurate assumption of linear progression used by J. S. Thompson in T.A.S.A., XIX, 265 and 268, and stated by Wickens in J.I.A., XLIII, 67, under which, for example, the mean population for a ten-year period could be obtained from the intercensal populations as at the beginning of each year by taking one-tenth of the sum of the yearly means. When there are marked seasonal fluctuations in the migration, as in the case of New Zealand, it may be desirable to weight the intercensal populations to allow for such fluctuations (cf. E. P. Neale, "A New Zealand Study in Seasonal Fluctuations of External Migration, with Special Reference to the Computation of Mean Annual Populations," J.R.S.S., LXXXVI, 226).

In applying the statistical method to various age groups, the process may be applied to each group separately, and the total of the estimates for all age groups would then be taken as the estimated total population. An alternative procedure for effecting the distribution by age groups, however, was used in the 1911 Australian Life Tables, where the scale of distribution expressed by the ratio π_t/P_t, where π_t is the population of a particular age group, was assumed to be a function of t, say, $f(t)$, and sufficiently accurate results were obtained by assuming linear progression, so that $f(t) = a + bt$, in which case the mean population over n years for an age group, being

$$\frac{1}{n}\int_0^n \pi_t \, dt \, ,$$

becomes

$$\frac{1}{n}\int_0^n (a + bt) P_t \, dt \, ,$$

which is evaluated by calculating a and b for each age group from the age distributions at the initial and terminal censuses and the integrals

$$\int_0^n P_t \, dt \quad \text{and} \quad \int_0^n t P_t \, dt$$

by approximate integration (see 1911 Census of Australia, Vol. I, pp. 85–87).

58. While this statistical method will frequently give close estimates of population for the whole of a country, it cannot be applied directly to the populations of particular localities therein, since no migration figures covering movements within each country are generally available. Special procedures are therefore necessary for the subdivision of the national figure into estimates of its component parts.

The first such methods for estimating local populations were based on the theory that the population of a particular locality could be assumed to bear some definite relation to the number of inhabited houses or family dwellings in the district, or the number of births or the children attending school in certain grades, or to economic data such as the number of water, gas, or electric meters. This theory was applied originally by taking account of only one such factor; and although it then reflects only one of a number of variable influences, it can produce good results in some cases because of its ability to take particular local characteristics into account (see 12th U.S. Census, Supplementary Analysis, p. 580, and discussions such as those of E. F. Young in American Journal of Sociology, XXXVIII, No. 4, and F. J. Eberle in J.A.S.A., XXXIII, 694).

E. C. Snow, also, has suggested the use of *multiple correlation* (see "The Application of the Method of Multiple Correlation to the Estimation of Post-Censal Populations," J.R.S.S., LXXIV, 575), by means of which the increase of population between two censuses is expressed as a linear function of two or three different variables such as (*a*) the increase of the births during the period over those of the preceding intercensal period, and the similar increase in the deaths, and in the marriages, or (*b*) the natural increase (i.e., births less deaths), and the increase in the number of inhabited houses, or (*c*) the increase in the inhabited houses and the increase in rateable values. While this method was shown to give some very good results, it is somewhat lengthy, and simpler methods can generally be used.

In the United States the Bureau of the Census, during many years of experimentation, has developed several procedures with the particular object of producing reliable estimates for State and local populations. Following early trials with a ratio method founded on the numbers of public utility consumers, city directories, voting registrations, and school censuses, the Bureau in 1936 published State figures based on natural increase with net migration estimated from comparisons of actual and expected school enrolments. For 1942 and 1943 the wartime registrations for ration books provided material for State and county estimates which were very extensive and unquestionably accurate (see also the footnotes to the table in par. 7, and par. 11, on the use of similar ration-book data for the publication of national population figures in the United Kingdom and Eire). For 1946 and 1947 estimates were prepared following the Bureau's development of two methods for computing net migration from school data:*

(*i*) In the simpler method it is assumed that "the difference between the percentage change in elementary school enrolment for the local area and the national percentage change in population of elementary school age is equal to the percentage change through net migration to or from the local area";

(*ii*) In a more elaborate process, which gave promise of improved results, "net migration is measured on the basis of the difference between the population of elementary school age as estimated from the school data and the expected population of that age had there been no migration since the base date [and] the expected population is computed by applying survival rates from an appropriate life table to the population cohort at the base date that became the population of elementary school age at the estimate date."

In every method of estimating local populations of States, counties, cities, towns, or other areas—and particularly in attempting to make postcensal estimates for dates in the near or distant future—it may also be necessary, of course, to make special allowances for factors likely to produce unusual disturbances, such as the establishment or disappearance of large plants or industries and other economic changes, or severe epidemics, or physical or sociological developments in or near the area which might sharply alter the prosperity or attractiveness of the locality. In wartime, moreover, distinction must be maintained between the civilian population and those in the armed forces.

59. When it is desired to compute estimates of population from the data of two censuses only by using some general hypothesis of population growth, the assumption of *arithmetical progression* has been employed widely, on account of its simplicity and because under many normal conditions it has been shown to give reasonable results (see the U.S. Census Bureau's estimates which were based on this assumption for many years; T.A.S.A., XVIII, 263; J. S. Thompson's "Note on Mean Population," T.A.S.A., XIX, 256; and some of the calculations in H. H. Wolfenden's Canadian estimates, T.A.S.A., XXXV, 283–89). By this method, if in a

---

* See "Population, Special Reports, P-47, No. 4," "Current Population Reports, Population Estimates, P-25, No. 12," and "Current Status of State and Local Population Estimates in the Census Bureau" by H. S. Shryock and N. Lawrence, in J.A.S.A., XLIV, 157, where the procedures are summarized, and the necessary precautions respecting the underlying assumptions and the precise school data to be used are discussed fully.

given age (or other) group π_1 be the population enumerated at one census, π_2 that at the next census n years later, and π_t the intercensal population at time t after the first census, then

$$\pi_t = \pi_1 + \frac{t}{n}(\pi_2 - \pi_1)$$

and the mean population over the n years, namely

$$\frac{1}{n}\int_0^n \pi_t \, dt \, ,$$

becomes $\frac{1}{2}(\pi_1 + \pi_2)$. Also, calling the total population at the first and second censuses P_1 and P_2 respectively, so that $P_1 = \Sigma\pi_1$ and $P_2 = \Sigma\pi_2$, it follows that the intercensal total population P_t may be calculated either from the group values as

$$\Sigma\pi_t = \Sigma\left[\pi_1 + \frac{t}{n}(\pi_2 - \pi_1)\right]$$

or directly from the totals as

$$P_1 + \frac{t}{n}(P_2 - P_1) \, ;$$

and the mean total population similarly will be given either as the sum of the group means or independently as

$$\frac{1}{n}\int_0^n P_t \, dt \, ,$$

that is, $\frac{1}{2}(P_1 + P_2)$.

60. The arithmetical progression method assumes a yearly increase of constant amount. Since, however, population begets population it has often been suggested that a preferable hypothesis will be that of *geometrical progression*, under which a constant rate of increase (instead of a constant amount) is assumed. This principle is frequently applicable as long as it is not used for the prediction of populations many years hence, or in cases where the density of population has become so great that a decreasing rate of increase is indicated.

The rate of increase r is obtained from the supposition that $\pi_2 = r\pi_1$. Taking one year as the unit, the intercensal population π_t is then $r^{t/n}\pi_1$ on the assumption that the progression is continuous, and the mean population for the n years is

$$\frac{1}{n}\int_0^n \pi_1 r^{t/n} dt \, ,$$

that is,

$$\left(\frac{r-1}{\lambda r}\right)\pi_1 \qquad \text{or} \qquad \frac{\kappa(r-1)}{\log r}\pi_1$$

where λ denotes Napierian and "log" the common logarithm, and κ is the modulus. Or taking the n years as the unit the intercensal population is $r^t\pi_1$ and the mean population

$$\int_0^1 \pi_1 r^t dt$$

which gives the same result as before.* If the mean population were required for a period not exactly coincident with the n years of the intercensal period the limits of integration would be suitably modified (see, for example, J.I.A., XLII, 261).

In calculating intercensal and mean populations, r is generally taken as the ratio of the numbers in the same group at the two censuses n years apart; so that if π_x^z denote the numbers at age x at the census in year z, r would be

$$\frac{\pi_x^z}{\pi_x^{z-n}}.$$

In predicting future populations this same principle is usually extended by taking π_x^{z+n} as $r\pi_x^z$, that is,

$$\pi_x^z\left(\frac{\pi_x^z}{\pi_x^{z-n}}\right).$$

Persons aged x at one census, however, are the survivors of the migration during the intercensal period and of those who were aged $x-n$ at the census n years previously. Hardy and Wyatt, therefore, in preparing the 1911 age-group estimates for the National Insurance Act and the National Health Tables in the United Kingdom, allowed for this variation in age by assuming that the rates of mortality and the net rates of migration at various ages over the years z to $z+n$ were similar to those of the period from $z-n$ to z, so that the ratio

$$\frac{\pi_x^{z+n}}{\pi_{x-n}^z}$$

would be equivalent to

$$\frac{\pi_x^z}{\pi_{x-n}^{z-n}},$$

* Cf. G. King, J.I.A., XLII, 260; C. H. Wickens, J.I.A., XLIII, 68; and J. S. Thompson, T.A.S.A., XIX, 258. On p. 257 of the last-mentioned paper an approximate method is also shown, by which the mean population over n years is taken as $1/n$ times the sum of the successive yearly geometric means.

whence $\pi_x^{z+n} = r'\pi_x^z$ where

$$r' = \frac{\pi_{x-n}^z}{\pi_{x-n}^{z-n}}$$

(see J.I.A., XLV, 411, and XLVII, 553).*

If this method—which may be called the *true G.P. method*—be applied to each age-group separately, by taking r in each case as the rate of increase shown by the particular group under consideration, then the total intercensal population P_t or the mean population must be taken merely as the sum of the various age-group figures. An independent calculation from P_1 and P_2, on the assumption that $P_2 = RP_1$, cannot be made, because in practice it is found that the rates of increase of the various groups and of the total population are not the same, with the result that it cannot be assumed that the total population also follows its own G.P.—for the sum of a number of G.P.'s is not itself a G.P.

61. This fact is not objectionable in some cases, as in the calculation of intercensal or mean populations for certain fixed age-groups. There are many instances in vital statistics, however, where intercensal estimates have to be made for thousands of subdivisions in such a way that when estimates for certain subdivisions of the total population, such as age-groups, have been made, these estimates must admit of further subdivision, and the total population also must permit of subdivision into other groups, such as by localities, without disturbing either the subdivisional estimates or the mean total population already calculated. The "true G.P. method" does not fulfil this condition. Several methods have therefore been suggested under which only the total population is assumed to follow its own G.P.—the various groups being assumed to progress in some manner (necessarily not so that each one follows its own G.P.) such that the total of the estimates of the various groups will actually produce the total population estimated, as assumed, upon its own G.P.

(*i*) Of these methods, the simplest may be called a *modified geometrical progression*. The procedure is to compute the A.P. value for each group and then to multiply each value by the constant ratio

$$\frac{\text{Total Population by G.P.}}{\text{Total Population by A.P.}}$$

The total population thus takes its G.P. value; and the group values are brought to an approximate G.P. basis, while retaining the proportionate distribution of A.P., in such a way that subsequent subdivisions may be

---

* Necessary modifications were introduced to allow for the decrease in the rates of mortality of 1901–11 (z to $z + n$) in comparison with those of 1891–1901 ($z - n$ to z).

effected easily without disturbing the original calculations. The method was used for a number of years by the Registrar-General of England and Wales for estimating local populations (see E. C. Snow, *op. cit.* in par. 58 here, and 72nd Registrar-General's Report, p. ix); it was suggested independently and examined by H. H. Wolfenden in T.A.S.A., XX, 225; and it was employed for the official Canadian population estimates in the Annual Report on Vital Statistics, 1922 (see also 1921 Census of Canada, I, xliv). It may be noted that in the case of a stationary population group the formula gives a result below the stationary value—which, although a slight theoretical defect, is an error on the safe side (see T.A.S.A., XX, 225). In practice, the method frequently gives good results (see, for examples, T.A.S.A., XX, 227, and XXXV, 283–88); and—as there stated —"particularly where it is found desirable to base the mean total population on G.P., while the various constituent groups show such divergent rates, as is usual, that neither A.P. nor G.P. can confidently be assumed for them, this method would meet the case, and it can be applied to any number of sub-groups with great facility."

(*ii*) The Registrar-General, however, later adopted a method which may be called *A. C. Waters' First Method*, from the name of its author who published it originally in J.R.S.S., LXIV, 293 (see also Part I, Supplement to 65th Report of the Registrar-General, p. cxvii; J.I.A., XLII, 263; T.A.S.A., XIX, 259; and R. Henderson's "Mortality Laws and Statistics," pp. 53–55). The condition that the sum of the group values shall equal the total G.P. population is fulfilled by assuming that the ratio of each group to the total population, viz., π_t/P_t, increases in A.P. so that $\pi_t = (a + bt)\, P_t$, say (as in the method of par. 57). Then, since the total population is founded upon G.P. so that $P_t = R^t P_1$, it follows that $\pi_t = P_1(a + bt)\, R^t$, and the mean population is therefore

$$P_1 \int_0^1 (a + bt)\, R^t\, dt = P_1 \left(\frac{R-1}{\lambda R}\right)\!\left\{ a + b\left(\frac{R}{R-1} - \frac{1}{\lambda R}\right)\right\}.$$

The values of a and b are determined from the fundamental assumption, which gives $\pi_1 = aP_1$ and $\pi_2 = (a + b)\, P_2$; and hence the mean population of the group becomes

$$\frac{1}{\lambda R}\left[\pi_1\left(\frac{R-1}{\lambda R} - 1\right) + \pi_2\left(1 - \frac{R-1}{R\lambda R}\right)\right],$$

and the sum of these values for the various groups is

$$\frac{1}{\lambda R}\left[P_1\left(\frac{R-1}{\lambda R} - 1\right) + P_2\left(1 - \frac{R-1}{R\lambda R}\right)\right] = \frac{R-1}{\lambda R}\,P_1,$$

which is the geometric mean as required. The formula, being of the form $f(R)\pi_1 + \phi(R)\pi_2$ where $f(R)$ and $\phi(R)$ depend only upon the total population, ensures consistency between estimates once made and subsequent subdivisions of those estimates; and the factors $f(R)$ and $\phi(R)$ when once calculated suffice for all the years and groupings in the intercensal period.

This method has been used in the construction of English Life Tables Nos. 6 and 7, the London Life Table, and by M. D. Grant in constructing his Canadian Life Tables (see T.A.S.A., XXXV, 291). It has, however, a slight theoretical defect. The fundamental assumption upon which it is based, namely, that the ratio

$$\frac{\text{Age Group}}{\text{Total Population}}$$

increases in A.P., while the total population increases in G.P., cannot contemplate a stationary population in any group—for with a stationary group b and the total population following a G.P. $y = aR^t$, the ratio

$$\frac{\text{Age Group}}{\text{Total Population}}$$

follows the curve

$$y = \frac{b}{aR^t}$$

which is a G.P. and not an A.P. as assumed. The result is that it gives a value in excess of the census populations in the case where $\pi_1 = \pi_2$ (see A. C. Waters, 70th Annual Report of the Registrar-General, p. cxxxii, and H. H. Wolfenden, T.A.S.A., XX, 221).

(*iii*) Waters consequently devised a second formula, which was intended to be free from the above defect and may be referred to as *A. C. Waters' Second Method* (see 70th Registrar-General's Report, p. cxxxii; A. T. Traversi, J.R.S.S., LXXX, 84 and 529; H. H. Wolfenden, T.A.S.A., XX, 222; and J. W. Glover, U.S. Life Tables, p. 353). If we suppose that $\pi_t = m\pi_1 + n\pi_2$, one condition must be introduced to give m and n determinate values; and if this condition be that when the group population is stationary, so that $\pi_1 = \pi_2$, then π_t must also remain unchanged so that $\pi_t = \pi_1$, we must have $m + n = 1$, so that $\pi_t = m\pi_1 + (1 - m) \pi_2$. And since the sum of the group values must equal the total population similarly estimated we must have $\Sigma\pi_t$, that is, $m\Sigma\pi_1 + (1 - m)\Sigma\pi_2$ equal to P_t or $mP_1 + (1 - m)P_2$, whence

$$m = \frac{P_2 - P_t}{P_2 - P_1}.$$

Consequently

$$\pi_t = \left(\frac{P_2 - P_t}{P_2 - P_1}\right) \pi_1 + \left(\frac{P_t - P_1}{P_2 - P_1}\right)\pi_2$$

from which, assuming as before that the total population follows its own

G.P. with ratio R, the mean population becomes

$$\left(\frac{R}{R-1} - \frac{1}{\lambda R}\right) \pi_1 + \left(\frac{1}{\lambda R} - \frac{1}{R-1}\right) \pi_2$$

which for practical calculations may be written

$$\pi_1 + \left(\frac{1}{\lambda R} - \frac{1}{R-1}\right)(\pi_2 - \pi_1).$$

In this last form Traversi has given an alternative demonstration, which clearly shows the fundamental assumption that π_1, in increasing to π_2, changes in such a manner that the increase $(\pi_2 - \pi_1)$ is supposed to follow the progression of the increment $(P_2 - P_1)$. Being again of the form $f(R)\pi_1 + \phi(R)\pi_2$, it permits the subdivision of results, and is very easily applied. The formula was used in the Registrar-General's Reports of 1911–14, in the United States Life Tables, 1901–10, etc. (on p. 354 of which is a clear example of the method of taking the limits of integration in dealing with an intercensal period which is not an integral number of years), and on account of the simplicity of its application in determining certain mean populations from the New Zealand data for 1911–15 and 1916–20 (see L. S. Polden, "The Construction of Mortality Tables from National Statistics with Special Reference to Some Investigations Conducted in Respect of the Population of New Zealand, and a Comparison of Mortality Rates between Australia and New Zealand," Actuarial Society of Australasia, 1926, and T.A.S.A., XXXV, 291). However, it does not completely rectify the defect in Waters' first formula, for it will give a mean population exceeding the A.M. (which is contrary to the principle that the A.M. is greater than the G.M.) in the case of a decreasing group when

$$\left(\frac{1}{\lambda R} - \frac{1}{R-1}\right) < \tfrac{1}{2}$$

(see J.R.S.S., LXXX, 89, and T.A.S.A., XX, 223; and H. H. Wolfenden, T.A.S.A., XXXV, 283–91, for its application to the calculations of post-censal estimates).

(*iv*) *A. T. Traversi's Method*, which was given in J.R.S.S., LXXX, 84 and 529, removes entirely the theoretical blemishes in Waters' two formulae by imposing, in effect, the condition that the mean population for each age group shall always fall between the A.M. and the G.M. The excess of the A.M. over the G.M. for a group being

$$\pi_1\left(\frac{1+r}{2}\right) - \pi_1\left(\frac{r-1}{\lambda r}\right) = \pi_1\left(\frac{i^2}{12} - \frac{i^3}{24} + \frac{19\,i^4}{720} - \cdots\right)$$

where $1 + i = r$, Traversi scales down the A.M. for each group in proportion to $i^2\pi_1$, the approximate difference between the A.M. and the G.M. His method of application is to calculate first the A.M. for the whole population and for each group, and then to scale down the group values as follows: "(*a*) Ascertain the difference between the results from A.P. and G.P. for the population as a whole, i.e.,

$$P_1\left(\frac{1+R}{2}\right) - P_1\left(\frac{R-1}{\lambda R}\right);$$

(*b*) Ascertain the value of $i^2\pi_1$ or

$$\pi_1\left(\frac{\pi_2}{\pi_1} - 1\right)^2$$

for each age group; (*c*) Divide up (*a*) in proportion to (*b*); (*d*) Deduct the result from the A.M. of each age group." Some numerical results by this method are shown in T.A.S.A., **XX**, 227, for mean populations, and in T.A.S.A., **XXXV**, 283–91, for postcensal estimates. A practical disadvantage for some purposes is that subsequent subdivisions or rearrangements of results once obtained cannot be made without disturbing the original calculations.

62. The assumption of G.P. is more defensible theoretically in the case of a population which increases mainly by an excess of births over deaths, while the change in a population increasing by immigration may sometimes be represented more nearly by an A.P. (cf. D. E. Kilgour, T.A.S.A., **XX**, 229). It has therefore been suggested that a *Combined Progression Method* might be used, by assuming that the increase each year is a constant proportion of the previous year's population plus a constant number. Thus with two census enumerations P_1 and P_2, n years apart, the population one year after the first census would be, say, $P_1R + I$; that after two years would be

$$(P_1R + I)R + I = P_1R^2 + I\left(\frac{R^2 - 1}{R - 1}\right);$$

and so on. The relation between the two census populations is therefore

$$P_2 = P_1R^n + I\left(\frac{R^n - 1}{R - 1}\right).$$

A difficulty with this method, however, is that unless a third census P_3 is also used similarly, in order to give two equations for the solution of R and I, the determination of R and I can only be effected approximately— as proposed, for example, by C. H. Wickens, J.I.A., **XLIII**, 62 (see also A. H. Mowbray, T.A.S.A., **XX**, 217).

The necessity of devising special methods for national populations affected by unusual waves of immigration is illustrated by the Canadian statistics from 1871 to 1921, for which close postcensal estimates for 1911 and 1921 resulted from the assumption that the decennial increase in population since 1901 could be measured as an A.P. plus the excess of the actual immigration over the "normal" average decennial immigration which had occurred from 1871 to 1901 (see H. H. Wolfenden, T.A.S.A., XXXV, 290).

(3) *The Prediction of Future Populations*

63. Although the theory underlying the assumption of G.P.—that population begets population—is often appropriate for the calculation of intercensal or mean populations from the data of the two nearest censuses, it should be used only with great caution in any attempt to predict postcensal populations on account of its tendency to give figures which may be much too high (cf. the first part of par. 60 here, and see H. H. Wolfenden, T.A.S.A., XXXV, 289, for a numerical illustration). In estimating postcensal populations, moreover, it is clearly advisable to select some hypothesis of population growth which aims to take cognizance of the particular features of the population under examination, without arbitrary assumptions concerning any supposed "law" of population increment (cf. Wolfenden, *op. cit.*, p. 290). The prediction of reasonably defensible postcensal estimates is essentially a problem of curve-fitting or extrapolation, whether it is based on the two nearest censuses or on many more; and it must always be remembered (in the words of Henry Schultz, "The Standard Error of a Forecast from a Curve," J.A.S.A., XXV, 184, and as emphasized in "The Fundamental Principles of Mathematical Statistics," p. 320) that "there is no necessary relation between the goodness of fit of a curve to past observations and its reliability for forecasting purposes; a curve may fit the data for the past one hundred years with a high degree of accuracy, and yet fail to predict the situation for the next year or so."

(*i*) Since the growth of populations under many circumstances is orderly and steady—without violent fluctuations—the methods of finite differences can sometimes be applied, or a parabolic curve can be fitted to the data by the method of moments or least squares. A third degree curve was thus found by H. S. Pritchett ("On a Formula for Predicting the Population of the United States," J.A.S.A., II, 278) to give a sound representation of the U.S. census populations from 1790 to 1890 (although the long-range predictions based on that curve are much too large and afford a good illustration of the dangers of extrapolation), and A. L. Bowley in

J.R.S.S., LXXXVIII, 77–79, gave least-square fittings of second degree parabolas to the populations of England and Wales and of France from 1801 to 1911, and of a third degree curve for the United States from 1790 to 1910. It was also shown by Wolfenden in T.A.S.A., XXXV, 289–90, that the populations of the Canadian Provinces could be estimated closely by such methods. Raymond Pearl and L. J. Reed ("On the Rate of Growth of the Population of the U.S. since 1790, and Its Mathematical Representation," Proceedings of the National Academy of Sciences, VI, 276) obtained improved results from the modified curve $P_t = a + bt + ct^2 + d(\log t)$. Bowley (in J.R.S.S., LXXXVIII, 77–78), moreover, gave an excellent representation of the population of England and Wales from 1801 to 1911 by means of the probability integral (see "The Fundamental Principles of Mathematical Statistics," p. 160, and compare E. B. Wilson's illustration of the growth in the number of epidemic scarlet fever cases in the Proceedings of the National Academy of Sciences, XI, 451). In some instances it may be more satisfactory to deal with the decennial (or quinquennial) rates of increase instead of with the actual populations.

(*ii*) Emphasis has already been laid upon the important restriction that curve-fitting methods of this kind are satisfactory only for short-term predictions; when they are applied to long-term estimates they usually fail to allow sufficiently for the slower rates of growth which frequently operate as the populations become denser, so that they tend to over-estimate the ultimate populations. One useful method of giving effect to this feature was Dr. T. H. C. Stevenson's determination of the decennial rates of growth of a particular community from those already experienced under the same densities of population by a similar community in which the development had already been practically completed (see the Journal of Hygiene, 1904, p. 207). Also, since the rates of growth and the densities of populations naturally approach limiting values, several analytical expressions have been suggested to represent those conditions. Thus Knibbs (in his "Mathematical Theory of Population," Appendix A, 1911 Census of Australia, pp. 26, 42, and 53) has discussed forms such as $\eta^{k+mt+nt^2}$, or $at^p + bt^q + ct^r + \ldots$, or $At^m e^{nt^p}$ (see also H. L. Moore's use of the last, with $p = 1$, as a "law of demand" in J.A.S.A., XVIII, 12); and Gompertz's formula kg^{c^z} and Makeham's expression $A + Bc^x$ have been tried with indifferent success (see R. B. Prescott, "Law of Growth in Forecasting Demand," J.A.S.A., XVIII, 471; L. E. Peabody, "Growth Curves and Railway Traffic," J.A.S.A., XIX, 476; and G. R. Davies, "The Growth Curve," J.A.S.A., XXII, 374).

(*iii*) The most widely discussed curve-fitting method for predicting future populations is the *Logistic* curve, which was proposed first by

Verhulst in 1838 and was rediscovered independently by Pearl and Reed in 1920. The assumption that the proportionate rate of increase over time, t, of a population, P_t, growing in a restricted area, will tend to decrease as the population becomes greater may be written in its simplest form as

$$\frac{1}{P_t}\left(\frac{dP_t}{dt}\right) = m - nP_t,$$

where m and n are constants; the solution of this differential equation gives

$$P_t = \frac{B}{1 + C e^{-kt}}.$$

This "logistic" curve starts from a lower asymptote, follows closely a G.P., reaches a point of inflexion, and thence proceeds symmetrically to an upper asymptote.

Convenient alternative forms are

$$P_t = \frac{A + B e^{k(t-\tau)}}{1 + e^{k(t-\tau)}},$$

where τ denotes the abscissa of the point of inflexion, A and B are the ordinates of the asymptotes, and k is a constant, or

$$P_t = \frac{L}{1 + e^{\frac{\beta - t}{a}}},$$

where L is the limiting population P_∞, a determines the horizontal scale, and β is the time from zero to the point of inflexion, or

$$P_{t'} = \frac{1}{1 + e^{-t'}},$$

where the scales are chosen so that L and a of the preceding expression are unity and the point of inflexion is at zero time.

Pearl and Reed also showed (in their papers on "The Mathematical Theory of Population Growth," Metron, III, 12, and "The Summation of Logistic Curves," J.R.S.S., XC, 729, and in Pearl's "Studies in Human Biology") that the essential symmetry of the preceding expressions for a single logistic can be modified into a sinuous curve by summing component logistics, in order to represent successive cycles of growth (as illustrated in H. Mühsam's "Note on Migration and Verhulst's Logistic Curve," J.R.S.S., CII, 445). The generalized form can be expressed as

$$P_t = d + \frac{k}{1 + m\, e^{a_1 t + a_2 t^2 + a_3 t^3}}.$$

In recent years the logistic curve has been fitted to a wide variety of populations in many countries, by several different methods (see "The Fundamental Principles of Mathematical Statistics," pp. 321 and 327; for graphical methods of fitting see E. B. Wilson, "The Logistic or Autocatalytic Grid," Proceedings of the National Academy of Sciences, XI, 451, W. A. Spurr and D. R. Arnold, "A Short-Cut Method of Fitting a Logistic Curve," J.A.S.A., XLIII, 127, and E. A. Rasor, "The Fitting of Logistic Curves by Means of a Nomograph," J.A.S.A., XLIV, 548). Undoubtedly the formula is capable of representing many series of known past populations with reasonable accuracy, and it can by summation of components or in its generalized form even be made to allow for sinuosities; but it cannot have much claim to be accepted as a "law" of growth, and its use for long-range predictions (in which the importance of the standard errors of the forecast values is to be emphasized) is surrounded inevitably by all the uncertainties and dangers of extrapolation (see Wolfenden, *op. cit.*, pp. 87–88, 169, 238, 320–21, and the discussions there noted).

(*iv*) Without attempting to make any mathematical assumption concerning the growth of the population, another procedure which can be applied when the necessary factors are available (or can be computed or selected with reasonable justification) is of course to project the various age, sex, or other groupings of the population by means of survival ratios which usually would be taken from a suitable life table.

In the notation of par. 64, a known population P_x^z, aged x last birthday according to a census taken at the beginning of a calendar year, would thus be projected, by the survival factor L_{x+n}/L_x from an appropriate life table, to give an estimate of the population n years hence which would then be aged $x + n$ last birthday; or similarly the data can often be handled more expeditiously and with little loss of accuracy by multiplying the known populations in, say, 5-year age groups by factors

$$\frac{T_{x+n} - T_{x+5+n}}{T_x - T_{x+5}}.$$

In practice it may be necessary to adjust the survivors so computed to allow for the number and age distribution of the estimated net migrants during the period of the prediction, while the technique can be elaborated on similar principles in order to subdivide the forecast populations according to sex, race, nativity (i.e., native or foreign-born) or other groups. In recent applications of these principles the calculations have usually been made by sex and race, in quinquennial age groups over successive 5-year projection periods. It is also often important to make the projections by means of survival and other factors which take into account such future changes in mortality rates, etc., as may be anticipated within reason.

The estimation of the populations n years hence at ages under n, which depend on the births during the n years of the prediction period, can be made (a) from assumed births during each of the n years, on the principle that each calendar year's actual births E_0^{z+k} would be multiplied by the life-table ratio L_{n-k-1}/l_0 to reach a prediction of the population aged $n - k - 1$ last birthday (see, for example, Greville's numerical illustration in the U.S. Life Tables and Actuarial Tables, 1939–41, p. 23), or (b) by developing fertility rates of women according to age, applying them to the appropriate female groups in order to estimate the births in the projection period, subdividing those births according to the sex ratio at birth* based on previous data, and then projecting these estimated male and female births to obtain the survivors at the end of the period. Method (b) has been adopted in the United States in all the recent calculations noted in the following paragraph.

Various projections for Great Britain (at intervals 5, 15, 30, 60, and 100 years from 1947) which were published in 1949 in the Report of the Royal Commission on Population have been derived by a somewhat different technique based on the view that the most important factors in population growth (apart from heavy waves of migration) are the trend in the marriage rate and the number of children born per married couple (i.e., the size of the resulting families, as defined in the footnote to par. 163 here, according to duration of marriage rather than by age). Both these factors are markedly dependent on economic conditions and threatened or actual wars, so that they fluctuate in a much sharper and more unpredictable manner than the relatively stable rates of mortality; they are, moreover, the underlying factors which determine the future numbers of births. Three series of projections were computed; all three assumed that mortality would continue to fall (over the next 30 years according to the trend of the decline during the last 50 years), and that marriage rates could be taken at the intermediate level of 1942–47; they differed, however, in the hypotheses respecting future family size—the first supposing that family size would remain constant at the same level as among couples married in 1927–38, the second that it would be constant at a level 6%

* The stability of the sex ratio at birth for each race, regardless of such factors as order of birth, age of mother, economic conditions, etc., and regardless of war, is indicated in R. J. Myers' papers "A Note on the Variance of Sex Ratios" (Human Biology, XV, 267), "Effect of the War on the Sex Ratio at Birth" (American Sociological Review, XII, 40), and "War and Post-war Experience in Regard to the Sex Ratio at Birth in Various Countries" (Human Biology, XXI, 257).

higher than the first, and the third that it would fall progressively to 80% of the first. Final adjustments also were shown to illustrate the effects of different assumptions with respect to net migration.

These general methods, which are essentially actuarial in nature, have been used on many occasions. Early examples are those of A. L. Bowley in 1924 with respect to "Births and Populations of Great Britain" (Journal of the Royal Economic Society, XXXIV, 188) and his 1926 League of Nations "Estimates of the Working Population of Certain Countries in 1931 and 1941." Other population projections which have been made at various times by several investigators in Great Britain are examined briefly, with some descriptions of the techniques involved, by P. R. Cox in chapters 12 and 13 of the Institute of Actuaries' and Faculty of Actuaries' book on "Demography." They have also been elaborated and applied very extensively by Warren S. Thompson and P. K. Whelpton (of the Scripps Foundation for Research in Population Problems) in respect of the U.S. populations,* by Frank W. Notestein and others for various European countries,† by R. J. Myers in the preparation of U.S. population projections for social insurance cost estimates,‡ and by the Royal

---

* The first forecasts of Thompson and Whelpton were prepared for the National Resources Planning Board in 1934 as "Estimates of Future Population by States"; in 1937 their "Population Statistics, National Data" gave six projections on differing assumptions; and in 1943 the National Resources Planning Board sponsored their revised and extended "Estimates of Future Populations of the United States, 1940–2000," in which twelve sets of estimates were given. In 1947 the Bureau of the Census published "Forecasts of the Population of the United States, 1945–1975" which was prepared by Whelpton alone. A new unit for the continuing official production of such estimates has now been created within the Bureau.

† These estimates were made in 1944 by Notestein and four members of the Office of Population Research of the League of Nations under the title "The Future Population of Europe and the Soviet Union; Population Projections, 1940–1970," with technical appendices and detailed methodological notes (see also T.A.S.A., XLV, 436).

‡ See "Illustrative U.S. Population Projections, 1946" (Actuarial Study No. 24, Social Security Administration) by R. J. Myers, where estimates of the U.S. population by age groups, for use in long-range cost estimates of the Old Age and Survivors Insurance program, are deduced, by the methods used by Thompson and Whelpton, up to the year 2050 on four bases: (A) Low fertility, high mortality, no immigration; (B) high fertility, low mortality, and immigration of 100,000 per annum; (C) high fertility, high mortality, no immigration; and (D) medium fertility, low mortality, and no immigration. The most recent estimates, prepared by R. J. Myers and E. A. Rasor for the actuarial cost estimates of the old-age and survivors insurance system, are now the "Illustrative United States Population Projections, 1952" (Actuarial Study No. 33, Social Security Administration). An earlier discussion of the problems involved in deciding upon the various factors required in this method is given in "Population, Birth, and Mortality Trends in the United States" by R. J. Myers, T.A.S.A., XLI, 66. The

Commission on Population in Great Britain.*

Because many different assumptions possessing varying degrees of plausibility must be made with regard to marriage rates, fertility, mortality, net migration, military losses, and other influences, such projections are usually prepared on several alternative bases, which often indicate ultimate conclusions with startling disparities. Their underlying uncertainties must therefore be clearly understood. The grave doubts, indeed, which must be expressed with regard to the validity of long-range population estimates of this general character are well substantiated by H. F. Dorn's paper in J.A.S.A., XLV, 311, on "Pitfalls in Population Forecasts and Projections" in the United States, and are further emphasized by the scepticism concerning the projections of the Royal Commission on Population in Great Britain which is recorded in J.I.A., LXXVI, 47–49.

---

projections made by the Committee on Economic Security in 1934 may also be noted as summarized in "Issues in Social Security" (A Report to the Committee on Ways and Means of the House of Representatives, January 17, 1946).

* See the Report of the Royal Commission on Population, 1949 (Cmd. 7695), and the discussions in J.I.A., LXXVI, 38, and J.R.S.S., CXIV, 38.

VI

THE MATHEMATICAL RELATIONSHIPS BETWEEN BIRTHS, DEATHS, AND POPULATIONS, AND THE FORMULAE FOR THE RATES OF MORTALITY

64. When the population data and death records of an actual community are used for the purpose of computing the fundamental probability of death, q_x, in the year of age x to $x + 1$, it is essential to keep clearly in view the different calendar years of observation. In constructing the formulae depicting the relationships between births, deaths, and populations in such an actual community, moreover, the assumption of a uniform distribution of deaths (with which the student will be familiar from his earlier knowledge of the conventional "life table")* will not be made until the conditions justifying its introduction are understood. In order thus to deal with these relationships involving both calendar years and years of age, and at the same time to examine the admissibility of the assumption of uniform distributions, it is necessary to employ a notation in which the required distinctions will be carefully maintained. The following symbols will therefore be employed in respect of the calendar year z:†

* It may be well here to emphasize again that q_x is the basic function which is required, and that the "life table," as it is described in such textbooks as E. F. Spurgeon's "Life Contingencies" and as it is universally employed in actuarial work, "is merely a convenient statistical device by which many complex formulae involving the fundamental rates of mortality, either without or with an associated rate of interest, may be translated from algebraical into arithmetical terms" (see H. H. Wolfenden, T.A.S.A., XXXV, 281). The "life table" represents a purely hypothetical community, subject to the q_x of the actual community, in which a constant number of births, l_0, occur each year and there is no immigration or emigration—so that $q_x = d_x/l_x$ where, in life-table notation, l_x is the number attaining precise age x and d_x is the number dying in the year of age x to $x + 1$. In this hypothetical "life-table community," as it may be called, the "number living" l_x is equivalent to the sum of the deaths at age x and beyond; and calendar years are not distinguished. The "central death rate" is $m_x = d_x/L_x$ where L_x is the population $\int_0^1 l_{x+t} dt$ in the year of age x to $x + 1$; and $L_x = l_x - d_x/2$ in that portion of the table (usually at ages 5 and up) where the customary life-table assumption of a uniform distribution of deaths over the year of age can be made.

† This notation is that given in H. H. Wolfenden's paper "On the Determination of the Rates of Mortality at Infantile Ages, from Statistics of the General Population," T.A.S.A., XXIV, 126, where it is employed as a simplification of that used by Professor J. W. Glover in the U.S. Life Tables, 1890, etc., pp. 329 et seq. The statements and demonstrations of all the formulae (1)–(18) and (21)–(39) here are also taken from the same paper.

P_x^z will denote the population aged x last birthday (i.e., in the year of age x to $x + 1$) at the beginning (i.e., on January 1) of the calendar year $z;$ and P_x^{z+1} will denote the population aged x last birthday (i.e., in the year of age x to $x + 1$) at the end (i.e., on December 31) of the calendar year z (being the beginning, i.e., January 1, of the calendar year $z + 1$).

D_x^z will denote the deaths aged x last birthday (i.e., in the year of age x to $x + 1$) in the calendar year z.

E_x^z will denote those who attain exact age x during the calendar year z. Thus P, D, and E will be used for the data of the actual community; and they are analogous, respectively, to the L, d, and l of the life table. The fundamental relation between them is

$$D_x^z = (P_x^z - E_{x+1}^z) + (E_x^z - P_x^{z+1}) \tag{1}$$

the rationale of which may be seen easily by taking a particular case, as follows: The deaths D_{25}^{1905}, say, in 1905 in the year of age 25–26 clearly arise from the births of 1879 and 1880. From the 1879 births the deaths occur between January 1, 1905, and attainment of age 26 in 1905, so that they number $(P_{25}^{1905} - E_{26}^{1905})$; from the 1880 births the deaths in the year of age 25–26 in 1905 occur between attainment of age 25 in 1905 and December 31, 1905 (i.e., January 1, 1906), when they are variously aged from 25 to 26, so that they number $(E_{25}^{1905} - P_{25}^{1906})$; and the sum of these two sections gives the total deaths D_{25}^{1905} as in the general formula (where $x = 25$, and the calendar year z is the year commencing January 1, 1905).

If we also denote by $_\delta D_x^z$ the deaths (in the first bracket) which occur between the beginning of the calendar year and attainment of age $x + 1$, and by $_a D_x^z$ the deaths (second bracket) between attainment of age x and the end of the calendar year, then

$$_\delta D_x^z = P_x^z - E_{x+1}^z \tag{2}$$
$$_a D_x^z = E_x^z - P_x^{z+1} \tag{3}$$

and

$$D_x^z = {_\delta D_x^z} + {_a D_x^z} . \tag{4}$$

Also, from (2) and (3) it follows that

$$P_x^z = {_\delta D_x^z} + {_a D_{x+1}^z} + P_{x+1}^{z+1} \tag{5}$$

By the successive application of these fundamental formulae it is then possible to relate the populations to the births from which they arise. For, applying (5) to the initial relation $E_0^z = P_0^{z+1} + {_a D_0^z}$ from (3) we get successively

$$\left.\begin{aligned}
E_0^z &= P_0^{z+1} + {_a D_0^z} \\
E_0^z &= P_1^{z+2} + {_a D_0^z} + {_\delta D_0^{z+1}} + {_a D_1^{z+1}} \\
E_0^z &= P_2^{z+3} + {_a D_0^z} + {_\delta D_0^{z+1}} + {_a D_1^{z+1}} + {_\delta D_1^{z+2}} + {_a D_2^{z+2}}
\end{aligned}\right\} \tag{6}$$

and so on.

These equations show the exact manner in which the births E_0^z may be derived by adding the appropriate deaths to the populations of later calendar years. Conversely, if the births are known, the populations may be computed therefrom by deducting the appropriate deaths, as here set out.*

65. From (3) and (2) it is clear that $_aD_x^z$ are the deaths in the year of age x to $x + 1$ in the calendar year z, out of those born in the calendar year $z - x$; while $_\delta D_x^z$, being the balance of the deaths in the year of age x to $x + 1$ in the calendar year z, were born in the preceding calendar year. Consequently, if we can obtain numerical values for the latter proportion $_\delta D_x^z/(_\delta D_x^z + _aD_x^z)$, which may be denoted by f_x^z, and therefore also for its complement $(1 - f_x^z)$, the calendar year's deaths may be divided according to the two generations from which they arise. Thus

$$f_x^z = \frac{_\delta D_x^z}{D_x^z},$$

and

$$1 - f_x^z = \frac{_aD_x^z}{D_x^z}.$$

In some countries, such as Germany and Austria, the deaths in each calendar year have been registered according to calendar year of birth as well as by year (or month) of age at death; and under such circumstances tabulations of the $_\delta D$ and $_aD$ deaths, and thence f_x^z and $(1 - f_x^z)$, follow directly (see, for example, Glover's U.S. Life Tables, p. 339, and J.I.A., LIII, 221).

In Great Britain, Canada, the United States, and most other countries, however, such tabulations of deaths by calendar year of birth are not generally available. An alternative procedure then is to calculate f_x^z from tabulations of the deaths by months of age. This, however, can usually be done only for the first year of age, and sometimes for the second, because the monthly deaths are not usually recorded for the later years of age. For those first years f_x^z can be found very closely by following the development of the calendar years' deaths as given in par. 64. For the deaths in, say, 1905 aged $0-\frac{1}{12}$ must arise from the births of December 1, 1904, to January 1, 1906; the deaths aged $\frac{1}{12}-\frac{2}{12}$ arise from the births of November 1, 1904, to December 1, 1905; and so on until finally the deaths aged $\frac{11}{12}-1$ arise from the births of January 1, 1904, to February 1, 1905. Consequently in order to find, say, $(1 - f_0^{1905})$, which, being $_aD/(_\delta D + _aD)$, is the proportion of the calendar year's deaths which arise from the

---

* A diagrammatic representation of this principle, which may be useful to some students, is given (largely from Czuber's Wahrscheinlichkeitsrechnung) by Glover in the U.S. Life Tables, 1890, etc., pp. 329 et seq.

births of the later of the two calendar years, we may take

$$(1 - f_0^z) = (\tfrac{12}{13}d_1 + \tfrac{11}{13}d_2 + \tfrac{10}{13}d_3 + \ldots + \tfrac{1}{13}d_{12}) \div \sum_{n=1}^{n=12} d_n,$$

where d_n = deaths in the nth month of the year of age. Or, using areas instead of ordinates as in the U.S. Life Tables, 1890, etc., p. 340, we should find similarly

$$(1 - f_0^z) = (\tfrac{23}{24}d_1 + \tfrac{21}{24}d_2 + \tfrac{19}{24}d_3 + \ldots + \tfrac{1}{24}d_{12}) \div \sum_{n=1}^{n=12} d_n.$$

A somewhat more precise method, which cannot be expressed readily by a formula, was used in the U.S. Life Tables and Actuarial Tables, 1939–41, pp. 117–18, where advantage was taken of tabulations of deaths under one year of age by age at death in months and also by calendar month of death. In most instances it is possible from this information to determine whether the birth occurred in the calendar year of death or in the preceding year. In cases of doubt (e.g., for deaths occurring in March at the age of two months in completed months) it was assumed that one-half of such deaths arise from the births of each of the two calendar years involved. An exception was made in the case of deaths in January at ages under one month, where data were available for certain subdivisions of the first month of life and appropriate factors were accordingly applied to the figures for these various subdivisions. By these rules the deaths $_\delta D_0^z$ were estimated, and f_0^z then followed.

The values of f_x^z which have been found by these methods have shown significant changes during recent years. For example, in the U.S. Life Tables, 1890, 1901, 1910, and 1901–10, the values for all calendar years finally adopted by Glover were $f_0^z = .28$ for males and .29 for females; $f_1^z = .41; f_2^z = .47; f_3^z = .48; f_4^z = .48;$ and at higher ages $f_x^z = .5;$ and for the New York State data employed in T.A.S.A., XXIII, 435, and XXIV, 126, the same values were used except $f_0 = .3$ as determined by Henderson from the 1909–11 N.Y. State data alone. Subsequent tabulations for the first year of age given by I. M. Moriyama and T. N. E. Greville (Bureau of the Census, Vital Statistics Special Reports, XIX, No. 21) indicate that for the U.S. birth registration area, as a result of the large decrease in mortality in the later subdivisions of the first year of life, f_0^z decreased fairly steadily from .263 in 1920 to .167 in 1942. In the U.S. Life Tables and Actuarial Tables, 1939–41, p. 118, the calculations produced $f_0^z = .207$ for all males in 1935, with variations which led to the adoption of different values, lying between extremes of .162 and .348, by race and sex in each year from 1934 to 1941; and at ages 1 to 4, as no U.S. data were available for their estimation, Glover's values were again employed after they had been confirmed approximately by a rough theoretical test (*op. cit.*, p. 135). In order, therefore, to obtain actual U.S. values for use in the preparation of future tables, a 10% sample (amounting to slightly over 6,000 cases) of the deaths at ages under 5 in 1944, 1945, and 1946 has since been tabulated according to year of birth, which indicated that, despite moderate irregularities, the values of f_x^z at ages 1–4 have approached closer to .5 since Glover's tables were constructed (see "Investigation of Separation Factors at Ages 1–4 Based on 10% Mortality Sample," Vital Statistics Special Reports, Federal Security Agency, XXX, No. 7).

Some additional material for Norway (1912–26 and 1934–35), Sweden (1915–45), and Denmark (1922–46) may be found in a paper by V. Valaoras on "Refined Rates for Infant and Childhood Mortality" (Population Studies, IV, 253).

66. The factor f_x^z divides the deaths ${}_\delta D_x^z + {}_a D_x^z$ of the year of age x to $x + 1$ which occur in the calendar year z (cf. also pars. 69 and 76 hereafter). In the development of the subsequent formulae it will be useful to employ also an analogous factor, k_x^z, for dividing the deaths ${}_a D_x^z + {}_\delta D_x^{z+1}$ of the year of age x to $x + 1$ which emerge directly by following the movement of the population over the year of age and thus involve two calendar years z and $z + 1$ (cf. pars. 68 and 75 hereafter); and we shall therefore use k_x^z to denote

$$\frac{{}_\delta D_x^{z+1}}{{}_a D_x^z + {}_\delta D_x^{z+1}},$$

namely, the proportion of the deaths of the year of age which occur between the commencement of the calendar year $z + 1$ and attainment of age $x + 1$ in that year. The numerical values of k_x^z are not generally required—for f_x^z is usually determined first, so that ${}_\delta D$ and ${}_a D$ result from them, and hence k_x^z follows. The actual values, however, are very close to f_x^z, since any variation between them is due solely to the variation in the volume of the data of the different calendar years; and in the life table, of course, k_x^z is equal to f_x (see T.A.S.A., XXIV, 141–42). For the first year of age, however, k_0^z has been calculated approximately in the Supplement to the 75th Registrar-General's Report, Part I, p. 5, and Part II, p. xxi, by assuming uniform distributions, and hence taking k_0^z as the proportion of the deaths 0–1 in the calendar year which occur in the second six months of age, according to the formula

$$(1 - k_0) = (d_1 + d_2 + \ldots + d_6) \div \sum_{n=1}^{n=12} d_n.$$

Such values, however, will in general be too low, because d_n decreases rapidly as n increases (see T.A.S.A., XXIV, 144).

Formulae for the Rates of Mortality

67. In now considering the various formulae by which q_x, the rate of mortality in the year of age x to $x + 1$, may be obtained from data which involve both years of age and calendar years, it is essential to remember clearly the manner in which a population moves (a) over the year of age, and (b) over the calendar year.

68. (a) The movement over the year of age is shown by the fact that the E_x^z who enter upon the year of age x to $x + 1$ during the calendar year z change, during (on the average) the latter part of that calendar year, by the occurrence of deaths $_aD_x^z$, to P_x^{z+1} at the end; and that these P_x^{z+1} persons then change, during (on the average) the first portion of the next calendar year $z + 1$, by the occurrence of the deaths $_\delta D_x^{z+1}$, to the E_{x+1}^{z+1} who attain the end of the year of age x to $x + 1$. Consequently

$$q_x = \frac{(E_x^z - P_x^{z+1}) + (P_x^{z+1} - E_{x+1}^{z+1})}{E_x^z} = \frac{E_x^z - E_{x+1}^{z+1}}{E_x^z} \qquad (8) *$$

$$= \frac{_aD_x^z + _\delta D_x^{z+1}}{E_x^z} . \qquad (9)$$

This may also be written

$$1 - \frac{P_x^{z+1}}{E_x^z} \cdot \frac{E_{x+1}^{z+1}}{P_x^{z+1}} ;$$

so that if we write $_ap_x^z$ for the probability, P_x^{z+1}/E_x^z, that a person attaining age x during the calendar year z will survive over (on the average) the latter part of the calendar year to the end of that year, and $_\delta p_x^{z+1}$ for the probability, E_{x+1}^{z+1}/P_x^{z+1}, that a person in the year of age x to $x + 1$ at the beginning of the calendar year $z + 1$ will survive over (on the average) the earlier part of the calendar year until attainment of age $x + 1$ during that year, then

$$q_x = 1 - _ap_x^z \cdot _\delta p_x^{z+1} . \qquad (10)$$

These formulae (8)–(10) will be called the "Type I formulae"—following T.A.S.A., XXIII, 271. It will be noted that the q_x so found is determined from the data of two calendar years, and therefore should strictly be written, say, $q_x^{z/z+1}$. The resulting values, consequently, as shown numerically in Table B, T.A.S.A., XXIV, 154, are a blend of the rates of those two years.

* The numbering of the formulae used in T.A.S.A., XXIV, 139 et seq., is retained here for ease of reference.

From the definitions that

$$_a p_x^z = \frac{P_x^{z+1}}{E_x^z} \quad \text{and} \quad _\delta p_x^z = \frac{E_{x+1}^z}{P_x^z}$$

it will be seen also, since $q = 1 - p$, from (3) that

$$_a q_x^z = \frac{_a D_x^z}{E_x^z},$$

and from (2) that

$$_\delta q_x^z = \frac{_\delta D_x^z}{P_x^z}.$$

69. (*b*) The movement over the calendar year, on the other hand, is shown by the fact that the population P_x^z at the beginning of the calendar year changes during (on the average) the first portion of that calendar year by the occurrence of deaths $_\delta D_x^z$, to the E_{x+1}^z who attain the end of the year of age x to $x + 1$ during the year; and that they are replaced by E_x^z who enter the year of age x to $x + 1$ during the year and who during (on the average) the second portion of the calendar year, by the occurrence of deaths $_a D_x^z$, are reduced to the population P_x^{z+1} at the end.

Hence, on account of the replacement of E_{x+1}^z by E_x^z during the calendar year, formulae analogous to (8) and (9) cannot be written down; but, using ratios, we have immediately

$$q_x = 1 - \frac{E_{x+1}^z}{P_x^z} \cdot \frac{P_x^{z+1}}{E_x^z} \tag{11}$$

$$= 1 - {_\delta p_x^z} \cdot {_a p_x^z}. \tag{12}$$

These are the formulae given by R. Henderson in T.A.S.A., XXIII, 437; and, as in T.A.S.A., XXIII, 272, they will be referred to as the "Type III formulae."[*] They give the true mortality, q_x^z, of the year of age x to $x + 1$ in the calendar year z.[†]

---

[*] The "Type II" formula for q, which is indicated in Glover's U.S. Life Tables, p. 334 (see also T.A.S.A., XXIII, 271), is simply

$$1 - \frac{P_{x+1}^{z+1}}{P_x^z}, \quad \text{or} \quad 1 - {_\delta p_x^z} \cdot {_a p_{x+1}^z},$$

and is obtained by following P_x^z to E_{x+1}^z and thence directly to P_{x+1}^{z+1}. It is not generally useful, however—for it does not give the rate of mortality of an exact year of age, but follows instead the year from the fractional age at the beginning of a calendar year to the fractional age at the end. Since, however, it involves the populations only, it may be employed to give a rate of mortality of the above character from census returns alone, as in par. 83 here.

[†] The following analysis given by H. H. Wolfenden in T.A.S.A., XXIV, 165, may also be of assistance: "The Type III formula, in order to derive the rate of mortality

70. The difference between the Type I formula (10) and the Type III formula (12) is merely that (10) is changed by substituting for $_\delta p_x^{z+1}$ the equivalent $_\delta p_x^z$. If the mortality shows no variation over successive calendar years, then $_\delta p_x^{z+1} = {_\delta p_x^z}$, and the Type I and Type III values will be identical. Alternatively, if, upon the same supposition that there is no variation over successive calendar years, $_a p_x^z$ in the Type I formula is replaced by its equivalent $_a p_x^{z+1}$, then any of the Type I formulae, which give $q_x^{z/z+1}$, will clearly be changed so that they will give q_x^{z+1}.

Thus, from (9),

$$q_x^{z/z+1} = \frac{D_x^{z+1}}{E_x^z \left(\dfrac{_a D_x^{z+1} + {_\delta D_x^{z+1}}}{_a D_x^z + {_\delta D_x^{z+1}}}\right)}. \tag{13}$$

But, when $_a p_x^z = {_a p_x^{z+1}}$, it follows, writing $_a q$ for $1 - {_a p}$, that

$$E_x^z {_a D_x^{z+1}} = E_x^z \left(E_x^{z+1} {_a q_x^{z+1}}\right) = E_x^z E_x^{z+1} {_a q_x^z} = E_x^{z+1} {_a D_x^z} \tag{14}$$

whence

$$q_x^{z+1} = \frac{D_x^{z+1}}{E_x^z \left(\dfrac{_\delta D_x^{z+1}}{_a D_x^z + {_\delta D_x^{z+1}}}\right) + E_x^{z+1}\left(\dfrac{_a D_x^z}{_a D_x^z + {_\delta D_x^{z+1}}}\right)} \tag{15}$$

$$= \frac{D_x^{z+1}}{k_x^z E_x^z + (1 - k_x^z) E_x^{z+1}}, \text{ where } k_x^z = \frac{_\delta D_x^{z+1}}{_a D_x^z + {_\delta D_x^{z+1}}}. \tag{16}$$

These are the true formulae for the rate of mortality in terms of those who attain age x during the calendar year.

---

from the data of the single calendar year z, instead of from the two calendar years z and $z + 1$ (as in Type I), assumes that $_a p_x^z$ may be compounded with $_\delta p_x^z$ instead of with $_\delta p_x^{z+1}$. The consequence of this is that p_x^z, being $_a p_x^z \cdot {_\delta p_x^z}$, involves, by definition, a substitution of one group for another—because (remembering that the objective is to obtain the rate of survival, or mortality, over the year of age, from the data of only one calendar year, notwithstanding the fact that a year of age necessarily involves, on the average, two calendar years) $_a p_x^z$ deals with a body of lives of whom P_x^{z+1} are surviving at the end of the period to which it relates, while $_\delta p_x^z$ is derived from a body of lives which starts as P_x^z instead of the preceding P_x^{z+1}. This substitution of P_x^z for P_x^{z+1}—both of which are populations in the year of age x to $x + 1$—implicitly assumes that P_x^z and P_x^{z+1} are of the same age constitution, to the extent that the probabilities

$$\frac{E_{x+1}^z}{P_x^z} \quad \text{and} \quad \frac{E_{x+1}^{z+1}}{P_x^{z+1}}$$

to which they give rise may be assumed to be identical. This is the fundamental basis of all the Type III formulae; and the Type III probability p_x^z may therefore be defined as the true (Type I) probability of (x) surviving to age $x + 1$, modified by the convenient supposition that $_\delta p_x^{z+1} = {_\delta p_x^z}$, that is, that there is no variation over successive calendar years."

Since k_x^z is very nearly equal to f_x (see par. 66), formula (16) may also be written approximately as

$$q_x^{z+1} = \frac{D_x^{z+1}}{f_x E_x^z + (1 - f_x) E_x^{z+1}}. \tag{17}$$

And this formula has frequently been modified further by assuming uniform progression in the movement of the population over the year of age (see par. 75 here, and T.A.S.A., XXIV, 142) so that $_aD_x^z = {}_\delta D_x^{z+1}$, that is, $k_x^z = \frac{1}{2}$, by which (16) becomes merely

$$q_x^{z+1} = \frac{D_x^{z+1}}{\frac{1}{2} E_x^z + \frac{1}{2} E_x^{z+1}}. \tag{18}$$

Another formula (published first by I. M. Moriyama and T. N. E. Greville—see par. 79 here) in terms of E_x^z, E_x^{z+1}, and D_x^{z+1}, but using f_x^{z+1} instead of k_x^z as in (16), is obtainable easily by writing the fundamental Type III relation (12) as

$$q_x^{z+1} = 1 - (1 - {}_\delta q_x^{z+1})\, {}_a p_x^{z+1} = {}_a q_x^{z+1} + {}_a p_x^{z+1} \cdot {}_\delta q_x^{z+1}.$$

Then from par. 68,

$$_a q_x^{z+1} = \frac{{}_a D_x^{z+1}}{E_x^{z+1}} = \frac{(1 - f_x^{z+1})\, D_x^{z+1}}{E_x^{z+1}}.$$

Also

$$_a p_x^{z+1} \cdot {}_\delta q_x^{z+1} = \frac{P_x^{z+2}}{E_x^{z+1}} \left(\frac{{}_\delta D_x^{z+1}}{P_x^{z+1}} \right) = \frac{{}_\delta D_x^{z+1}}{E_x^{z+1}} \left(\frac{P_x^{z+2}}{P_x^{z+1}} \right);$$

by formula (25) given hereafter this is

$$\frac{{}_\delta D_x^{z+1}}{E_x^z},$$

which from par. 65 is

$$\frac{f_x^{z+1} D_x^{z+1}}{E_x^z}.$$

Hence we find

$$q_x^{z+1} = \frac{(1 - f_x^{z+1})\, D_x^{z+1}}{E_x^{z+1}} + \frac{f_x^{z+1} D_x^{z+1}}{E_x^z}. \tag{18a}$$

71. Formulae (15)–(18a) for q_x^{z+1} proceed upon principle (b) of par. 69, by which the calendar years' deaths are related to the births from which they arise. Analogous formulae, however, may also be found which, following principle (a), par. 68, start from the births of the calendar year and trace the deaths of the two calendar years to which they give rise. Thus from (9),

$$q_x^{z/z+1} = \frac{D_x^z \left(\dfrac{{}_a D_x^z}{D_x^z} \right) + D_x^{z+1} f_x^{z+1}}{E_x^z} = \frac{D_x^z (1 - f_x^z) + D_x^{z+1} f_x^{z+1}}{E_x^z}, \tag{21}$$

which becomes, when f_x^z is the same for all values of z,

$$q_x^{z/z+1} = \frac{D_x^z(1 - f_x) + D_x^{z+1}(f_x)}{E_x^z},$$ (22)

and when f_x is taken as $\frac{1}{2}$,

$$q_x^{z/z+1} = \frac{\frac{1}{2}D_x^z + \frac{1}{2}D_x^{z+1}}{E_x^z}.$$ (23)

These formulae still give the Type I mortality $q_x^{z/z+1}$, whereas the analogous Nos. (15)–(18a) give, as is more desirable, the Type III mortality, q_x^{z+1}, of the calendar year. Formulae (15)–(18a) are therefore preferable; and consequently they are generally used in practice.

72. All the preceding formulae express q in terms of E. Where, however, as is usual for ages above 5, the census populations are sufficiently reliable, it is desirable to deduce q directly from those populations and the deaths of the calendar years. That is, a Type III formula is required in terms of P and D only, and is obtainable as follows: Substituting $_aD_x^z + P_x^{z+1}$ for E_x^z according to (3) in the denominator of (13) we find

$$q_x^{z/z+1} = \frac{D_x^{z+1}}{(_aD_x^z + P_x^{+1})\left(\dfrac{D_x^{z+1}}{_aD_x^z + _\delta D_x^{z+1}}\right)}$$

$$= \frac{D_x^{z+1}}{D_x^{z+1}(1 - k_x^z) + P_x^{z+1}\left(\dfrac{_aD_x^{z+1}}{_aD_x^z + _\delta D_x^{z+1}}\right) + P_x^{z+1}(k_x^z)}.$$ (24)

In order to transform this to a Type III formula we take, as in par. 70, $_aq_x^z = _aq_x^{z+1}$, that is,

$$\frac{E_x^z - P_x^{z+1}}{E_x^z} = \frac{E_x^{z+1} - P_x^{z+2}}{E_x^{z+1}};$$

and from this and (14) it follows that

$$\frac{P_x^{z+2}}{P_x^{z+1}} = \frac{E_x^{z+1}}{E_x^z} = \frac{_aD_x^{z+1}}{_aD_x^z},$$ (25)

by which (24) becomes

$$q_x^{z+1} = \frac{D_x^{z+1}}{P_x^{z+1} + (1 - k_x^z)[P_x^{z+2} - P_x^{z+1} + D_x^{z+1}]}$$ (26)

$$= \frac{D_x^{z+1}}{P_x^{z+1} + \left(\dfrac{_aD_x^z}{_aD_x^z + _\delta D_x^{z+1}}\right)(P_x^{z+2} - P_x^{z+1} + D_x^{z+1})}.$$ (27)

This is the generalization of the usual formula for obtaining q by dividing the deaths by the mean population plus half the deaths.

73. Where E and P are both available, (27) may also, by equation (1), be written in the convenient form

$$q_x^{z+1} = \frac{D_x^{z+1}}{P_x^{z+1} + (1 - k_x^z)(E_x^{z+1} - E_{x+1}^{z+1})} . \qquad (28)$$

74. In order now to obtain a formula in terms of E and the increase of population $P_x^{z+2} - P_x^{z+1} = \delta_x^{z+1}$ say, as is sometimes required (see pars. 79 and 92), the Type I formula (13) may at once be transformed by (25) into

$$q_x^{z+1} = \frac{D_x^{z+1}}{E_x^{z+1} - (P_x^{z+2} - P_x^{z+1})\left(\dfrac{k_x^z E_x^{z+1}}{P_x^{z+2}}\right)} . \qquad (29)$$

This formula may also be modified slightly by writing

$$k_x^z \cdot \frac{E_x^z}{P_x^{z+1}} \qquad \text{for} \qquad k_x^z \cdot \frac{E_x^{z+1}}{P_x^{z+2}}$$

by formula (25).

FORMULAE FOR THE RATES OF MORTALITY ON THE ASSUMPTION OF UNIFORM DISTRIBUTIONS*

75. The formulae of pars. 67–74 have all been obtained without the introduction of any assumption other than that $q^z = q^{z+1}$; and they are therefore suitable for the calculation of the rates of mortality at infantile ages, where f_x^z and k_x^z are not equal to $\frac{1}{2}$ and the assumption of uniform distributions is consequently inadmissible. For ages above 5, however, that assumption may be employed; and the manner in which it is introduced, and the modifications which result in the preceding expressions, may therefore now be considered.

In par. 68 it was explained how the population moves over the year of age x to $x + 1$ by E_x^z changing to P_x^{z+1} by the deaths $_aD_x^z$, and then again changing from P_x^{z+1} to E_{x+1}^{z+1} by the deaths $_bD_x^{z+1}$. In order to maintain a uniform distribution of the deaths over the year of age, $_aD_x^z$ will therefore

---

* The method used here for stating the assumption of uniform distribution over the year of age in the Type I population by means of equations (30)–(32), and the assumptions of uniform movement in the Type III population by the relations (34)–(35) over the year of age and (37)–(38) over the calendar year, was published originally, together with the greatly simplified proofs to which the method leads (as shown in pars. 75–77 here), by H. H. Wolfenden in the paper "On the Determination of the Rates of Mortality at Infantile Ages, from Statistics of the General Population" (T.A.S.A., XXIV, 146–49) previously mentioned in the footnote to par. 64.

In addition to those demonstrations, the student may be referred to the alternative series of even shorter parallel proofs given in the same paper on pp. 155–58 (portions of which are reproduced here), and also to the further comments on pp. 165–66 thereof.

equal $_\delta D_x^{z+1}$. This may also be put as

$$(E_x^z - P_x^{z+1}) = (P_x^{z+1} - E_{x+1}^{z+1}),\tag{30}$$

that is,

$$\left(1 - \frac{P_x^{z+1}}{E_x^z}\right) = \left(\frac{P_x^{z+1}}{E_x^z}\right)\left(1 - \frac{E_{x+1}^{z+1}}{P_x^{z+1}}\right),\tag{31}$$

which is

$$_a q_x^z = {}_a p_x^z \cdot {}_\delta q_x^{z+1}.\tag{32}$$

This last equation therefore states, in terms of probabilities, the assumption of a uniform distribution of deaths over the year of age, in a population of Type I. The same equation is also seen to be true in the ideal Type I population of the life-table; for with uniformly distributed deaths, $(l_x - l_{x+\frac{1}{2}}) = (l_{x+\frac{1}{2}} - l_{x+1})$, and this, as above, may be written $|_{\frac{1}{2}} q_x = {}_{\frac{1}{2}} p_x \cdot |_{\frac{1}{2}} q_{x+\frac{1}{2}}$—that is, the probability of (x) dying in the first half of the year of age equals the probability of his dying in the second half.

Applying, therefore, the assumption of uniform distribution of deaths as embodied in equations (30) and (32) to the fundamental Type I formula (8), the latter at once becomes

$$q_x^{z/z+1} = \frac{E_x^z - E_{x+1}^{z+1}}{P_x^{z+1} + \left(\dfrac{E_x^z - E_{x+1}^{z+1}}{2}\right)} = \frac{{}_a D_x^z + {}_\delta D_x^{z+1}}{P_x^{z+1} + \left(\dfrac{{}_a D_x^z + {}_\delta D_x^{z+1}}{2}\right)}.\tag{33}$$

This formula is analogous to the usual

$$q_x = \frac{d_x}{L_x + \dfrac{d_x}{2}}$$

of the life table, and to the Type III formulae (27)–(28) and (36).

Another new type of proof for (33) was also given by H. H. Wolfenden in T.A.S.A., XXIV, 155–56, based on the Lemma that (as may be seen by putting $\dfrac{X}{Y} = \dfrac{a}{b} = k$) if $\dfrac{X}{Y} = \dfrac{a}{b}$, then

$$\frac{X}{a} + \frac{Y}{b} = \frac{2\,(X+Y)}{a+b}.$$

For the Type I formula is, as previously stated,

$$q_x^{z/z+1} = 1 - {}_a p_x^z \cdot {}_\delta p_x^{z+1}.\tag{10}$$

Introducing the condition of uniformity (32) by using it to eliminate $_\delta p_x^{z+1}$ from (10) we get $q_x^{z/z+1} = 2\,{}_a q_x^z$, and eliminating $_a p_x^z$ similarly we obtain

$$q_x^{z/z+1} = \frac{2\,{}_\delta q_x^{z+1}}{1 + {}_\delta q_x^{z+1}}.$$

From these two relations, therefore,

$$q_x^{z/z+1} = {}_aq_x^z + \frac{\delta q_x^{z+1}}{1 + \delta q_x^{z+1}}$$

$$= \frac{{}_aD_x^z}{E_x^z} + \frac{\delta D_x^{z+1}}{2P_x^{z+1} - E_{x+1}^{z+1}}$$

$$= \frac{X}{a} + \frac{Y}{b}$$

where

$$X = {}_aD_x^z, \ a = E_x^z, \ Y = {}_\delta D_x^{z+1}, \text{ and } b = 2P_x^{z+1} - E_{x+1}^{z+1}. \qquad \text{(A)}$$

Now the uniformity condition when expressed as (30) means that

$${}_aD_x^z = {}_\delta D_x^{z+1}, \text{ or here } X = Y,$$

and from (30) also $E_x^z = 2P_x^{z+1} - E_{x+1}^{z+1}$, that is, $a = b$. Consequently, $\frac{X}{Y} = \frac{a}{b}$, and this relation and (A), by the Lemma, immediately produce (33).

76. Coming now to the movement of the populations over the calendar year, as required in the formulae of Type III, it was shown in par. 69 how, in the calendar year z to $z + 1$, P_x^z passes to E_{x+1}^z, and is replaced by E_x^z which passes to P_x^{z+1} at the end. Applying the above principles, the movement may therefore be followed, in such populations, either (*i*) over the year of age, or (*ii*) over the calendar year.

(*i*) In tracing the year of age (in the calendar year) we have to follow E_x^z to P_x^{z+1}, which is then replaced by P_x^z and passes to E_{x+1}^z; and therefore, in order for E_x^z to pass uniformly to E_{x+1}^z as required, we must have

$$(E_x^z - P_x^{z+1})P_x^z = P_x^{z+1}(P_x^z - E_{x+1}^z), \qquad (34)$$

that is,

$${}_aq_x^z = {}_ap_x^z \cdot {}_\delta q_x^z. \qquad (35)$$

This equation, expressive of uniform movement over the year of age in the Type III population, is, of course, obtainable also from the condition (32) for uniform movement over the year of age in the Type I population, by substituting ${}_\delta q_x^z$ for ${}_\delta q_x^{z+1}$ as in the case of the similar transformations from Type I to Type III previously discussed in par. 70.

The introduction of condition (34)–(35) into the Type III formula (11) will therefore produce the true calendar year formula for the particular case of uniform movement over the year of age—the resulting formula being

$$q_x^z = \frac{D_x^z}{\dfrac{P_x^z + P_x^{z+1}}{2} + \dfrac{D_x^z}{2}}. \qquad (36)$$

This may be shown as follows:

Condition (34) is $_aD_x^z P_x^z = {_\delta}D_x^z P_x^{z+1}$, from which

$$f_x^z = \frac{P_x^z}{P_x^z + P_x^{z+1}}.$$

Hence (11), or

$$\frac{E_x^z P_x^z - E_{x+1}^z P_x^{z+1}}{E_x^z P_x^z},$$

which may be put as

$$\frac{_aD_x^z + \dfrac{P_x^{z+1}}{P_x^z} \cdot {_\delta}D_x^z}{E_x^z} = \frac{D_x^z + \left(\dfrac{P_x^{z+1}}{P_x^z} - 1\right) {_\delta}D_x^z}{E_x^z} = \frac{D_x^z}{E_x^z \left[1 + f_x^z \left(\dfrac{P_x^{z+1}}{P_x^z} - 1\right)\right]^{-1}},$$

becomes

$$\frac{D_x^z}{\dfrac{E_x^z}{P_x^{z+1}} \left(\dfrac{P_x^z + P_x^{z+1}}{2}\right)}.$$

But

$$\frac{E_x^z}{P_x^{z+1}} = \frac{1}{_a p_x^z} = (1 + {_\delta}q_x^z) \text{ from } (35),$$

$$= 1 + \frac{{_\delta}D_x^z}{P_x^z} = 1 + \frac{f_x^z D_x^z}{P_x^z} = 1 + \frac{D_x^z}{P_x^z + P_x^{z+1}},$$

by means of which (36) emerges at once.

Wolfenden's alternative type of proof given in par. 75, based on the Lemma there stated, also produces formula (36) easily. For (as pointed out in T.A.S.A., XXIV, 157), from the Type III formula (12) and the uniformity condition (35) it follows, by exactly the same method as before, that then

$$q_x^z = {_a}q_x^z + \frac{{_\delta}q_x^z}{1 + {_\delta}q_x^z}$$

$$= \frac{X}{a} + \frac{Y}{0}$$

where

$$X = {_a}D_x^z, \; a = E_x^z, \; Y = {_\delta}D_x^z, \text{ and } b = 2P_x^z - E_{x+1}^z. \tag{C}$$

[In the original paper in T.A.S.A., XXIV, 157, a transposition in these expressions for a and b occurred in formula (3e), and the first two portions of formula (3i) should be inverted.]

Also, as before, from the uniformity condition when written in the extended form (34) we see that

$${_a}D_x^z P_x^z = P_x^{z+1} {_\delta}D_x^z, \quad \text{or} \quad \frac{X}{Y} = \frac{P_x^{z+1}}{P_x^z},$$

while again from (34)

$$E_x^z P_x^z = P_x^{z+1} (2P_x^z - E_{x+1}^z), \quad \text{or} \quad \frac{a}{b} = \frac{P_x^{z+1}}{P_x^z}.$$

Hence $\dfrac{X}{Y} = \dfrac{a}{b}$, and from (C) and the Lemma (36) follows directly.

77. (*ii*) If we now suppose, instead of the above uniform movement over the year of age, that the population is to show a uniform progression over the calendar year, we follow P_x^z to E_{x+1}^z, which is then replaced by E_x^z and passes to P_x^{z+1}; so that we must have

$$(P_x^z - E_{x+1}^z)E_x^z = E_{x+1}^z(E_x^z - P_x^{z+1}), \tag{37}$$

that is,

$$_\delta q_x^z = {}_\delta p_x^z \cdot {}_a q_x^z. \tag{38}$$

This last equation expresses the condition that there is an equal probability that a person living at the beginning of the calendar year will die in the first portion or the second portion of that calendar year, just as equation (35)—and similarly (32)— expressed the condition of equal probability of death in the first and second portions of the year of age.

Consequently, introducing this condition (37)–(38) into the Type III formula (11) we obtain the true calendar year formula for the particular case of uniform movement over the calendar year—the formula being

$$q_x^z = \frac{D_x^z}{E_x^z - \frac{1}{2}(P_x^{z+1} - P_x^z)}, \tag{39}$$

which may be shown thus:
From (37), $_a D_x^z E_{x+1}^z = {}_\delta D_x^z E_x^z$, whence

$$f_x^z = \frac{E_{x+1}^z}{E_x^z + E_{x+1}^z}.$$

Hence (11), as in the preceding paragraph, becomes

$$\frac{D_x^z}{E_x^z \left[1 - \dfrac{(P_x^{z+1} - P_x^z)E_{x+1}^z}{E_x^z P_x^z + E_{x+1}^z P_x^{z+1}} \right]};$$

and this, by (37), at once reduces to the required form (39). Or, in exactly the same manner, (39) may be obtained by introducing the condition of uniform movement into the generalized formula (29).

The alternative type of proof based on the Lemma stated in par. 75 again leads to formula (39) in a very simple manner, as was shown by Wolfenden in T.A.S.A., XXIV, 158.* For, by the method used in similarly

* Both the proofs given in this paragraph (which, as already remarked in the footnote to par. 75, depend on the fact that (38) can be used to state the uniformity assump-

reaching (33) and (36), the introduction of the condition of uniformity (38) into the Type III formula (12) leads to

$$q_x^z = {}_\delta q_x^z + \frac{{}_a q_x^z}{1 + {}_a q_x^z}$$

$$= \frac{X}{a} + \frac{Y}{b} \text{ where } X = {}_\delta D_x^z, \ a = P_x^z, \ Y = {}_a D_x^z, \text{ and } b = 2E_x^z - P_x^{z+1}. \quad \text{(D)}$$

Also, the uniformity condition (37) states that

$${}_\delta D_x^z E_x^z = E_{x+1}^z {}_a D_x^z, \qquad \text{being} \qquad \frac{X}{Y} = \frac{E_{x+1}^z}{E_x^z},$$

while again from (37) $P_x^z E_x^z = E_{x+1}^z(2E_x^z - P_x^{z+1})$, or

$$\frac{a}{b} = \frac{E_{x+1}^z}{E_x^z}.$$

Hence $\dfrac{X}{Y} = \dfrac{a}{b}$, and from (D) and the Lemma (39) can be written down immediately.

The Practical Application of the Preceding Formulae

78. In considering the practical applicability of the preceding formulae it is necessary to distinguish carefully between the "infantile" ages and the higher ages. The former may usually be treated as comprising the five ages 0–4 last birthday, inclusive, where f_x^z is not equal to $\frac{1}{2}$ and consequently uniform distributions cannot be assumed (see par. 65).

In practice, f_0^z must be chosen carefully. At each age from 1 to 4 in modern life-table constructions, which involve only a few calendar years, f_x^z can usually be taken without variation in respect of z. Moreover, at ages 2, 3, and 4 (and sometimes, but not always, at age 1) satisfactory values of q will generally emerge if f_x is given the approximate value $\frac{1}{2}$ (cf. H. H. Wolfenden, T.A.S.A., XXV, 149–52, and the Vital Statistics Special Report on an "Investigation of Separation Factors at Ages 1–4 Based on 10% Mortality Sample" noted in par. 65 here). For ages 5 and beyond $f_x^z = \frac{1}{2}$ may also be employed for all practical purposes, so that at those ages the assumption of uniform distributions can be made.

79. The Type III formula (11)–(12), therefore, should be used at the infantile ages whenever possible—for it gives the theoretically true q_x^z directly without the introduction of any subordinate assumptions. The

---

tion in terms of probabilities) are very much easier and quicker than the lengthy demonstrations involving definite integrals and differential equations which had been published previously in Czuber's "Wahrscheinlichkeitsrechnung" and elsewhere in European literature—see T.A.S.A., XXIV, 149.

Type I formula (8)–(9), and its modifications (21)–(23) and (33), and the Type II formula (footnote, par. 69), are not so desirable—the former involving the two calendar years z and $z + 1$, while Type II does not follow an integral year of age.

Of the various modifications of the Type III formula, Nos. (15)–(16), which by the use of k_x^z find q_x^{z+1} from the births and those who attain each subsequent age x, naturally give sound results because no arbitrary assumption is involved; in practice, however, the necessity of determining k_x^z is not convenient. No. (17) consequently has often been used (as stated, for example, by the Registrar-General of England and Wales, 83rd Annual Report, 1920, p. xxviii) because it employs the more accessible f_x and usually provides a close approximation (see the numerical illustrations given by H. H. Wolfenden in T.A.S.A., XXIV, 154; and I. M. Moriyama and T. N. E. Greville, "Effect of Changing Birth Rates upon Infant Mortality Rates," Bureau of the Census, Vital Statistics Special Reports, XIX, No. 21, p. 409). No. (18), with its assumption of uniform movement over the year of age, will produce reasonable results when a number of calendar years are employed in which the births and deaths are fairly uniform (see T.A.S.A., XXIV, 151 and 154); it has formed the basis of the methods employed in the English Life Tables Nos. 1 to 8 at infantile ages (see pars. 87 et seq. here). No. (18a) was first published by Moriyama and Greville (*op. cit.*) as a convenient formula requiring f_x^z instead of k_x^z; being derived without any subordinate assumption from the fundamental Type III, it necessarily produces sound results; and it is used in the United States by the National Office of Vital Statistics for their annual computations of infant mortality rates.*

Formulae (26)–(28) may sometimes be useful at the infantile ages (see, for example, Henderson's "Mortality Laws and Statistics," p. 96), so long as the populations used therein may be assumed to be reliable (see par. 92 here).

Formula (29), with the factor in the denominator taken as

$$\frac{k_x^z E_x^z}{P_x^{z+1}},$$

has been used in the U.S. Abridged Life Tables, 1919–20, for the first year of age; and, as shown in T.A.S.A., XXV, 149–52, it may be applied readily for the other infantile ages as well—for the above factor may be taken

---

* In reports on vital statistics in some countries a rough approximation is often made by calculating merely the ratio of deaths in the first year of age during a calendar year to the number of children born during the year, i.e., D_0^z/E_0^z. That method, however, as will be seen at once from formulae (15)–(18a) and (21)–(23), may give misleading results under the usual circumstances of changing birth and death rates.

either from known values or from the consistent tables of P_x^z, P_x^{z+1}, E_x^z, and f_x^z which may be built up as in par. 92 hereafter.

80. Of the formulae which result from the assumptions of uniform distributions, (36)—or occasionally the less usual form (33)—is generally used as the basis of the calculations at all ages except the infantile ages, where it overstates the mortality seriously. It is commonly applied by using the corresponding form for the central death rate, m_x—the ratio of the deaths during the year to the population in the middle of the year.

Formula (39) also results in an overstatement of the mortality at the infantile ages if it is applied directly. This is shown in T.A.S.A., XXIV, 150–54, where the numerical results of all these formulae are compared, and also in T.A.S.A., XXV, 149–52. At those ages, therefore, it should be used either in its general form (29) (in which case uniform distributions are not assumed), or it should be applied over shorter age periods than an entire year of age—as was actually done by Glover in the U.S. Life Tables, 1890, etc. (p. 343, par. 112), where for the first year of age the formula was applied to each separate month of age. An extension of formula (39), with the denominator taken as $E_x^z - \frac{1}{2}(P_x^{z+1} - P_x^z) + \frac{1}{2}(NM)_x$ when the net migration at age x last birthday, $(NM)_x$, is sufficient to affect the results, is examined by T. N. E. Greville in R.A.I.A., XXXI, 368–73, and is there related to the corresponding formula by which the "exposed to risk" can be computed from the individual records of insured lives (see Greville, *loc. cit.*, "Census Methods of Constructing Mortality Tables and Their Relation to Insurance Methods," and H. H. Wolfenden, T.A.S.A., XLIII, 258, "On the Formulae for Calculating the 'Exposed to Risk' in Constructing Mortality and Other Tables from the Individual Records of Insured Lives," in which formula (31) is the basis of that employed by Greville).

VII

THE CONSTRUCTION OF MORTALITY TABLES
FROM POPULATION STATISTICS

81. With the formulae of the preceding section at hand, the methods of constructing mortality tables from population statistics may now be considered in detail. They fall into three divisions, according as the statistics employed are (1) *Death Returns only;* (2) *Census Returns only;* or (3) *Death and Census Returns—supplemented frequently by Birth Returns at the Infantile Ages.*

(1) *Construction of Mortality Tables from Death Returns Only*

82. In the case of the hypothetical stationary community of the life table, a mortality table could be formed by recording the deaths, d_x, in each year of age, summing them to obtain l_x, and thence computing $q_x = d_x/l_x$. It is clear, however, that this principle will be disturbed if the number of annual births varies, or if there is any immigration or emigration; and since varying birth rates and migrations are found to exist in all actual communities, it would be necessary to introduce corrections* for those variations in order for the principle to be applicable in practice. Such corrections, however, cannot be determined accurately, because the variations in birth rates and migrations are themselves interwoven, and are of a fluctuating character, while the migration statistics are usually defective.

Two historically important examples of the application of this method are Halley's Breslau Table, which was constructed in 1693 from the deaths in the city of Breslau, Germany, in the years 1687–91 (see J.I.A., I, 42, and XVIII, 251, and Henderson's "Mortality Laws and Statistics," p. 2), and Dr. Richard Price's Northampton Tables which were published in 1771 and 1783 from the deaths in the Parish of All Saints, Northampton, England (see J.I.A., XVIII, 107). Both these early writers were cognizant of the necessity for the population being stationary, in order for

* The nature of the requisite correction in the case of a population with an increasing number of annual births is shown on p. 6 of George King's Institute of Actuaries' Text Book, Part II (which may still be consulted for the clearness of its presentation) and the possible effect of migration upon the principle of summing the d column to get the number of living, l, is illustrated by an example in Spurgeon's Life Contingencies (with which the actuarial student may be assumed to have become familiar in his early reading).

the method to be strictly applicable. Halley remarked that "the method requires, if it were possible, that the People we treat of should not at all be changed, but die where they were born, without any Adventitious Increase from Abroad, or Decay by Migration elsewhere," and that this condition "seems in a great measure to be satisfied by the late curious Tables of the Bills of Mortality at the City of Breslaw"; while he further commented that "in the Five years mentioned . . . there were born 6,193 Persons, and buried 5,869, that is born per annum 1,238, and buried 1,174, whence an Encrease of the People may be argued of 64 per annum . . . ; but this being contingent, and the Births certain, I will suppose the People of Breslaw to be encreased by 1,238 Births annually" (*loc. cit.*). Dr. Price, on the other hand, had to deal with an excess (469) of burials over christenings, for which he corrected by assuming an immigration into Northampton at age 20. Although both the Breslau and Northampton tables were defective by reason of the arbitrary assumptions which were made in overcoming the discrepancies between the births and total deaths, they are important as being the first complete mortality tables published, and as examples of the difficulties encountered in attempting to construct such tables in the absence of census returns.*

* Arne Fisher, in a paper in Proc. Casualty Actuarial Society, Vol. IV, and a book entitled "An Elementary Treatise on Frequency Curves, and Their Application in the Analysis of Death Curves and Life Tables," has claimed that mortality tables can be constructed from deaths alone by (i) classifying the deaths, by age groups, according to certain groups of causes of death; (ii) calculating the proportionate death ratios (i.e., the proportion of deaths for each cause-group to the total deaths from all causes, for each age group) which depend on the deaths alone and are absolutely independent of the numbers exposed to risk; (iii) expressing these ratios as Charlier frequency functions—the groups in (i) being, in fact, so chosen that these ratios conform to Charlier curves "whose parameters are known or chosen beforehand"; and then (iv) assuming that we can pass from the fluctuating actual community to the stationary hypothetical community of the life table by imposing the condition (which subsists in the life table) that the total deaths from all causes at all ages shall equal the radix of the mortality table—the total deaths from all causes at each age (namely d_x) which correspond to that radix being determined by least squares from a series of observation equations which arise from the frequency curves of (iii) and the assumption (iv). The very fact, however, that the ratios in (ii) are independent of the numbers at risk necessarily renders any such method unsafe; for it is easily conceivable that in two communities, A and B, the actual rates of mortality in B might, for example, be k times those in A and yet their proportionate death ratios might be identical—in which case the relation $q_x^B = k q_x^A$ ought to emerge, whereas Fisher's method of proceeding from the identical ratios as the basic data would produce exactly the same q_x for A and B (except so far as either or both q_x^A or q_x^B found by his method might be altered by the uncertain process of grouping differently the various causes of death) (see also par. 146 here, and the reviews in J.I.A., LIV, 206, and J.A.S.A., XIX, 114). [The entirely different principle illustrated by Prof. Karl Pearson in his "Chances of Death" must

For the purposes of this Study it is not necessary to describe all the early attempts to construct mortality tables because in most cases they merely provided technically deficient estimates based on unsatisfactory material, and they are now quite obsolete. It may be of interest, however, to record the following: (1) Tables of e_x were estimated by the Roman jurisconsult Macer, and by Ulpian, about the 3rd century, and Ulpian's table was used in Italy until the end of the 18th century (see J.I.A., VI, 313, and XXXIV, 159, and H. H. Wolfenden's review in T.A.S.A., XXVII, 470, of C. F. Trenerry's "The Origin and Early History of Insurance"). An examination of Ulpian's table led M. Greenwood to conclude (in J.R.S.S., CIII, 246) that Ulpian had simply interpolated between values which had been taken arbitrarily for the expectation of life at ages below 30 and at 60. (2) Graunt's classic work in 1661 on the London Bills of Mortality (see par. 17 here) may be considered to have foreshadowed the modern mortality table; Graunt clearly seems to have realized that he could form a life table by a summation of deaths, and—as Greenwood remarked in J.R.S.S., XCVI, 79—"that was Graunt's discovery, and the only contemporary who realized its immense importance was . . . Halley." (3) In the United States Barton published a fragmentary table based on the mortality of part of Philadelphia in 1782 and 1788–90; and Wigglesworth's Massachusetts Table, constructed in 1793 from deaths alone, was used as an authority in Massachusetts courts for many years (see J.A.S.A., II, 638, and "Length of Life; A Study of the Life Table" by L. I. Dublin and A. J. Lotka—reviewed by H. H. Wolfenden in T.A.S.A., XXVII, 240—for additional details of these and other early tables of doubtful validity).

(2) *Construction of Mortality Tables from Census Returns Only*

83. It is clear that if the average age of a population group P_x^z be assumed to be $x + \frac{1}{2}$, and that of the corresponding group P_{x+n}^{z+n} at a census n years later be $x + n + \frac{1}{2}$, then if there has been no disturbance from migration, and if the birth and death rates have been uniform, the ratio P_{x+n}^{z+n}/P_x^z may be taken as $_np_{x+\frac{1}{2}}$ (see also footnote, par. 69). If, however, the group has been increased by a number of immigrants I, and decreased by emigration amounting to E, during the n years, and if D' deaths among

---

not be confused with Fisher's method. Pearson simply showed the possibility of splitting the death curve $l_x\mu_x$ of the life table itself into a series of superimposed frequency curves—and no suggestion was made of reversing the process, either directly or by the use of ratios as in Fisher's method. A brief summary of Pearson's analysis in the case of English Life Table No. 4 is given in "The Fundamental Principles of Mathematical Statistics," p. 315].

the net migrants $I - E$ have occurred so that the surviving migrants at the second census are $I - E - D'$, then $_np_{x+\frac{1}{2}}$ will be obtainable from the expression

$$\frac{P_{x+n}^{z+n} - (I - E - D')}{P_x^z};$$

and if, as is usually the case in practice, the enumerated populations have arisen from an irregular series of annual births, it will also be necessary to estimate their rates of increase in order to combine them with the above expression and so obtain $_np_{x+\frac{1}{2}}$ from a population which may be assumed to be approximately stationary.

It is, however, very difficult to make these adjustments. The statistics of migration are frequently incomplete, and are seldom available according to age; the deaths D' among them, although comparatively small, would usually have to be estimated; and the rates of increase of the population groups are not easy to determine, and generally are not uniform. A detailed example of a correction of this type for migration was given by H. G. W. Meikle in his report (noted in par. 34(b) here) on the Indian census returns of 1921—although under the particular circumstances of the Indian populations at that time he concluded that the effect of migration upon the age distribution was unimportant, and that it was even less significant with regard to the rates of mortality which eventually emerged.

84. Notwithstanding these difficulties, the construction of approximate mortality tables from census enumerations only* (without any tabulations of the deaths) was undertaken of necessity in the United States prior to the establishment of death registration—Levi W. Meech having computed and published such tables in the second edition of his "System and Tables of Life Insurance." In India also the method has been employed extensively for the same reason.

The principles have been illustrated in the case of India by G. F. Hardy in three reports epitomized in J.I.A., XXV, 217, by T. G. Ackland in J.I.A., XLVII, 315, and by H. G. W. Meikle and L. S. Vaidyanathan in their reports on the censuses of 1921 and 1931 already noted in par. 34(b). Complete details of the various processes employed are given in those

---

* As noted in the footnote to par. 17 here, the United States census schedules from 1850 to 1900 included questions (though with unsatisfactory results) with respect to deaths in the year preceding the census. In the report on the census of 1860 (see also J.I.A., XIII, 289) Dr. Edward Jarvis consequently gave (p. 524) a life table for whites based on that census and the deaths so reported to the enumerators; but although his table thus was based on census data only, the method of construction clearly utilized death statistics and therefore did not follow the principles under discussion here.

publications. In Ackland's investigation, for example, which related to the decennium 1901–11, a preliminary correction for errors of age (see par. 52 here) was first used. Having thus obtained a more reliable age distribution for both the 1901 and 1911 censuses, per 100,000 of each sex, the arithmetic mean was taken as the mean population, by age groups, for the period 1901–11—corrections being introduced in the cases of Madras and the United Provinces to allow for the effects of emigration upon the mean population figures thus ascertained. These mean populations were then graduated—the values thence derived at each age giving a graduated mean population at each age for the period 1901–11. In order now to deduce the rates of mortality, the corrected age group figures for 1901 and 1911 were compared and the rate of increase of the population over the decennium was obtained for each age group—the rates so found being graduated to give r_x, the graduated rate of decennial increase at age x; and since the graduated mean population for 1901–11 as previously found represents approximately the population of correct age distribution at the middle point of the decennium, it was then possible by multiplying and dividing by $r_x^{\frac{1}{2}}$ to obtain the populations at the same age in 1911 and 1901 respectively, from which $_{10}p_{x+\frac{1}{2}}$ follows directly, and thence p_x by interpolation. A simpler alternative process, which was used by Ackland for some of the Provinces, and was adopted in the subsequent reports of Meikle and Vaidyanathan, is to multiply and divide by $r_x^{\frac{1}{20}}$ instead of $r_x^{\frac{1}{2}}$, thus obtaining the estimated population at each age six months after and six months before the middle point of the decennium, from which $p_{x+\frac{1}{2}}$ is obtained directly and thence p_x by interpolation.

Such methods, however, are not often required under modern conditions; and in practice they can give only approximate results.

(3) *Construction of Mortality Tables from Death and Census Returns—Supplemented Frequently by Birth Returns at the Infantile Ages*

85. The more usual method of construction, which is adopted whenever the data permit, is to employ both the registered deaths and the census returns in order to obtain m_x (or sometimes q_x) directly from the observations, without the necessity of introducing doubtful assumptions as in the preceding methods which use either death or census returns only. As censuses are usually taken at decennial intervals, many tables have been constructed in the past on the basis of the mean populations living throughout the intercensal period and the corresponding ten years' deaths, in order to avoid the danger of reflecting unduly the fluctuations in mortality which may occur in particular calendar years. With improv-

ing mortality, however, such tables will give rates of mortality higher than those prevailing in the last years of the decennium. When the data are of sufficient extent, it is therefore preferable to base the investigation upon the results of one census only (with the incidental advantage of thereby avoiding the calculation of the mean population over a ten-year period) and the deaths for, say, two or three adjacent years, so long as those years have not been abnormal by reason of wars, epidemics, or excessive migration.

In now considering the details of the various methods of construction which fall under this heading (3), it is desirable to take up first (A) The Infantile Ages, then (B) The Adult Ages, and finally certain supplementary methods for (C) The Oldest Ages, and the "Juvenile" Ages (i.e., those between the Infantile and Adult Ages). The range of ages included by the term "infantile" will, as in par. 78, be taken as the five ages from 0 to 4, last birthday, inclusive.

(A) INFANTILE AGES

86. On account of the unreliability of the numbers enumerated by the census at infantile ages, as explained in pars. 29–32, it has been customary, in the long series of English Life Tables published by the Registrars-General of England and Wales, to discard the census statistics and to deduce the rates of mortality from the more reliable registrations of births and deaths. In the U.S. and Canada, however, birth registrations also are incomplete (see par. 46); and it is then necessary to correct or re-calculate the births or populations in order to apply methods as described in par. 92 hereafter.

THE ENGLISH LIFE TABLE METHODS

87. The basic principle of the English Life methods is to accept the birth and death registrations as correct and consistent (see par. 24), and to calculate q_x directly therefrom—migrations being ignored as unimportant at these ages. The constructions in Tables 1 to 8 were based on the assumption that formula (18) would give sufficiently accurate results (cf. T.A.S.A., XXIV, 151 and 154)—allowance for the varying births and deaths of different calendar years being made implicitly by using the data of a number of calendar years. The various ways in which such data may be arranged can be seen from the following classifications (taken from H. H. Wolfenden's paper on "The Determination of the Rates of Mortality at Infantile Ages, from Statistics of the General Population," T.A.S.A., XXIV, 127–31):

If b_n denotes the births in the nth calendar year and $_nd_x$ the deaths aged

x last birthday in the nth calendar year, then on these assumptions

The Births		The Corresponding Deaths
$\frac{1}{2}(b_1 + b_2)$		$_2d_0\ _3d_1\ _4d_2\ _5d_3\ _6d_4$
$\frac{1}{2}(b_2 + b_3)$		$_3d_0\ _4d_1\ _5d_2\ _6d_3\ _7d_4$
$\frac{1}{2}(b_3 + b_4)$	produce	$_4d_0\ _5d_1\ _6d_2\ _7d_3\ _8d_4$
$\frac{1}{2}(b_4 + b_5)$		$_5d_0\ _6d_1\ _7d_2\ _8d_3\ _9d_4$
$\frac{1}{2}(b_5 + b_6)$		$_6d_0\ _7d_1\ _8d_2\ _9d_3\ _{10}d_4$

The rates of mortality for the first five years of age may now be determined from such data in a number of ways, which may be classified as follows:

88. *Farr's Method.*—(*i*) The principle employed by Dr. Farr in the English Life Table No. 1, in the Healthy English Life Table No. 1 (see J.I.A., IX, 134, and XLII, 229), and in the English Life Table No. 3 was to proceed, in the above scheme, directly *along the line*, thus:

$$q_0 = \frac{_2d_0}{\frac{1}{2}(b_1 + b_2)}\,;\ q_1 = \frac{_3d_1}{\frac{1}{2}(b_1 + b_2) - _2d_0}\,;\ q_2 = \frac{_4d_2}{\frac{1}{2}(b_1 + b_2) - _2d_0 - _3d_1}\,;$$

$$q_3 = \frac{_5d_3}{\frac{1}{2}(b_1 + b_2) - _2d_0 - _3d_1 - _4d_2}\,;\text{and}\ q_4 = \frac{_6d_4}{\frac{1}{2}(b_1 + b_2) - _2d_0 - _3d_1 - _4d_2 - _5d_3}.$$

The several values of q were thus determined from the same group of births, by employing successively the deaths of five different calendar years which appear along the line in the above scheme. In order to obtain a wider basis than is given by the data of only one line, several lines may of course be combined—as in the English Life No. 3; or, as in the Healthy English Table, the average of the results of several lines may be employed.

(*ii*) Instead of finding q_0, q_1, etc., directly, as in (*i*), by involving the deaths in the denominators, the values of q_0, $_1|q_0$, $_2|q_0$, etc., could be found as follows—the values of q being easily deducible therefrom:

$$q_0 = \frac{_2d_0}{\frac{1}{2}(b_1 + b_2)}\,;\ _1|\,q_0 = \frac{_3d_1}{\frac{1}{2}(b_1 + b_2)}\,;\ \dots\,;\ _4|\,q_0 = \frac{_6d_4}{\frac{1}{2}(b_1 + b_2)}\,;$$

and a wider basis could similarly be obtained by combining the data of several lines or by averaging the various results.

89. *The Methods of English Life Tables Nos. 5 to 8.*—Farr's method, as already pointed out, employs the deaths of successive years, and consequently it may be objected that it will not produce the rates of mortality of any particular period. Another method of selecting the data was therefore employed in several later tables, by which the deaths are taken *along the diagonal* in the scheme of par. 87 (instead of along the line) so that for each age they are supplied by the same calendar year.

(*i*) When q is calculated directly by this means the formulae may therefore be written down at once as

$$q_0 = \frac{{}_6 d_0}{\frac{1}{2}(b_5 + b_6)}; \; q_1 = \frac{{}_6 d_1}{\frac{1}{2}(b_4 + b_5) - {}_5 d_0}; \; q_2 = \frac{{}_6 d_2}{\frac{1}{2}(b_3 + b_4) - {}_4 d_0 - {}_5 d_1};$$

$$q_3 = \frac{{}_6 d_3}{\frac{1}{2}(b_2 + b_3) - {}_3 d_0 - {}_4 d_1 - {}_5 d_2}; \; \text{and} \; q_4 = \frac{{}_6 d_4}{\frac{1}{2}(b_1 + b_2) - {}_2 d_0 - {}_3 d_1 - {}_4 d_2 - {}_5 d_3}.$$

The principle of this method—extended to include a number of calendar years' deaths—was used in the London Life Table, and the English Life Tables Nos. 5, 6, 7, and 8 (see, for example, Supp. to 75th Report of the Registrar-General, Part I, p. 5).*

(*ii*) This same method of proceeding along the diagonal may again be applied to the calculation of $q_{0,1} | q_0$, etc., from which the values of q would be deduced—the formulae being:

$$q_0 = \frac{{}_6 d_0}{\frac{1}{2}(b_5 + b_6)}; \; {}_1| q_0 = \frac{{}_6 d_1}{\frac{1}{2}(b_4 + b_5)}; \; \ldots; {}_4| q_0 = \frac{{}_6 d_4}{\frac{1}{2}(b_1 + b_2)}.$$

This is the principle used by Moors and Day, J.I.A., XXXVI, 167, and also by C. H. Wickens, J.I.A., XLIII, 74.

90. *Pell's Method.*—The method of Dr. Farr, which proceeds along the line in the scheme of par. 87 and so requires the extraction of the births of two years and the deaths of five calendar years, and the method just stated in par. 89, which proceeds along the diagonal and so employs the births of six years and the deaths of one year, may clearly be combined and extended without the necessity of examining the data of any further calendar years. The data so combined will be included *within the triangle* formed by the top line, the diagonal, and the left side; and the formulae,

---

* On the supposition that the total of the census populations under 5 was correct though erroneously distributed, an adjustment was used in the London Life Table and English Life Tables Nos. 5 and 6 by which the total "numbers living" under 5, as computed from the birth and death statistics on the principles of par. 89(*i*), were brought to coincide with the numbers enumerated by the census (see the official volumes of those tables; Newsholme's Vital Statistics (3rd Edition), p. 274; T. E. Hayward, J.R.S.S., XLII, 451; J. Buchanan, Proceedings 6th International Congress of Actuaries, II, 610; and G. King, Supplement 75th Registrar-General's Report, I, 5–13). In English Life Table No. 8 and later tables, however, this adjustment was discarded because King showed clearly that it reduced the "numbers living" erroneously, and so produced an overstatement of mortality, since the census populations (instead of being inaccurately distributed) were actually deficient at ages 0 and 1 (see also H. H. Wolfenden, T.A.S.A., XXIV, 131–34, and pars. 29–31 here).

which are most compactly stated for the deferred probabilities, are clearly

$$q_0 = \frac{{}_2d_0 + {}_3d_0 + {}_4d_0 + {}_5d_0 + {}_6d_0}{\frac{1}{2}(b_1 + b_2) + \frac{1}{2}(b_2 + b_3) + \ldots + \frac{1}{2}(b_5 + b_6)};$$

$$_1|\,q_0 = \frac{{}_3d_1 + \ldots + {}_6d_1}{\frac{1}{2}(b_1 + b_2) + \ldots + \frac{1}{2}(b_4 + b_5)};$$

$$_2|\,q_0 = \frac{{}_4d_2 + {}_5d_2 + {}_6d_2}{\frac{1}{2}(b_1 + b_2) + \ldots + \frac{1}{2}(b_3 + b_4)};$$

$$_3|\,q_0 = \frac{{}_5d_3 + {}_6d_3}{\frac{1}{2}(b_1 + b_2) + \frac{1}{2}(b_2 + b_3)};$$

and

$$_4|\,q_0 = \frac{{}_6d_4}{\frac{1}{2}(b_1 + b_2)}.$$

These are the formulae of Professor Pell's method, J.I.A., XXI, 264 (see also T.A.S.A., XXIV, 130).

91. *The Methods of English Life Tables Nos. 9 and 10.*—All the procedures outlined in pars. 87–90, as used in English Life Tables 1 to 8, employ the basis of formula (18) with its assumption of uniform movement over the year of age. In constructing English Life Table No. 9 based on the deaths of 1920–22, and the Northern Ireland Life Tables, 1926 (for the references see par. 120 here), the violent fluctuations in the numbers of births during and after the war of 1914–18 necessitated the abandonment of the uniformity assumption of formula (18); and as returns of births were available for each quarter of each calendar year, it was assumed that the births in each quarter were distributed uniformly so that, on the principle of par. 89 (*i*) suitably modified, the formulae were

$$q_0 = \frac{D_0^{1920} + D_0^{1921} + D_0^{1922}}{\frac{1}{8}(\beta_1^{19} + 3\beta_2^{19} + 5\beta_3^{19} + 7\beta_4^{19}) + (\beta^{20} + \beta^{21}) + \frac{1}{8}(7\beta_1^{22} + 5\beta_2^{22} + 3\beta_3^{22} + \beta_4^{22})},$$

$$q_1 = \frac{D_1^{1920} + D_1^{1921} + D_1^{1922}}{\frac{1}{8}A + (\beta^{19} + \beta^{20}) + \frac{1}{8}B - (D_0^{1919} + D_0^{1920} + D_0^{1921})}$$

where $A = \beta_1^{18} + 3\beta_2^{18} + 5\beta_3^{18} + 7\beta_4^{18}$

and $B = 7\beta_1^{21} + 5\beta_2^{21} + 3\beta_3^{21} + \beta_4^{21}$,

and so on, where for example β_n^{19} represents the births in the *n*th quarter of 1919, and β^{19} denotes the births during the whole of 1919.

For English Life Table No. 10 based on the deaths of 1930–32, and the corresponding table for Scotland (see par. 120 here), the preceding method was again adopted at ages 1 to 5; at age 0, however, a further elaboration was introduced by using quarterly deaths as well as quarterly births—the probabilities of death being determined for each quarter of the year of age and then summed to give q_0. Denoting by $D_{0/3}^z$, $D_{3/6}^z$, . . . , the deaths in the first, second, . . . , quarters of the year of age, and by $q_{0/3}$, $q_{3/6}$, . . . , the corresponding probabilities of death, the formulae were

$$q_{0/3} = \frac{D_{0/3}^{1930} + D_{0/3}^{1931} + D_{0/3}^{1932}}{\frac{1}{2}\beta_4^{29} + \beta^{30} + \beta^{31} + \beta^{32} - \frac{1}{2}\beta_4^{32}}$$

$$q_{3/6} = \frac{D_{3/6}^{1930} + D_{3/6}^{1931} + D_{3/6}^{1932}}{\frac{1}{2}\beta_3^{29} + \beta_4^{29} + \beta^{30} + \beta^{31} + \beta_1^{32} + \beta_2^{32} + \frac{1}{2}\beta_3^{32}}$$

and so on.*

THE METHODS DEVELOPED IN THE UNITED STATES

92. In the United States and Canada (as pointed out in pars. 45–47) birth registrations have always been incomplete, and death registrations

* It is sometimes desired to compute values of q_0 from the experience of a period shorter than a year, such as a quarter or a month. Quarterly infant mortality rates accordingly have been published by the Registrar-General of England and Wales, and monthly rates are published by the National Office of Vital Statistics in the United States. The Registrar-General's method (which is also employed by the National Office of Vital Statistics) for computing these rates consists in allocating the infant deaths in a particular month or quarter, subdivided by age at death (under 1 day, 1 day, 2 days, 3–6 days, 7–13 days, 14–20 days, 21 days to 1 month, and thereafter for each month) to the month or quarter of birth by means of factors (varying slightly according to the number of days in the month); the infant deaths so allocated to each month or quarter are then divided by the number of births occurring in that month or quarter; and the ratios are summed to represent the monthly or quarterly rates (see the 83rd Annual Report of the Registrar-General for England and Wales, and the U.S. Vital Statistics report by Moriyama and Greville noted in par. 79 here). This method, however, is somewhat laborious; an abridgment has therefore been used by DePorte for computing q_0 on a monthly basis. Instead of allocating infant deaths to the precise month of birth, De-Porte's method in effect allocates deaths of infants under 1 month and over 1 month of age to the approximate or average month of birth; the deaths under 1 month of age occurring during a particular month are divided by the number of births during the month, and the infants surviving the first month but dying before reaching their first birthdays are divided by the monthly average number of births for the 11-month period preceding the month of death; and the two ratios are then added (see J. V. DePorte, "Rate of Infant Mortality Adjusted to a Rapidly Changing Birth Rate," Health News, New York State Department of Health, XXI [1944], and discussion thereof in the paper by Moriyama and Greville where DePorte's abridged method is shown to be sufficiently accurate for most practical purposes).

may not be wholly reliable in all areas. The enumerated populations, moreover, as in other countries, are deficient at ages 0 and 1 (see pars. 29–32). Under these circumstances the methods of pars. 87–91 are not appropriate, and special procedures have been devised on the basis of the formulae stated here in Section VI. The problem, in general terms, is to compute q_x at each age from 0 to 4 from some arrangement of (*a*) the deficient births, E_0^z; (*b*) the deaths, D_x^z, which often are assumed to be correct, although in certain areas deficiencies may exist; and (*c*) the census populations, P_x^z, which are deficient at ages 0 and 1, but generally are reliable for ages 2, 3, and 4 in total.

(*i*) In the U.S. Life Tables 1890, 1901, 1910, and 1901–10, the method used by J. W. Glover followed that given in Czuber's "Wahrscheinlichkeitsrechnung," and was discussed further by R. Henderson in T.A.S.A., XXIII, 435, and H. H. Wolfenden in T.A.S.A., XXIV, 136, and XXV, 148. The registered deaths D_x^z in each year of age, and the enumerated populations at each age from 2 upwards, were assumed to be correct. The deaths were then divided into their $_sD_x^z$ and $_aD_x^z$ components by means of values of f_x^z, which were found as in par. 65. The births E_0^z were then computed directly from the population aged, say, 2 last birthday (or similarly from that aged 3 or 4), by formula (6)—the population P_2^{z+3} being computed in the U.S. Life Tables on the assumption of its own G.P. It was then assumed that, although the absolute values of P_0 and P_1 are unsound, nevertheless the arithmetical increase $P_x^{z+1} - P_x^z$ for each age may be taken as correct—the populations at dates other than the census date being estimated, in the U.S. Life Tables, by their own G.P.'s in each case. The data then consisted of a computed number of births E_0^z, the original deaths $_sD_x^z$ and $_aD_x^z$, and computed values of $(P_x^{z+1} - P_x^z)$, which may be denoted by δ_x^z, at each age.

Two courses are then open. We may apply equation (1) in the form $E_{x+1}^z = E_x^z - \delta_x^z - D_x^z$ to build up, from the births E_0, a column E_x^z (see U.S. Life Tables, p. 343, and T.A.S.A., XXIV, 137); and from E_x^z so constructed, with D_x^z, and δ_x^z which is assumed to be correct, q_x^z may be computed by a formula which again must involve only E, D, and δ—such as (29) with the factor

$$\frac{k_x^z E_x^{z+1}}{P_x^{z+2}}$$

taken from known values (see T.A.S.A., XXV, 150), or (39) so long as in the first year of age at least it is applied by months of age (see par. 80 here). Or, this limitation on the permissible formulae for q_x^z may be removed by adding the further simple step of recomputing the separate values of P_x^z and P_x^{z+1} from E_x^z, δ_x^z, and the D's by formulae (2) and (3); for by so doing a table of P_x^z, P_x^{z+1}, δ_x^z, E_x^z, and the D's will be obtained which will be consistent throughout, so that any of the formulae for q_x^z may be applied to it (see T.A.S.A., XXV, 151).

(*ii*) In Glover's procedure the calculation of the births from the populations aged 2 (or over) by the direct equations (6) necessitates the use of the deaths of two (or more) calendar years subsequent to the period under observation; and it was pointed out by R. Henderson (J.A.S.A., XVIII, 552) that this resulted in a small understatement of the original populations aged 2–4 in the U.S. Life Tables, with a consequent slight overstatement of the mortality. The assumption that the original increases δ_x^z are correct is also of doubtful validity; for it implicitly assumes that each of the populations P_x^{z+1} and P_x^z is affected by an error of the same amount, so that their difference δ_x^z is correct—notwithstanding considerable uncertainty as to the nature of those errors (see T.A.S.A., XXIV, 138). Henderson therefore suggested a method in T.A.S.A., XXIII, 435 ("The Adjustment of Population Returns at Infantile Ages in the Absence of Birth Statistics") in which it was assumed that the total populations aged 2, 3, and 4 are correct in total but subject to redistribution, and that all the populations increase in a G.P. with ratio r (or in an A.P.) as found from those populations aged 2–4. Hence by an obvious application of equation (5) a new value of P_4^z was determined by the formula

$$P_4^z = \frac{(P_2^z + P_3^z + P_4^z) - [\,(\delta D_2^z + {}_aD_3^z) + (1+r)\,(\delta D_3^z + {}_aD_4^z)\,]}{1 + r + r^2}\,,$$

where $P_x^{z+1} = rP_x^z$ (in the G.P. method); and then, working backwards therefrom by applying formula (5) at each age, the individual values of P were established, and finally the births emerged from formula (3).

This method produces a consistent table in which all the fundamental relations (1)–(4) are maintained, so that q_x^z may be calculated from it by any of the available formulae of pars. 67 et seq.—preferably by No. (11); and it has the advantage that the recomputed births and corrected populations are determined from the data of the observation period alone (see T.A.S.A., XXIII, 439; XXIV, 150 and 153; and XXV, 151).

(*iii*) Henderson's process used the same value of r throughout. In the construction of the U.S. Abridged Life Tables, 1919–20, which were prepared by Miss Elbertie Foudray,* it was noted, however, that the birth

---

* It may also be of interest to note here that other methods devised by Miss Foudray in the preparation of United States life tables for 1920–29 and 1930–39 are discussed, with particular reference to corrections at ages over 5 for net migration and inconsistencies due to age or other errors, by T. N. E. Greville in R.A.I.A., XXXI, 370–73.

rates had varied considerably for several calendar years, and it was therefore concluded that the assumption of a uniform G.P. or A.P. would not
be permissible. Miss Foudray consequently devised a method under which
the deficient populations P_0^{z+1} were first corrected on the assumption of a
fixed percentage deficit of 9% for whites and 25% for Negroes (see par. 31
here), the births E_0^z thence following by formula (3). This recalculated E_0^z
for 1919, in comparison with the registered births of 1919, then gave the
percentage by which the registered births of 1919 were assumed to be deficient; and this percentage deficiency was then assumed to be applicable
for the calculation of the true births from the registered births of previous
calendar years. From these corrected births of previous calendar years and
the registered deaths of those years it was then possible to calculate P_x^z
and P_x^{z+1} at each age by subtracting the appropriate deaths from the births
in accordance with formula (6). The column E_x^z then followed by formula
(1). In applying this method Miss Foudray computed only the increases
δ_x^z, or $P_x^{z+1} - P_x^z$, at each age, and was therefore restricted to the use of
formula (29) for q_x^z which does not involve the actual P's when the factor
in the denominator is taken from known values. As pointed out by
H. H. Wolfenden in T.A.S.A., XXV, 150, however, this restriction is not
necessary; for the separate values of P_x^{z+1} and P_x^z emerge directly by the
above process, and as they satisfy the fundamental relations (1)–(4), q_x^z
may be computed by any formula—preferably by No. (11).

(*iv*) In preparing the U.S. Life Tables, 1939–41, T. N. E. Greville used
the true Type III formula (11). After due examination (see pars. 46 and
47 here), it was assumed that the degree of under-registration was the
same for births and infant deaths, so that q_0 could be derived from the
registered data without adjustment. The deaths D_x^z were therefore
divided into their $_\delta D_x^z$ and $_a D_x^z$ components by using the factors f_x^z determined as stated in par. 65 here. Then P_0^z follows from the previous year's
births E_0^{z-1} and deaths $_a D_x^{z-1}$ by formula (3); $E_1^z = P_0^z - {}_\delta D_0^z$ by formula
(2); $P_0^{z+1} = E_0^z - {}_a D_0^z$ by formula (3); and these values with E_0^z give q_x^z by
formula (11).

Before proceeding to the higher ages, the values of E_1^z so found were
adjusted for under-reporting. The degree of adjustment required was
computed with due regard for the fact that at ages 5 and beyond the
census data and registered deaths were assumed implicitly to be incomplete by the same percentage, so that at those ages they could be used
without correction. The factors for adjusting E_1^z were obtained by estimating E_1 from the births between April 1, 1930, and March 31, 1937 by two
independent methods based on evident applications of formulae (2), (3),
and (6), namely: (*a*) by subtracting the appropriate reported infant

deaths occurring among the reported births of that period, and (*b*) by adding to the census populations at each age from 3 to 9 the reported deaths this group experienced in previous years in passing from age 1 to the census date. The adjustment factor, formed as the ratio of (*a*) and (*b*), was divided into E_1^z computed from the recorded births and deaths. From the value of E_1^z thus adjusted, corrected values of E_x^z and P_x^z for use in formula (11) at ages 1 to 4 were then derived on the assumption that the deaths could be taken as correct.

In comparing these several methods, it will be noted that Glover's procedure computes the births from the supposedly correct populations aged 2 and over and the deaths in calendar years subsequent to the observation period, and produces an approximate Type III q_x^z. Henderson's method calculates the births from the data of the observation period alone, and gives the correct Type III q_x^z. Miss Foudray's process requires the births and deaths of calendar years prior to the observation period, and finds an approximate Type III q_x^z (although more correct values can be obtained as shown in T.A.S.A., XXV, 149–52). Greville's approach also uses the births and deaths of calendar years prior to the observation period, and finds the correct Type III q_x^z.

93. (*i*) As a result of the nature of the adjustments at infantile ages described in pars. 87–92 it is generally sufficient to adopt the values of q_x which emerge therefrom without any further graduation. Where graduation is found to be desirable Makeham's second formula has been suggested (see "Investigations Concerning a Law of Infantile Mortality," Australian Association for the Advancement of Science, XIV [1913], 526, and Vol. I, Statistician's Report, 1911 Census of Australia, p. 325, by C. H. Wickens, and Greville's comments in the U.S. Life Tables and Actuarial Tables, 1939–41, p. 137). Two other modifications of Makeham's first formula to provide for the rapid change in values during the infantile ages have also been proposed by J. F. Steffensen and F. S. Harper (see "The Fundamental Principles of Mathematical Statistics," p. 80).

(*ii*) In proceeding from q_x to the customary life-table functions, l_x and d_x are calculated from an arbitrary radix in the usual manner. The function L_x, however, which at ages 5 and over where $f_x = \frac{1}{2}$ is taken with sufficient accuracy as

$$\frac{l_x + l_{x+1}}{2},$$

must be computed at the infantile ages where $f_x \neq \frac{1}{2}$ as $l_{x+1} + f_x d_x$ or $l_x - (1 - f_x)d_x$ in accordance with formulae (2) and (3) respectively (see also pars. 65 and 66)—these expressions also being equivalent to

$L_x = f_x l_x + (1 - f_x) l_{x+1}$. For L_0, moreover, where data are often available for various subdivisions of the first years of life, a more accurate value can be obtained by making separate calculations for those subdivisions by the formula $T_x - T_{x+t} = \dfrac{t}{2}(l_x + l_{x+t})$ and adding the results (as in the U.S. Life Tables, 1939–41, p. 133).

(*iii*) Another special problem is that of determining values for the force of mortality, μ, at ages 0, 1, and 2, because the usual approximate formula

$$\mu_x = \frac{8(l_{x-1} - l_{x+1}) - (l_{x-2} - l_{x+2})}{12 l_x}$$

is inapplicable for $x = 0$ and 1, and at age 2 is unsuitable since it involves l_0. In the U.S. Life Tables, 1939–41, p. 137, μ_1 and μ_2 therefore were found by Waring's (Lagrange's) formula (see footnote, par. 52) from the five unequally spaced values $l_{\frac{1}{2}}, l_1, l_2, l_3,$ and l_4 for μ_2, and $l_{\frac{1}{2}}, l_{\frac{1}{2}}, l_1, l_2,$ and l_3 for μ_1.

In preparing those tables, also, Greville paid particular attention to the estimation of a realistic value for μ_0 (which has some academic interest even though its practical utility is slight). After a review of methods previously used for the calculation of μ_0 in official reports in Australia and Belgium, and elsewhere in actuarial literature by King and Spurgeon—all of which seem to have underestimated the value seriously—the procedure finally adopted was to fit a Gompertz curve to the l_x values at birth and at the ages of 1 day and 2 days in order to give effect to the extremely rapid decrease in the death rate immediately after birth.

94. In the procedures of pars. 87–91 for the English life tables and pars. 92(*i*)–(*iv*) with respect to those constructed in the United States, migrations have always been ignored as unimportant. Among the processes devised for the 1939–41 United States life tables as described in par. 92(*v*), however, a final adjustment was made for immigration at ages 1 to 4 since the deaths recorded at those ages may include some deaths of children who entered the country as immigrants. The method which was used as a sufficiently close approximation was to multiply the computed mortality rate at each age by the ratio of the native population to the total population at that age. This ratio is very close to unity, and the effect of the adjustment was negligible. At age 0 this method is not appropriate, because the small amount of immigration which occurs is believed to be heavily concentrated in the latter part of the first year of life, while the mortality is very much heavier in the early part. The expedient was therefore adopted of applying the adjustment ratio only to the probability of death, $_sq_0$, for the second portion of the first year of life. These

adjustments at ages 0 to 4 might result in a slight understatement of the mortality rates as they assume that no emigration occurred, although this is partially offset by the fact that the number of deaths subtracted from the births to obtain the exposed to risk may include some deaths of immigrant children (see T. N. E. Greville, "U.S. Life Tables and Actuarial Tables, 1939–41," pp. 119–20).

(B) ADULT AGES

95. The preceding methods of treating the data at infantile ages are necessary by reason of the unreliability of the census returns at those ages. For the later ages—in accordance with the principles of pars. 53 and 54 here, and sometimes after preliminary adjustments for errors of digit concentration of the types discussed in par. 52—the census returns and death statistics can usually be taken as being approximately correct in certain specified quinquennial or decennial age groups. Furthermore, at ages above 4 last birthday (as stated in pars. 65 and 78), f_x^z may generally be taken as $\frac{1}{2}$, so that a uniform distribution of deaths may be assumed and m_x may be found directly by dividing the calendar year's deaths by the mean population in accordance with the usual $m_x = d_x/L_x$ of the life table (and the analogous formulae (27), (33), and (36) hereof for q_x^z). The problem to be dealt with at these later ages is consequently that of re-distributing the approximately correct quinquennial or decennial group-ings of the deaths and populations into the values at each age, in such a manner that the irregularities at individual ages will be removed without disturbing unduly the totals in each group.

The various methods which have been developed in constructing the best known population tables will therefore now be reviewed in chrono-logical order. Of the methods to be thus described, the student at the commencement of his reading should note particularly the following ap-praisal of their present comparative utilities: (*a*) The graphic method (par. 96) may still be useful under some circumstances. (*b*) Farr's meth-ods (par. 97) are now of historical interest only. (*c*) The later English Life Table methods (par. 98) introduced important basic ideas in the "curve of sines" and the handling of grouped data. (*d*) The tangential and oscu-latory reproducing interpolation formulae on Sprague's principles (pars. 99–103) and Henderson's principles (pars. 104–6), and the tangential and osculatory non-reproducing formulae on Jenkins' principles (par. 107), have been used so extensively and have become so well established as al-most routine procedures in many countries because they have produced sufficiently good results with considerable facility, that their continued use may still be anticipated in some quarters notwithstanding their demonstrable and acknowledged weaknesses. (*e*) The more flexible interpolation and fitting methods developed by Reid and Dow, Kerrich, and Greville (pars. 108–11) are important as being essential links in the theoretical development of the general problem, and as affording improved practical techniques, although they have not been adopted widely in practical work on account of their comparative complexity and the previously established popularity of the simpler methods of pars. 99–107. (*f*) The newer method of applying linear compounding coefficients to effect reproducing or non-reproducing interpolations minimizing the mean square error in a specified order of differences (pars. 115–17) involves a simple computation routine and may be expected to show improved results; the recent censuses in several countries may afford opportunities for its further exploration. (*g*) The practical usefulness of the theoretically interesting "interlocking" formulae (par. 118) remains to be established. (*h*) The idea of reproducing subtabulation minimizing the sum of the squares of all differences of a given order by difference-equation operations (par. 119), while again theoretically interesting, does not seem likely to produce sufficiently improved results to justify its comparatively laborious working processes.

(*i*) *Graphic Method*

96. A graphic treatment was naturally one of the first methods to be applied on account of its apparently simple nature. The deaths and populations in the age groups can be represented separately by a series of rectangles, from which the values for individual years of age may be ascertained by drawing a curve through the tops of those rectangles in such a manner that the areas representative of each age group shall be unaltered. By then reading the values for each age from the death curve and from the population curve, m_x is obtained directly by dividing the former by the latter, and thence p_x follows by the usual

$$p_x = \frac{2 - m_x}{2 + m_x};$$

or p_x may be obtained directly from the deaths and populations by the relation

$$p_x = \frac{2L_x - d_x}{2L_x + d_x}.$$

This graphic method was used originally by Milne in the construction of the Carlisle Table (see G. King, J.I.A., XXIV, 186, and XLII, 226, and see J.I.A., XVI, 221, for an interesting account of the life of Dr. John Heysham, compiler of the data used by Milne). It was also illustrated by

Burridge (J.I.A., XXIII, 309, and XXIV, 333), Moors and Day (J.I.A., XXXVI, 151), and Grant (J.I.A., XL, 125). Notwithstanding its apparent simplicity, however, it is difficult to read the individual values from the curve with sufficient accuracy. It may therefore be desirable in some cases to represent the data approximately by a mathematical formula, such as by a Makeham function (see par. 125 here); and then, using this as a base line, to graduate graphically the differences between the resulting series and the original data (see G. F. Hardy, J.I.A., XXV, 229). A further graphic graduation of the values of m_x or p_x as determined from the population and death curves may also be advantageous (cf. J.I.A., XXIII, 321, and XXIV, 203 and 339).

(ii) Dr. Farr's Methods

97. In the construction of the earliest English Life Tables the deaths and populations were available in the age groups 5–9, 10–14, thence decennially to 94, with a final group for ages 95 and over; and Dr. Farr assumed that by dividing the deaths by the population in these groups the resulting function, which is analogous to the

$$\frac{l_x - l_{x+n}}{T_x - T_{x+n}}$$

of the life table, could be taken as the central death rate for the year of age central to the group, namely $m_{x+\frac{n-1}{2}}$, or as the force of mortality for the central point of age, that is, $\mu_{x+\frac{n}{2}}$ —these two functions being assumed to be identical. It was therefore supposed that the data in these age groups would thus yield immediately the numerical values of m_7, m_{12}, $m_{19.5}$ (or μ_{20}), $m_{29.5}$ (or μ_{30}), and so on. The values of p_7 and p_{12} thence follow by the formula of par. 96—a special adjustment being made to the value at age 12 "to allow for the turn of the curve" (J.I.A., IX, 135). At the subsequent ages two different methods were used in passing to p_{20}, p_{30}, etc. In *Farr's First Method*, which presumably was used by him in preparing English Life Tables Nos. 1 and 2 (see J.I.A., XLII, 288) it was assumed that $m_{29.5} = m_{19.5}r^{10}$ from which m_{20} was obtained as $m_{19.5}r^{\frac{1}{2}}$, and the subsequent intervals were treated similarly—p_{20}, p_{30}, etc., thence following as usual. In his *Second Method*, which was applied to the English Life Table No. 3 and the Healthy English Table No. 1, the values of p_{20}, etc., were determined by calculating log p_x directly from the supposed values of μ_x by the formula

$$\log_{10} p_x = -\frac{\kappa^2 (r - 1)}{\log_{10} r} \mu_x,$$

which was obtained as follows: Assuming (as in the similar assumption with regard to m in the first method) that $\mu_{x+10} = r^{10}\mu_x$, so that $\mu_{x+t} = r^t\mu_x$ as in Gompertz's formula, it follows, since

$$\operatorname{colog}_e p_x = \int_0^1 \mu_{x+t}\,dt\,, \qquad \text{that } \operatorname{colog}_e p_x = \int_0^1 \mu_x r^t\,dt = \frac{r-1}{\log_e r}\,\mu_x\,;$$

from which the above formula results, κ being the modulus. The logarithms of p_7, p_{12}, p_{20}, p_{30}, etc., were then made the subject of interpolation by ordinary third differences to get the values at each age.

The principal objection to Farr's method lies in the inaccuracy of the assumption that, in effect,

$$\frac{l_x - l_{x+n}}{T_x - T_{x+n}}$$

can be taken as an approximation to $m_{x+\frac{n-1}{2}}$ or $\mu_{x+\frac{n}{2}}$; for, as shown by King in J.I.A., XLII, 232–33, that assumption "leads to erroneous results of serious magnitude."* His method may now be considered as of historical interest only.

(iii) Later English Life-Table Methods

98. Some years after the production of English Life Table No. 3, No. 4 was constructed by applying to the rates of mortality of No. 3 the ratios in which the mean annual death-rates shown by the data of the two tables had altered (see J.I.A., XXVII, 494; XXIX, 29; and XLII, 288). A complete change of method, however, was subsequently made in the preparation of the next tables—namely, Nos. 5 and 6, the corresponding Healthy English Tables Nos. 2 and 3, and the London Life Table. The procedures which were then adopted are generally associated with the names of Dr. John Tatham and A. C. Waters (see J.I.A., XLII, 234–35). They are entirely free from the questionable assumptions made by Dr. Farr.

* Dr. M. Greenwood in J.I.A., LVIII, 153, however, expressed the opinion that "this seems to do some little injustice to the old tables." He stated that in The Lancet (1922), II, 739, he had computed the expectations of life at various ages by King's method for comparison with Farr's, with the following results: "At late ages the error was, of course, relatively large—for example, at age 75 there was an error of nearly 6 months in the expectation of life; but at an age as late as 45 the effect of the correction [by King's method] was to alter the expectation of life by 22 days, and for the purposes for which Dr. Farr used those tables perhaps the error was not very serious." V. P. A. Derrick has also pointed out in J.I.A., LVIII, 159, that the understatement of mortality by Farr's method at the older ages "was compensated by the probability that the records themselves already overstated mortality through age misstatements in the original data, so that really Dr. Farr's mortality rates at these ages might be regarded, in his opinion, as superior to those given later by the improved method of Mr. King."

In these tables the data consisted of the populations and deaths in certain fixed age groups, which could not be altered since tabulations by single years were not available. Under such circumstances, and also when the data by single years have been thrown into appropriate age groups on the principles of pars. 53–54, the data consist in effect of values of populations $(T'_x - T'_{x+n})$ and deaths $(l'_x - l'_{x+n})$, where x is the first age of the group and n its range, and T'_x and l'_x denote in the actual community the population and deaths at age x and beyond in the same manner that T_x and l_x are used in the life-table community. Summing from the bottom upwards, therefore, we get T'_x and l'_x for the points of divisions of the groups. Thus when the original age groups were quinquennial to 15, thence decennial to 95, with a final group at 95 and over, as in the English Life Tables to No. 6 inclusive, the values so obtained were for ages 0, 5, 10, 15, 25, 35, . . . , 95. The values at individual ages may then be obtained by interpolation, and the first differences taken negatively give values of the population L'_x and deaths d'_x of the actual community in each year of age, from which m_x follows by dividing the deaths by the population as in par. 95, and hence p_x or q_x as usual.

Numerous variations in detail have been made in applying these principles. In English Life Table No. 5 the values of $(2T'_x + l'_x)$ and $(2T'_x - l'_x)$ were calculated for the points of division, and the similar values at ages one year older were obtained by interpolation; then $(2L'_x + d'_x)$ and $(2L'_x - d'_x)$, and hence

$$p_x \left(= \frac{2L'_x - d'_x}{2L'_x + d'_x} \right),$$

were found by differencing at the points of division, and from these values the series p_x was completed by interpolation. In the London Life Table $(2L'_x + d'_x)$ and $(2L'_x - d'_x)$ were obtained at each age from interpolations of $\log (2T'_x + l'_x)$ and $\log (2T'_x - l'_x)$, while in English Life No. 6 the interpolations were based on $\log (2T'_x)$ and $\log l'_x$. Other appropriate functions, such as T'_x and l'_x directly, $\log q_x$, or $\log (q_x + .1)$ may be used as in the later developments of these methods described in par. 99. The ratios of T'_x and of l'_x to the corresponding T_x and l_x values of a smoothly graduated life table, or functions such as

$$\log \frac{T'_x}{T_x} \quad \text{or} \quad \log \frac{p'_x}{p_x},$$

also provide a valuable method of performing such graduations with reference to a standard table (see A. Henry, J.I.A., XLVII, 407; Henderson's

"Mortality Laws and Statistics," p. 60; "The Fundamental Principles of Mathematical Statistics," pp. 85–86; and par. 111 here).

In all these tables, moreover, an important innovation was the employ- ment of a double process of interpolation (by constant fourth differences), and the blending of the results by the *Curve of Sines* with the object of smoothing the breaks of continuity which occur at the points of division when ordinary interpolations are made from separate abutting series. (The importance of smoothing the discontinuities which thus occur at the points of junction with ordinary interpolations, resulting from the fact that each such interpolation segment "cuts its successor at an angle" [cf. J. E. Kerrich's description, J.I.A., LXVI, 88], may be seen readily from the diagrams on p. 22*a* of the monograph "Elements of Graduation" by M. D. Miller et al.—published by the Actuarial Society of America and the American Institute of Actuaries, 1946). By this method, for example, "at ages 26–34, inclusive, there was one set of values derived from the group with central age 25, and another from the group with its centre at age 35. A mean of the two values at each age was formed by multiplying the first set by the following factors:

(1)	.97553	(4)	.65451	(7)	.20611
(2)	.90451	(5)	.50000	(8)	.09549
(3)	.79389	(6)	.34549	(9)	.02447

and the second by these factors reversed, and by adding together the two products at each age. By this means the greatest weight was given to these terms nearest the centre of a group, and the least to those farthest from it. The factors are empirical, and are derived from the 'curve of sines'; they are the numerical values of the expression

$$\frac{1}{2}\left(1 + \cos\frac{\pi x}{10}\right),$$

when x is given successive integral values from 1 to 9" (see 65th Annual Report of the Registrar-General, Part I, p. xvii). The method produced results which George King described at that time as being "exceedingly well graduated." It is of interest to note, as shown in J.I.A., XLII, by Lidstone (p. 284) and J. Buchanan (p. 382), that Sprague's fifth difference osculatory formula (see par. 100) uses, in effect, a blend of two ordinary interpolations in proportions very similar to those of the "curve of sines."*

(*iv*) *Tangential and Osculatory Reproducing Interpolation Formulae on Sprague's Principles*

---

* Other "overlapping" methods of ordinary interpolation may also frequently give good results—see J.I.A., L, 126.

99. On account of the empirical and comparatively laborious nature of the "curve of sines" process, George King next suggested in J.I.A., XLII, 238, that tangential or osculatory reproducing interpolation* could be applied more readily; and in that paper he reconstructed the Carlisle table and the English Life Tables Nos. 3 and 6 (males) by the use of Sprague's fifth difference osculatory formula (see par. 100 here) and also by Karup's third difference tangential formula (which King produced independently—par. 101).

In these reconstructions a preliminary calculation was first made of the values of T'_x and l'_x for quinquennial ages throughout instead of for the decennial ages 15, 25, 35, etc., as in the original data—the ordinary formulae for bisection of groups being used. The interpolations were then performed, for purposes of investigation, in four different ways, namely, (A) By applying Sprague's fifth difference osculatory formula to find T'_x and l'_x, and hence, by differencing, L'_x and d'_x at each age; (B) By using log T'_x and log l'_x as the basis of the fifth difference osculatory interpolation; (C) By finding quinquennial values of log q_x by ordinary interpolation from the quinquennial values of T'_x and l'_x, and thence log q_x at each age by the fifth difference osculatory method; and (D) By proceeding as in C, except that the Karup-King third difference tangential formula was employed.

This principle of using tangential or osculatory interpolation as thus suggested by King was adopted in a number of instances. In the United

---

* The term *osculatory*—following Sprague's designation of his original process (par. 100), and its subsequent wide use to describe also the Karup-King formula (par. 101) and others—has been employed generally in actuarial literature to cover all those formulae for which one or more derivatives of adjacent curve segments are equal at the points of junction. Strict mathematical terminology, however, suggests that this label is applied correctly only when equality of at least the first and second derivatives is required, so that, conformably, the word *tangential* (as suggested by H. S. Beers, T.A.S.A., XLVI, 83–84), might be used for those formulae which produce equal first derivatives only. These two distinctive terms are therefore adopted here.

The designations (a) *reproducing* and (b) *non-reproducing* are also used, as explained further in the text, in order to maintain a clear distinction between (a) the tangential or osculatory formulae which (on Sprague's or Henderson's principles) are true interpolation formulae *reproducing* the given values, and (b) the tangential or osculatory formulae which (on Jenkins' principles) do *not* reproduce the given values and consequently introduce into the procedures an element of graduation or smoothing. (The term "non-reproducing" seems preferable to the word "modified" which, following Jenkins' original paper, has been used frequently to describe these non-reproducing formulae.)

States the fifth difference formula was applied in 1910 with King's Construction A by J. W. Glover in preparing a mortality table for the Registration States (J.A.S.A., XII, 85); H. L. Rietz and C. H. Forsyth in 1911 employed it for the production of a rural U.S. life table (R.A.I.A., I, 9); C. H. Forsyth adopted it again in 1914 in constructing tables for the registration area for 1901–10 (J.A.S.A., XIV, 228); and Construction A (with slight variations) was used extensively by Glover in the U.S. Life Tables 1890, 1901, 1910, and 1901–10. The third difference formula, with which King experimented in Construction D, has not been so used; it has, however, been employed recently by Greville for the special interpolation problems between ages 12 and 27 in all the U.S. life tables of 1939–41 (see p. 126 thereof), and it has formed an important part of King's later development of his "pivotal value" method which is described in par. 120 here.

100. *Sprague's fifth difference osculatory formula* secures smoothness at the points occupied by the original data by providing that the curve of the fifth degree passing through the central interval u_2 to u_3 in the given six-point series u_0, u_1, u_2, u_3, u_4, and u_5 shall have, at the point whose ordinate is u_2, the same tangent and radius of curvature (i.e., the same first and second differential coefficients, being second order contact) as the partial Newton-Stirling curve of the fourth order through $u_0 \ldots u_4$, and shall similarly, at the point whose ordinate is u_3, have the same tangent and radius of curvature as the partial curve of the fourth order through $u_1 \ldots u_5$. In this process the other important condition laid down is that the formula must reproduce the given values exactly, i.e., it shall be a *reproducing* interpolation formula only (cf. par. 107 where the subsequent development of non-reproducing osculatory formulae is discussed). The derivation of the formula, which was introduced in 1880 by T. B. Sprague (J.I.A., XXII, 270), is shown conveniently by King in J.I.A., XLII, 239; and an alternative demonstration has been given by G. J. Lidstone in J.I.A., XLII, 394, which is assisted by the diagram included with this proof in the U.S. Life Tables, 1890, etc., p. 345.*

The formula may be stated in a number of ways:

(*a*) In terms of ordinary advancing differences when derived as above

---

* Although osculatory reproducing formulae beyond Sprague's 5th differences and 2nd order contact are not usually required for practical purposes, it may be noted that J. F. Reilly (in R.A.I.A., XIII, 4, and XIV, 12) generalized Sprague's and Lidstone's proofs for differences of odd order $2h + 1$ and contact of order k, and showed in particular the expressions with 5th differences and 3rd order contact, 7th differences and 2nd order contact, and 7th differences and 3rd order contact.

for the interval from u_2 to u_3 it is $(x < 1)$

$$u_{2+x} = u_2 + x\Delta u_0 + \frac{(x+3)\,x}{2}\,\Delta^2 u_0 + \frac{(x+2)\,(x+1)\,x}{6}\,\Delta^3 u_0$$

$$+ \frac{(x+2)\,(x+1)\,x\,(x-1)}{24}\,\Delta^4 u_0 + \frac{x^3\,(x-1)\,(5x-7)}{24}\,\Delta^5 u_0$$

in which the first three terms may be written otherwise as

$$u_0 + (x+2)\,\Delta u_0 + \frac{(x+2)\,(x+1)}{2}\,\Delta^2 u_0 .$$

In this form it is seen to differ from the usual interpolation formula only in the fifth difference term; and it is applied easily by calculating the leading differences for subdivided intervals as shown in the papers already mentioned.

(b) An alternative form given by Karup (Trans. 2nd International Actuarial Congress, p. 82) in which the differences are taken centrally is

$$u_x = u_0 + x\Delta u_0 + \frac{x\,(x-1)}{2}\,\Delta^2 u_{-1} + \frac{x\,(x^2-1)}{6}\,\Delta^3 u_{-1}$$

$$+ \frac{x\,(x^2-1)\,(x-2)}{24}\,\Delta^4 u_{-2} + \frac{x^3\,(x-1)\,(5x-7)}{24}\,\Delta^5 u_{-2}$$

for which he gives a special working process of considerable facility which is well illustrated by J. Buchanan in J.I.A., XLII, 385–92.

(c) The last form may be expressed at once in W. F. Sheppard's very convenient central difference notation, in which

$$\delta u_x = u_{x+\frac{1}{2}} - u_{x-\frac{1}{2}} \text{ and } \mu\delta^n u_x = \tfrac{1}{2}\,(\delta^n u_{x+\frac{1}{2}} + \delta^n u_{x-\frac{1}{2}}),$$

so that

$$\delta u_{\frac{1}{2}} = u_1 - u_0 (= \Delta u_0),\ \delta^2 u_0 = u_1 - 2u_0 + u_{-1}(= \Delta^2 u_{-1}),$$

$$\delta^3 u_{\frac{1}{2}} = u_2 - 3u_1 + 3u_0 - u_{-1}(= \Delta^3 u_{-1}),$$

$$\delta^4 u_0 = u_2 - 4u_1 + 6u_0 - 4u_{-1} + u_{-2}(= \Delta^4 u_{-2}),$$

and so on, and $\mu\delta u_0 = \tfrac{1}{2}(\delta u_{\frac{1}{2}} + \delta u_{-\frac{1}{2}})$ etc. (see Buchanan, J.I.A., XLII, 370 and 379, and Henderson, T.A.S.A., XXII, 175); and when written in "Everett's form," in which $y = 1 - x$ for symmetry, it becomes

$$u_x = xu_1 + \frac{x\,(x^2-1)}{6}\,\delta^2 u_1 + \frac{x^3\,(x-1)\,(5x-7)}{24}\,\delta^4 u_1$$

$$+ yu_0 + \frac{y\,(y^2-1)}{6}\,\delta^2 u_0 + \frac{y^3\,(y-1)\,(5y-7)}{24}\,\delta^4 u_0 \tag{40}$$

as given by Buchanan in J.I.A., XLII, 379 (where $\xi = y$), and in Henderson's "Mortality Laws and Statistics," p. 76 (formula 6) for interval t.

The working process in this form is very simple, as shown in J.I.A., XLII, 390, and T.A.S.A., XXII, 194.*

101. *The Karup-King third difference tangential formula* was deduced originally in 1898 by J. Karup in Trans. 2nd International Actuarial Congress, p. 83, and was subsequently derived independently in 1907 by King in J.I.A., XLI, 545. An alternative demonstration is given by Lidstone in J.I.A., XLII, 394. The formula—which is again a "reproducing" interpolation formula—provides that the third degree curve through the central interval u_1 to u_2 of the four-point series u_0, u_1, u_2, and u_3 shall have at u_1 and u_2 the same tangents (first differential coefficients) as the partial Newton-Stirling curves of the second degree through $u_0 \ldots u_2$ and $u_1 \ldots u_3$ respectively. It may be expressed in the following forms:

(*a*) In terms of ordinary advancing differences it is

$$u_{1+x} = u_1 + x\Delta u_0 + \frac{x(x+1)}{2}\Delta^2 u_0 + \frac{x^2(x-1)}{2}\Delta^3 u_0 ;$$

and in this form it is easily applied as shown by King in J.I.A., XLII, 245, and Supplement (Part I) to the Registrar-General's 75th Report, p. 52.

(*b*) Karup gives it in terms of differences taken centrally as

$$u_x = u_0 + x\Delta u_0 + \frac{x(x-1)}{2}\Delta^2 u_{-1} + \frac{x^2(x-1)}{2}\Delta^3 u_{-1} .$$

(*c*) In Everett's form $(y = 1 - x)$ with Sheppard's notation it becomes

$$u_x = xu_1 + \frac{x^2(x-1)}{2}\delta^2 u_1 + yu_0 + \frac{y^2(y-1)}{2}\delta^2 u_0 \qquad (41)$$

as shown by Buchanan, J.I.A., XLII, 378, and also by Henderson in T.A.S.A., XXII, 189, and "Mortality Laws and Statistics," p. 77 (formula 7) for interval t. The numerical work in this form is extremely convenient (cf. J.I.A., XLIII, 159–60).

102. The preceding "reproducing" formulae of pars. 100 and 101 are designed to secure smoothness of junction of the interpolated results at the points occupied by the original data. It is also to be remembered,

---

* Still using Sprague's basic assumptions except that the differential coefficients were determined from the mean of their values in the partial curves, J. Buchanan in J.I.A., XLII, 374, reached a variation of Sprague's formula of par. 100(*c*) in which the coefficient of $\delta^4 u_1$ was

$$\frac{x^3(x-1)(3x-4)}{12}$$

and similarly for $\delta^4 u_0$. (See also T.F.A., XII, 124, and W. A. Jenkins in R.A.I.A., XV, 90, and T.A.S.A., XXVIII, 198.)

however, as stated in par. 95, that the problem here under consideration is ordinarily not merely one of smoothing, but is primarily that of redistributing the approximately correct quinquennial (or decennial) groupings into the values at each age so that, while the irregularities at individual ages will be removed, the totals in each group will not be unduly disturbed.

In 1913, accordingly, S. T. Shovelton (J.I.A., XLVII, 284) investigated the effect of introducing directly the condition of reproduction of grouped data. Requiring that the interpolation curve shall be of the fourth degree and that it shall have the same ordinates and tangents at the point of junction as the partial curves based on five given values, he imposed an additional condition designed to effect the reproduction of grouped data. If the ungraduated values are grouped in fives and pivotal values (see par. 120 here) are then found by King's formula (49), and if the formula in question is next applied to obtain intermediate graduated values, it was required that the quinquennial sums of the graduated and ungraduated values shall agree to and including the fifth differences of these sums. The resulting expression thus became, in Everett's form, *Shovelton's six-point tangential formula*

$$u_x = x u_1 + \frac{x(x^2-1)}{6} \delta^2 u_1 + \frac{x^2(x-1)(x-5)}{48} \delta^4 u_1$$
$$+ y u_0 + \frac{y(y^2-1)}{6} \delta^2 u_0 + \frac{y^2(y-1)(y-5)}{48} \delta^4 u_0 \tag{42}$$

which was shown to give a very satisfactory interpolation (see also R.A.I.A., XXXIV, 57).

Shovelton also gave an alternative derivation of the formula in which the condition of reproduction of grouped values is replaced by the requirement that the area under the interpolation curve in each interval shall be equal to the average of the areas under the partial curves in the same interval. It was found, incidentally, that Sprague's fifth difference formula satisfies the condition as to the area under the interpolation curve. In the case of a third degree formula based on five given values, Shovelton also showed that both his methods of derivation produce the Karup-King formula of par. 101.

103. In determining the differential coefficients for the tangential or osculatory "reproducing" formulae of the preceding paragraphs, the partial curves are taken of one degree less than that of the final curve. This restriction, however, is not necessary; and it was consequently shown in 1906 by R. Henderson (T.A.S.A., IX, 215–17) that Karup's third difference formula of par. 101 could be improved, without going as far as

Sprague's original fifth difference method, by determining a third difference curve with its first differential coefficients equal to those of two partial Newton-Stirling fourth degree curves (instead of merely taking second difference partial curves as in Karup's formula). The resulting expression in Everett's form is *Henderson's six-point tangential formula*

$$u_x = x u_1 + \frac{x(x^2-1)}{6}\, \delta^2 u_1 + \frac{x^2(1-x)}{12}\, \delta^4 u_1$$
$$+ y u_0 + \frac{y(y^2-1)}{6}\, \delta^2 u_0 + \frac{y^2(1-y)}{12}\, \delta^4 u_0 \tag{43}$$

as given by him in his "Mortality Laws and Statistics," p. 77 (formula 8, for interval t) and used on p. 97 thereof. It may also be written as

$$u_x = u_0 + x\,\delta u_{\frac12} + \frac{x(x-1)}{2}\, \mu B_{\frac12} + \frac{x(x-1)(x-\frac12)}{6}\, C_{\frac12} \tag{44}$$

where $B_x = \delta^2 u_x - \frac16 \delta^4 u_x$ and $C_x = \delta^3 u_x - \frac12 \delta^5 u_x$ as in T.A.S.A., IX, 215–17, and XXII, 195 (example No. 3).

This formula materially reduces the labour of applying Sprague's formula—for, as shown in T.A.S.A., IX, 216, the fourth and fifth differences which are retained are in effect applied "merely as corrections to the second and third orders respectively."

(v) *Tangential and Oscillatory Reproducing Interpolation Formulae on Henderson's Principles*

104. The formulae of pars. 100–103 are all derived on Sprague's original principle of equating certain functions of the curve to the corresponding functions of two ordinary partial curves at a central interval, in addition to the requirement that the given values must be reproduced. The selection of these partial curves is, of course (as remarked by Jenkins in T.A.S.A., XXVIII, 198), somewhat arbitrary. Henderson accordingly in 1921 enunciated the new principle that it is preferable to discard the use of partial curves, and instead simply to impose the condition that the successive intervals are to be filled in by curves of the specified degree with their constants so determined that the corresponding differential coefficients at the points of junction shall be equal to each other (cf. R.A.I.A., XIII, 23). He retained, however, Sprague's other basic requirement that the two curves must exactly reproduce the given values. Following this principle, therefore, we may take formula (44), which is a general expression for a function of the third degree between u_0 and u_1, and "determine $\mu B_{\frac12}$ and $C_{\frac12}$ from the conditions that the values of the first and second differential coefficients should be continuous at the points of junction, if differences of the sixth and higher orders vanish." We thus obtain easily,

as in T.A.S.A., XXII, 190, $C_x = \delta B_x$ and $B_x + \frac{1}{6}\delta^2 B_x = \delta^2 u_x$. This last difference equation gives $B_x = \delta^2(1 + \frac{1}{6}\delta^2)^{-1}u_x = \delta^2 u_x - \frac{1}{6}\delta^4 u_x$ approximately, by neglecting differences of the sixth and higher orders. Also $C_{\frac{1}{2}} = \delta B_{\frac{1}{2}} = \delta_3 u_{\frac{1}{2}} - \frac{1}{6}\delta^5 u_{\frac{1}{2}}$. *Henderson's approximately osculatory formula* is consequently

$$u_x = xu_1 + \frac{x(x^2-1)}{6}\ (\delta^2 u_1 - \tfrac{1}{6}\delta^4 u_1)$$

$$+ yu_0 + \frac{y(y^2-1)}{6}\ (\delta^2 u_0 - \tfrac{1}{6}\delta^4 u_0)\,.$$

(45)

The numerical work is very convenient, as shown in T.A.S.A., IX, 219.

The discontinuity in the first differential coefficient, which results from the relation $B_x = \delta^2 u_x - \frac{1}{6}\delta^4 u_x$ being only an approximate solution of the difference equation $B_x + \frac{1}{6}\delta^2 B_x = \delta^2 u_x$, is $\frac{1}{36}\delta^6$ (as is shown easily in T.A.S.A., XXII, 186; see also T.A.S.A., IX, 221, and R.A.I.A., XV, 88). The formula is now mainly of historical interest as having occupied a prominent place in Henderson's departure from the basic principles originally used by Sprague.

105. In view of the discontinuity of $\frac{1}{36}\delta^6$ which is thus involved in formula (41), Henderson subsequently showed (see R.A.I.A., XIII, 24, following T.A.S.A., XXV, 30) that an exact solution of the difference equation $B_x + \frac{1}{6}\delta^2 B_x = \delta^2 u_x$ can be obtained by writing it in the form

$$\delta^2 u_x = B_x + \frac{r}{(1+r)^2}\ \delta^2 B_x$$

so that

$$\frac{r}{(1+r)^2} = \tfrac{1}{6}$$

and consequently $r = 2 - \sqrt{3} = \frac{4}{15}$ with sufficient accuracy, where r is applied by means of the relations $B_x' = \delta^2 u_x + r(\delta^2 u_x - B_{x-1}')$ and $B_x = B_x' + r(B_x' - B_{x+1})$. Two arbitrary initial values are necessary for B_x' and B_x in these relations. They may be determined so that the first and last second differences of B_x will vanish, which from the difference equation at once gives $\delta^2 u_x$ as the initial value of B_x. For B_x' "we start with an approximate value and work as if it were correct; then to the values of B_x so derived we apply a set of corrections k, $-rk$, $r^2 k$, $-r^3 k$ where k is so determined that the corrected values of B_x will satisfy the required conditions." The following example gives the actual work of deriving corrected values of B_x, using $\frac{4}{15}$ for r (see R.A.I.A., XIII, 25; note also Henderson's numerical comparisons in T.A.S.A., XXXV, 280, based on Grant's Canadian data, which there showed a better sum of 3rd differences regardless of sign than the Karup-King 3rd difference formula, but a result not as good as Jenkins' 5th difference non-reproducing formula (47)).

x	u_x	Δu_x	$\delta^2 u_x$ $=\Delta^2 u_{x-1}$	B'_x	Uncor- rected B_x	Correction	Corrected B_x
5......	21.899	− .404	....	− .341	− .372	− .077	− .449
10......	21.495	− .609	− .205	− .169	− .226	+ .021	− .205
15......	20.886	− .642	− .033	+ .003	+ .045	− .006	+ .039
20......	20.244	− .755	− .113	− .144	− .153	+ .001	− .152
25......	19.489	− .877	− .122	− .116	− .111	....	− .111
30......	18.612	−1.008	− .131	− .135	− .136	....	− .136
35......	17.604	−1.140	− .132	− .131	− .131	....	− .131
40......	16.464	−1.269	− .129	− .128	− .130	....	− .130
45......	15.195	−1.385	− .116	− .113	− .119	....	− .119
50......	13.810	−1.476	− .091	− .085	− .092	....	− .092
55......	12.334	−1.532	− .056	− .048	− .057	....	− .057
60......	10.802	−1.544	− .012	− .002	− .013	....	− .013
65......	9.258	−1.506	+ .038	+ .049	+ .039	....	+ .039
70......	7.752	−1.419	+ .087	+ .097	+ .087	....	+ .087
75......	6.333	−1.287	+ .132	+ .141	+ .136	....	+ .136
80......	5.046	−1.129	+ .158	+ .163	+ .158	....	+ .158
85......	3.917	....	....	....	+ .180	....	+ .180

The osculatory interpolation on the principle of par. 104 may now be performed exactly, instead of approximately as in formula (45), by using these corrected values of B_x as if they were the actual second differences in Everett's ordinary central difference formula

$$u_x = xu_1 + \frac{x(x^2-1)}{6}\delta^2 u_1 + yu_0 + \frac{y(y^2-1)}{6}\delta^2 u_0.$$

106. The production of a set of exact tangential or osculatory reproducing formulae on Henderson's principles of par. 104—namely, that the corresponding differential coefficients of each curve at the common point must be equal to each other (but not necessarily equal to any predetermined values as laid down by Sprague), and that the given values must be reproduced—was investigated next by W. A. Jenkins in 1926 (R.A.I.A., XV, 87 and 191). The third difference tangential formula emerging on these assumptions was, interestingly enough, the Karup-King formula (which, as stated in par. 101, was derived originally by Sprague's method of using values for the first differential coefficients predetermined from partial curves). For the fifth difference case with 2nd order contact,*

---

* The condition that the given values must be reproduced, i.e., that the two curves must take the given value at the common point, was met by taking $\varphi(x) = x(x-1)\psi(x)$, and $\psi(x)$ was assumed to be a polynomial. Then $\psi(x) = a_0 + a_1 x + a_2 x^2$ gives Jenkins' formula above; $\psi(x) = a_0 + a_1 x + a_2 x^2 + a_3 x^3$ (which is redundant to

however, *Jenkins' fifth difference osculatory reproducing formula* was found to be

$$u_x = xu_1 + \frac{x(x^2-1)}{6}\,\delta^2 u_1 - \frac{x^3(x-1)}{12}\,\delta^4 u_1$$
$$+ yu_0 + \frac{y(y^2-1)}{6}\,\delta^2 u_0 - \frac{y^3(y-1)}{12}\,\delta^4 u_0. \tag{46}$$

(vi) Tangential and Osculatory Non-reproducing Interpolation Formulae on Jenkins' Principles

107.* All the preceding formulae derived by Sprague's assumptions which use partial curves, or from Henderson's which discard the partial curves and simply require that the differential coefficients shall be continuous, have in common the other basic condition that (being "reproducing" formulae for interpolation) the two curves must take the given value at the common point. When such formulae have been used, as in many of the population tables, to fill in the values between certain predetermined points, it has been found—unless the values at those points themselves lie upon a smooth curve—that the whole curve which finally results will show many undulations and points of inflexion, even though it will be free from discontinuities (cf. J. Buchanan, T.F.A., XII, 124). In order to meet this weakness W. A. Jenkins in 1927 (T.A.S.A., XXVIII, 198) therefore released the two curves from the requirement that they must take the given value at the common point, and instead permitted, in effect, that the interpolated value shall differ from the given value by a fraction of its 2nd difference in the 3rd difference formula, or of its 4th difference in the 5th difference formula. Since the predetermined points are thus not to be reproduced, the resulting non-reproducing formulae (which earlier were called "modified" formulae) will evidently effect some adjustment of those values in addition to performing a tangential or osculatory interpolation for the intermediate values. Jenkins gave a general expression, and the 3rd and 5th difference formulae, in T.A.S.A.,

---

the extent of one degree in x since the term a_3x^3 is not necessary) produces Sprague's formula (40) when $a_2 = -\frac{7}{24}$, and Buchanan's (see footnote to par. 100) when $a_2 = -\frac{1}{3}$; and $\psi(x) = a_0 + a_1x$ gives Henderson's (45). The proofs used by Jenkins are shown clearly in his papers (*loc. cit.*)—on which Greville's remarks in T.A.S.A., XLV, 217–18 should now be noted.

* The wording of this paragraph and some later paragraphs is taken, with slight variations, from "The Fundamental Principles of Mathematical Statistics." Section XI, pp. 119–48, of that volume, which gives "An Outline of a Course in Graduation" (covering the principal methods proposed up to 1942), and the accompanying technical discussions and references elsewhere therein, should be consulted for a more complete and detailed presentation of the basic theory and the practice of graduation than is necessary in the condensed treatment appropriate for this Study.

XXVIII, 199–206, and the general form for even orders of differences, with the 4th difference formula, in T.A.S.A., XXXI, 10–12 and 24–30; the proof of the 5th difference formula is also given conveniently in T.F.A., XII, 138 (on which the comment by Reid and Dow in T.F.A., XIV, 189, should be noted), and in Miller's "Elements of Graduation," p. 70, while W. G. P. Lindsay produced an elegant alternative demonstration in T.F.A., XIV, 211.

Jenkins' fifth difference osculatory non-reproducing formula which he thus reached is

$$u_x = x u_1 + \frac{x(x^2 - 1)}{6} \delta^2 u_1 - \frac{x^3}{36} \delta^4 u_1$$
$$+ y u_0 + \frac{y(y^2 - 1)}{6} \delta^2 u_0 - \frac{y^3}{36} \delta^4 u_0 .$$

$$(47)$$

The correction to each given value amounts to $\frac{1}{36}$ of the negative of the 4th central difference, as may be seen by putting $x = 0$ (and $y = 1$) in (47). In practice it is consequently important to choose the formula which extends into an order of differences alternating in sign, for otherwise the graduated series will lie everywhere above or below the observed points; in mortality experiences, therefore, where the 2nd differences are usually not negligible while the 4th differences change in sign frequently, it was pointed out by Jenkins that the 4th or 5th difference formulae are suitable but that the 3rd difference expression is unsatisfactory.

This formula is appropriate (subject to the nature of the differences just mentioned), and has been used frequently (for example, above age 32 in the U.S. Life Tables and Actuarial Tables, 1939–41, p. 125) when the given values (or the "pivotal" values—see pars. 120–24) are not sufficiently smooth to serve without some further adjustment as the basis of reproducing osculatory interpolation.

(vii) The General Problem of Determining Tangential and Osculatory Formulae of the Reproducing and Non-reproducing Types

108. The various well-known reproducing and non-reproducing formulae of Sprague (with Reilly's generalizations), Buchanan, Karup-King, Shovelton, Henderson, and Jenkins which have been stated in pars. 100–107 are, in reality, particular expressions resulting from the selection of certain special methods of giving effect to the basic conditions on which they were derived. The first paper which directed attention to one aspect of this fact was that by A. R. Reid and J. B. Dow in 1933 (T.F.A., XIV, 185); in 1935 a much wider discussion was given by J. E. Kerrich (J.I.A., LXVI, 88); and in 1944 T. N. E. Greville (T.A.S.A., XLV, 202) developed

the general theory systematically with the object of "presenting the subject as an integrated whole rather than a collection of isolated formulas."*

109. In their paper Reid and Dow pointed out that Jenkins' 5th difference non-reproducing formula (47) is only one of many satisfying the prescribed conditions, since one arbitrary constant is avoided by the restriction implicit in Jenkins' derivation that no differences beyond the 5th are to appear in the final formula. Relaxing this limitation, therefore, *Reid and Dow's general fifth difference osculatory non-reproducing formula* emerged as

$$u_x = xu_1 + \frac{x(x^2-1)}{6}\,\delta^2 u_1 + \left(bx - \frac{x^3}{36}\right)\delta^4 u_1 + \tfrac{1}{6}\,b x^3 \delta^6 u_1$$
$$+\, yu_0 + \frac{y(y^2-1)}{6}\,\delta^2 u_0 + \left(by - \frac{y^3}{36}\right)\delta^4 u_0 + \tfrac{1}{6}\,b y^3 \delta^6 u_0 \tag{48}$$

where b is an arbitrary constant (giving Jenkins' (47) when $b = 0$). Writing u_x^J for Jenkins' (47), the relation between it and (48) is

$$u_x = u_x^J + b\left[(x\,\delta^4 u_1 + \tfrac{1}{6}x^3\,\delta^6 u_1) + (y\,\delta^4 u_0 + \tfrac{1}{6}y^3\,\delta^6 u_0)\right];$$

Reid and Dow consequently suggested that in practice u_x^J should first be calculated, and that the flexibility afforded by the b term should be used to improve the results as may be desirable—the procedures which they actually adopted being noted in par. 123 hereafter since they are of a type belonging to the methods there discussed.

110. Kerrich's treatment gave a more general approach under both Sprague's and Jenkins' conditions, and produced expressions from which the formulae of Reid and Dow, as well as those of Sprague, Buchanan, Karup-King, Jenkins, and others are obtainable immediately as special cases.†

---

* Although the mathematical techniques employed lie beyond the scope of this Study, research workers should note also that I. J. Schoenberg has given (in 1946–48) an elegant treatment of graduation and interpolation expressible in linear compound form (see footnote to par. 123 here) in his papers "Contributions to the Problem of Approximation of Equidistant Data by Analytic Functions" (Quarterly of Applied Mathematics, IV, 45 and 112) and "Some Analytical Aspects of the Problem of Smoothing" (Courant Anniversary Volume, 1948, 351). Using characteristic functions and Fourier integrals, he derives the basic functions of the well-known interpolation formulae in remarkably compact form, of which a brief summary is stated by T. N. E. Greville in "Recent Developments in Graduation and Interpolation" (J.A.S.A., XLIII, 434). In 1952 Schoenberg extended his approach still further in an address "On Smoothing Operations and Their Generating Functions" (Bulletin of the American Mathematical Society, LIX, 199).

† Kerrich also pointed out the similarity between osculatory interpolation and the method of "pseudo-analytical" graduation which (following the idea of Felix Klein) has been presented by H. C. Nybölle (Nordic Statistical Journal, I, 103, and J.I.A.,

111. Greville's paper dealt with the theory of tangential or osculatory interpolation with equal intervals by developing the most general expression for any order of contact, and showed how to derive a tangential or osculatory formula satisfying predetermined requirements as to continuity of derivatives, reproduction or non-reproduction of the given values, number of terms, correctness to a stated order of differences, and the values of any arbitrary parameters not fixed by those conditions. (For example, the Karup-King formula (41) herein is a tangential, reproducing, four-point formula, correct to second differences, and using third degree curves; it can be derived by specifying these properties, and is the only formula possessing them). An unlimited number of such formulae can thus be written down, amongst which are all the particular formulae previously known (pars. 100–107 here), as well as a number of other useful expressions which had not been given before (and some of no practical value on account of the very general nature of the conditions imposed). The freedom of choice is thus so wide that, as Greville showed with numerical examples,* a formula can in fact be determined which will incorporate in a single operation the desired amount of non-reproduction with the type of interpolation selected.

Among the various formulae which he published, Greville directed at-

---

LXVI, 63) and further examined by J. F. Steffensen (Aktuárské Vĕdy, 1932, of which an English abstract prepared by Kerrich appears in J.I.A., LXVI, 125). The objectives of "pseudo-analytical" graduation are thus described in Kerrich's paper (*loc. cit.*, 92): "The result aimed at is to pass a smooth curve among the observations in such a way that any ordinate can readily be calculated, and such that the curve possesses a preassigned number of continuous successive derivatives whose values can also be readily calculated at all points on the curve. This curve and its derived curves are then regarded as defining the underlying function sought and its successive derivatives." Accordingly, a set of approximate derivatives is first calculated from the observed values by some practicable method such as approximate formulae for derivatives in terms of observations, with subsequent graphical smoothing; if the graduating curve is to have, for example, continuous first and second derivatives (because to go beyond second derivatives would usually involve very heavy numerical work), the calculated second derivatives are then assumed to form a polygonal arc of straight line segments; "these linear segments are integrated interval by interval, and the constants of integration adjusted so that each integrated element joins the next"; and finally these parabolic elements are integrated similarly, so that the resulting graduating curve is built of a set of osculating cubic arcs.

* In an application to somewhat intractable material, he first used the operator $1 - \frac{3}{7}\delta^4 - \frac{2}{21}\delta^6$, which (see H. H. Wolfenden, T.A.S.A., XLVI, 97, and XXVI, 100–103, and "The Fundamental Principles of Mathematical Statistics," 132–37 and 282–84) is De Forest's "best R_0" 7-term "fitting" formula $v_0 = \frac{1}{21}[7u_0 + 6u_{\pm 1} + 3u_{\pm 2} - 2u_{\pm 3}]$ which minimizes the mean square error in v, and then tried two specially determined "best R_0" operators employing 2nd and 5th difference corrections.

tention to 15 new tangential formulae (with first order contact) and 10 new osculatory formulae (with 2nd order contact), and also to 7 (obtained by giving particular values to certain arbitrary parameters in the first 25) which were specially designed to incorporate the best or nearly best R_0 fitting. The results were presented in condensed tables, from which the Everett forms can be written down at once. As examples—but without implying their invariable superiority by their statement here, where they are shown as illustrations only—one of the new tangential formulae (Greville's (69), Table I) is

$$u_x = u_{\frac{1}{2}} + \tfrac{1}{2}\,(x^2 - \tfrac{1}{4})\,\delta u_1 + \tfrac{1}{48}x^2\,(4x - 7)\,\delta^3 u_1$$
$$-\tfrac{1}{2}\,(y^2 - \tfrac{1}{4})\,\delta u_0 - \tfrac{1}{48}y^2\,(4y - 7)\,\delta^3 u_0$$

and one of his osculatory non-reproducing expressions (his (88), Table II) is

$$u_x = u_{\frac{1}{2}} + [\tfrac{1}{2}\,(x^2 - \tfrac{1}{4})\,\delta u_1 + \tfrac{1}{24}\,(x^2 - \tfrac{1}{4})\,(x^2 - \tfrac{9}{4})\,\delta^3 u_1$$
$$+ \tfrac{1}{240}x^3\,(x^2 - \tfrac{149}{16}x + \tfrac{89}{8})\,\delta^5 u_1]$$
$$- [\tfrac{1}{2}\,(y^2 - \tfrac{1}{4})\,\delta u_0 + \tfrac{1}{24}\,(y^2 - \tfrac{1}{4})\,(y^2 - \tfrac{9}{4})\,\delta^3 u_0$$
$$+ \tfrac{1}{240}y^3\,(y^2 - \tfrac{149}{16}y + \tfrac{89}{8})\,\delta^5 u_0]$$

while among the best or nearly best R_0 expressions the formula actually used in his numerical illustration (No. 109, Table IVB) is

$$u_x = xu_1 + \tfrac{1}{4}x\,(x + \tfrac{8}{3})\,\delta^2 u_1 + \tfrac{1}{6}x^2\delta^4 u_1$$
$$- yu_0 - \tfrac{1}{4}y\,(y + \tfrac{8}{3})\,\delta^2 u_0 - \tfrac{1}{6}y^2\delta^4 u_0$$

(viii) Methods of Calculation, and Treatment of the End Terms, with Tangential and Osculatory Interpolation Formulae; and the Unequal Interval Case

112. As noted in the preceding paragraphs (see also H. Freeman's "Mathematics for Actuarial Students," II, 73, and Greville's comments in R.A.I.A., XXXII, 86), the numerical work involved in calculating the differences and using the Everett types of these interpolation formulae is generally quite convenient. An alternative method which now is usually preferable, however, because it eliminates the calculation of the differences (except for the end values) and can be applied rapidly with modern calculating machines, is to express and employ the formulae in terms of the given u's in linear compound form (see par. 123), by means of the relations stated in par. 100(c)—see, for examples, John Boyer's paper "Osculatory Interpolation in Practice" (R.A.I.A., XXXI, 337) and M. D. Miller's monograph "Elements of Graduation," pp. 25–26.

113. The values at the two ends which are not reached by a symmetrical interpolation formula can be handled by one of the following methods: (1) Employing comparable unsymmetrical formulae to find the interpolated values at the ends; (2) extending the interpolated values by assuming that the missing values of the last order of differences are constant (and that the next therefore vanish), completing the difference table by addition, and applying the symmetrical formula; (3) making a hypothetical extension of the series of given values, from which the remaining interpolations are performed by using the symmetrical formula; (4) continuing the interpolated values, as computed in the last interval dealt with by the usual application of the symmetrical formula, by assuming constant differences; (5) using special interpolation curves determined to satisfy specified conditions and joining smoothly with the interpolated values resulting from the symmetrical formula.

Method (1) is illustrated by formulae such as those given by Jenkins for No. (47) here in respect of the two intervals at each end (see T.A.S.A., XXVIII, 209, and Buchanan, T.F.A., XII, 135 and 140). Method (2) is discussed by G. J. Lidstone in T.F.A., XII, 277 ("Note on the Computation of Terminal Values in Graduation by Jenkins' Modified Osculatory Formula"), where it is pointed out that the formulae of method (1) are tacitly based on certain artificial values of the missing differences, and that the same result is obtained by inserting 0 in the places of the missing values of $\delta^4 u$ preceding the first value of $\delta^4 u$ yielded by the data, and similarly at the other end. Buchanan, however, objected in T.F.A., XIV, 209, that this method in effect assigns definite magnitudes to the missing u's, and that the resulting curve consequently may be distorted; he therefore advocated the use of reasonable hypothetical values as in method (3). Method (4) was suggested and used by Greville in T.A.S.A., XLV, 239. The special processes of method (5) are discussed in par. 128 here.

In addition to the comments on particular methods just noted, reference may be made to the papers by Boyer in R.A.I.A., XXXI, 337, and Greville in T.A.S.A., XLV, 237.

114. In practice the data from which the interpolations are to be made can usually be obtained at equal intervals. It may be noted, however, that the unequal interval case for reproducing formulae on Sprague's principles (par. 99–101 here) has been examined by T. G. Ackland in J.I.A., XLIX, 369, and by J. F. Reilly (in its general form) in R.A.I.A., XV, 34.

(ix) Reproducing and Non-reproducing Interpolation Minimizing the Mean Square Error in a Specified Order of Differences

115. Although the tangential and osculatory formulae of the preceding paragraphs are based on the principles of interpolation, they deal, in fact,

with the problem of graduation by constructing a continuous curve with one or more of its derivatives satisfying specified conditions, and in such a way that any interpolated value and the values of the derivatives are all viewed as important.* It may be argued, however, that actually the values of mortality table functions are seldom required for other than integral ages, and that consequently it would be more practicable, and no less logical, to regard such a function as a discrete series of numbers rather than to think of it in terms of a continuous curve.

116. In order to approach the problem in this manner, the theory of minimizing the mean square error of a linear compound, as it was first stated in actuarial literature by E. L. De Forest, can be applied readily. De Forest's basic assumption (see H. H. Wolfenden, "On the Development of Formulae for Graduation by Linear Compounding, with Special Reference to the Work of Erastus L. De Forest," T.A.S.A., XXVI, 81, and "The Fundamental Principles of Mathematical Statistics," pp. 132–34 and 283–84) was that, if u_r is an observed value and U_r the true value so that $u_r = U_r + e_r$ where e_r is the error, it may be assumed that the e's are independent and that the mean square of each is (say) e^2—or, to use other language, it may be assumed that the errors in the observed values are independent random variables with mean zero and variance e^2. If it is further supposed that differences of U beyond order j are zero, it follows that $\Delta^m u_r = \Delta^m e_r$ for $m > j$. In his derivations of linear compound graduation formulae of the type of No. (56) here, De Forest adopted the logical position that theoretically the smoothest results would be produced by minimizing the mean square error in $\Delta^{i+1} v$ (rather than in $\Delta^i v$ as employed by many subsequent writers)—this use of Δ^{i+1} instead of Δ^i having been supported also by Wolfenden in his paper on De Forest's work (*op. cit.*, pp. 109–10; and R.A.I.A., XXXVII, 33) and later by T. N. E. Greville (in R.A.I.A., XXXIV, 39, and XXXVI, 259). The mathematical technique for thus minimizing the mean square error in v (to give the best fitting formulae—such as No. (61) of par. 123 here), or in $\Delta^{i+1} v$ (for maximum smoothness), is explained fully in the first references given in this paragraph, and is also shown by Greville in R.A.I.A., XXXIV, 22–23 and 30. In those explanations, and in the further developments to be now discussed, it is important to recall that (*a*) the assumption that differences of U beyond order j are zero means that the true $\Delta^{i+1} U_r$ is zero but the observed $\Delta^{i+1} u_r$ is not zero; (*b*) as shown in the "The Funda-

---

* This viewpoint is regarded even more emphatically in the somewhat analogous "pseudo-analytical" method (see footnote to par. 110), for there the avowed objective is to produce first from the data a smooth series of derivatives and thence to return to the original function by successive integrations (cf. J.I.A., LXVI, 68 et seq.).

mental Principles of Mathematical Statistics," pp. 23–25 (formula (27) with $\sigma_1^2 = \sigma_2^2 = \ldots = \sigma_n^2 = e^2$) the mean square error of a linear compound $l_1F_1 + l_2F_2 + \ldots + l_nF_n$ of any number of independent observed qualities $F_1, F_2, \ldots, F_n$ each obeying the Normal Curve of Error with mean square errors e^2 is $(l_1^2 + l_2^2 + \ldots + l_n^2)e^2$; (*c*) when a graduated value *v* is determined by linear compounding from a range of observed *u*'s as in (56) here, the mean square error in *v* itself is therefore $(\Sigma l_r^2)e^2$; (*d*) similarly, when *v* again is to be found as a linear compound of *u*'s as in (56), the mean square error in $\Delta^{j+1}v$ when $j = 4$ (as shown in T.A.S.A., XXVI, 110, for the case of $\Delta^4 v$ when $j = 3$) is $\Sigma(\Delta^5 l_r)^2 e^2$; (*e*) it is thus apparent that when, on De Forest's assumptions, we minimize the mean square error in the $(j + 1)$th differences we are really—to give two alternative statements—minimizing the sum of the squares of the $(j + 1)$th differences, or (as stated by Greville in T.S.A., I, 356) we are minimizing the sum of the squares of the coefficients which express the $(j + 1)$th differences of the interpolated values in terms of the given values themselves.

(*i*) These assumptions and procedures, as they have been described in the publications to which reference has been made, are concerned basically with graduation by linear compounding of the observed *u*'s. The same technique obviously can be employed in the allied process of interpolating at certain points from a set of observed *u*'s—the problem usually encountered in dealing with population statistics being the interpolation of the intermediate values from data at quinquennial points. In 1945, therefore, Greville (in R.A.I.A., XXXIV, 22–33) adopted De Forest's assumptions, and the principles stated in the preceding paragraph, in order to find the linear compounding coefficients for this problem of subdivision of given intervals, and gave the results for reproducing interpolations when the mean square error in the $(j + 1)$th differences is to be minimized with $j = 1, 2, 3,$ and 4 (his Tables 1, 3, 4, and 6). The detailed proof for the case of $j = 4$ (Greville's Table 6, and Table I here) is shown in R.A.I.A., XXXIV, 27–33; and a shorter form of proof, which depends on the mathematical analogy between graduation and interpolation formulae pointed out by H. Vaughan in J.I.A., LXXII, 482, is given by Greville for the case of $j = 3$ (Table 4, *loc. cit.*, p. 26) in his paper "On the Derivation of Discrete Interpolation Formulas," in T.S.A., I, 343. For the usual case of subdividing given intervals into fifths (thus using six terms), and taking $j = 4$ so that the mean square error in the 5th differences is minimized, the coefficients as deduced by Greville in R.A.I.A., XXXIV, 27–33 (and Table 6 on p. 28), are shown here in Table I (where the printed value $-.1266$ for $v_{1.4}$ when $x = 4$ in R.A.I.A., XXXIV, 28, is corrected, as

TABLE I

PART A—TO BE USED FOR THE FIRST TWO INTERVALS

x	COEFFICIENTS OF u_x TO OBTAIN:							
	$v_{.2}$	$v_{.4}$	$v_{.6}$	$v_{.8}$	$v_{1.2}$	$v_{1.4}$	$v_{1.6}$	$v_{1.8}$
0.....	$+.6763$	$+.4177$	$+.2221$	$+.0851$	$-.0420$	$-.0514$	$-.0400$	$-.0195$
1.....	$+.4489$	$+.7819$	$+.9839$	$+1.0529$	$+.8484$	$+.6314$	$+.3904$	$+.1679$
2.....	$-.0466$	$-.1286$	$-.1726$	$-.1346$	$+.2184$	$+.4844$	$+.7424$	$+.9314$
3.....	$-.1966$	$-.2026$	$-.1266$	$-.0446$	$-.0056$	$-.0476$	$-.0896$	$-.0866$
4.....	$+.1559$	$+.1749$	$+.1249$	$+.0559$	$-.0276$	$-.0266$	$-.0096$	$+.0049$
5.....	$-.0379$	$-.0433$	$-.0317$	$-.0147$	$+.0084$	$+.0098$	$+.0064$	$+.0019$

PART B—TO BE USED EXCEPT FOR THE FIRST TWO AND LAST TWO INTERVALS

x	COEFFICIENTS OF u_x TO OBTAIN:			
	$v_{n+.2}$	$v_{n+.4}$	$v_{n+.6}$	$v_{n+.8}$
$n-2$.....	$+.0017$	$+.0136$	$+.0088$	$+.0027$
$n-1$.....	$-.0921$	$-.1096$	$-.0776$	$-.0311$
n........	$+.9234$	$+.7184$	$+.4464$	$+.1854$
$n+1$....	$+.1854$	$+.4464$	$+.7184$	$+.9234$
$n+2$....	$-.0311$	$-.0776$	$-.1096$	$-.0921$
$n+3$.....	$+.0027$	$+.0088$	$+.0136$	$+.0117$

PART C—TO BE USED FOR THE LAST TWO INTERVALS

x	COEFFICIENTS OF u_x TO OBTAIN:							
	$v_{z-1.8}$	$v_{z-1.6}$	$v_{z-1.4}$	$v_{z-1.2}$	$v_{z-.8}$	$v_{z-.6}$	$v_{z-.4}$	$v_{z-.2}$
$z-5$..	$+.0019$	$+.0064$	$+.0098$	$+.0084$	$-.0147$	$-.0317$	$-.0433$	$-.0379$
$z-4$..	$+.0049$	$-.0096$	$-.0266$	$-.0276$	$+.0559$	$+.1249$	$+.1749$	$+.1559$
$z-3$..	$-.0866$	$-.0896$	$-.0476$	$-.0056$	$-.0446$	$-.1266$	$-.2026$	$-.1966$
$z-2$..	$+.9314$	$+.7424$	$+.4844$	$+.2184$	$-.1346$	$-.1726$	$-.1286$	$-.0466$
$z-1$..	$+.1679$	$+.3904$	$+.6314$	$+.8484$	$+1.0529$	$+.9839$	$+.7819$	$+.4489$
z....	$-.0195$	$-.0400$	$-.0514$	$-.0420$	$+.0851$	$+.2221$	$+.4177$	$+.6763$

pointed out by Greville, to $-.0266$). In that table the different coefficients for the first two and last two intervals arise, of course, from the inability of any symmetrical formula to reach the ends.

The corresponding coefficients for ascertaining the single-age values from five-year group totals—a problem which is encountered frequently in handling population statistics—have been supplied by Greville for publication in this Study, and are shown in Table II.

TABLE II

(*Notation:* $W_x = w_x + w_{x+1} + w_{x+2} + w_{x+3} + w_{x+4}$)

PART A—TO BE USED FOR THE FIRST TWO INTERVALS

x	COEFFICIENT OF W_x TO OBTAIN:									
	w_0	w_1	w_2	w_3	w_4	w_5	w_6	w_7	w_8	w_9
0.....	+.3237	+.2586	+.1956	+.1370	+.0851	+.0420	+.0094	−.0114	−.0205	−.0195
5.....	−.1252	−.0744	−.0064	+.0680	+.1380	+.1936	+.2264	+.2296	+.2020	+.1484
10.....	−.0786	+.0076	+.0376	+.0300	+.0034	−.0248	−.0396	−.0284	+.0130	+.0798
15.....	+.1180	+.0136	−.0384	−.0520	−.0412	−.0192	+.0024	+.0136	+.0100	−.0068
20.....	−.0379	−.0054	+.0116	+.0170	+.0147	+.0084	+.0014	−.0034	−.0045	−.0019

PART B—TO BE USED EXCEPT FOR THE FIRST TWO AND LAST TWO INTERVALS

x	COEFFICIENTS OF W_x TO OBTAIN:				
	w_{5n}	w_{5n+1}	w_{5n+2}	w_{5n+3}	w_{5n+4}
5n−10....	−.0117	−.0019	+.0048	+.0061	+.0027
5n−5.....	+.0804	+.0156	−.0272	−.0404	−.0284
5n........	+.1570	+.2206	+.2448	+.2206	+.1570
5n+5.....	−.0284	−.0404	−.0272	+.0156	+.0804
5n+10....	+.0027	+.0061	+.0048	−.0019	−.0117

PART C—TO BE USED FOR THE LAST TWO INTERVALS

x	COEFFICIENTS OF W_x TO OBTAIN:									
	w_{z-10}	w_{z-9}	w_{z-8}	w_{z-7}	w_{z-6}	w_{z-5}	w_{z-4}	w_{z-3}	w_{z-2}	w_{z-1}
z−25..	−.0019	−.0045	−.0034	+.0014	+.0084	+.0147	+.0170	+.0116	−.0054	−.0379
z−20..	−.0068	+.0100	+.0136	+.0024	−.0192	−.0412	−.0520	−.0384	+.0136	+.1180
z−15..	+.0798	+.0130	−.0284	−.0396	−.0248	+.0034	+.0300	+.0376	+.0076	−.0786
z−10..	+.1484	+.2020	+.2296	+.2264	+.1936	+.1380	+.0680	−.0064	−.0744	−.1252
z−5...	−.0195	−.0205	−.0114	+.0094	+.0420	+.0851	+.1370	+.1956	+.2586	+.3237

(*ii*) The preceding method is a process of reproducing interpolation. If, however, reproduction of the given values is not required, corresponding sets of coefficients for non-reproducing interpolation can be obtained on De Forest's assumptions and the technique already discussed. Thus in R.A.I.A., XXXIV, 24–29 (Tables 2, 5, and 7), Greville has stated the coefficients (except at the ends) for non-reproducing interpolations minimizing the mean square error in the $(j + 1)$th differences for $j = 1$ (with 3 terms) and for $j = 3$ (with 5 and 6 terms), and has suggested with respect to the end intervals that the best practical solution will be to extend the given values in a reasonable manner at both ends so that the coefficients deduced for the middle intervals can be used throughout.

117. The methods and linear compounding coefficients which have been described in par. 116 are all based on De Forest's assumption (which also has been used extensively by many later authorities—see T.A.S.A., XXVI, 81 et seq.) that if u_r is an observed value of U_r, so that $u_r = U_r + e_r$, the e's are independent random variables with zero mean and variance e^2; and the interpolations are made by minimizing the mean square error in $\Delta^{j+1}v$, i.e., in the $(j+1)$th differences of the interpolated values, in conjunction with the further supposition that the values of the true $\Delta^{j+1}U_r$ are actually zero. The development of this interpolation method by Greville in 1945, as already stated, is thus in reality an application of De Forest's graduation procedures to the allied problem of interpolation, and it is so explained in par. 116 because it is important for this relationship to be understood. This importance is emphasized, moreover, by the fact that in 1944 (previous to Greville's work) H. S. Beers had proceeded from a somewhat different assumption by a different type of derivation, in which he did not make direct use of the theory of minimizing the mean square error although that theory would have produced identically the same results as he obtained (see R.A.I.A., XXXIV, 37).

The different assumption from which Beers started was, in effect (as just noted), that the 5th differences of the observed values are independent random variables with mean zero and variance (say) g^2—the g^2 for the assumed constant mean square error (variance) of each $\Delta^5 u_r$ in this assumption being adopted in this Study for the purpose of distinguishing it clearly from the assumed constant mean square error (variance) of each u_r in De Forest's basis which was followed by Greville and in par. 116 here. Since under both assumptions exactly the same type of procedure is available in order to find the linear compounding coefficients for minimizing the mean square error in the $(j+1)$th differences, it will be seen that on Beers' assumptions, as in statement (e) for De Forest's assumptions in par. 116, it can be said alternatively that we are really minimizing the sum of the squares of the $(j+1)$th differences, or (as explained by Greville in T.S.A., I, 354) we are minimizing the sum of the squares of the coefficients which express the $(j+1)$th differences of the interpolated values in terms of the $(j+1)$th differences of the given values.

(i) The first coefficients which were published on this assumption that the $(j+1)$th differences of the observed values are independent random variables with mean zero and variance g^2 concerned a reproducing interpolation with $j = 4$ (see H. S. Beers, "Six-Term Formulas for Routine Actuarial Interpolation," R.A.I.A., XXXIII, 245). Those coefficients were derived by a method which included in its conditions a requirement that the sum of the interpolated values in any interval should equal the sum of the corresponding values which would be obtained by ordinary 5th difference interpolation. Greville, however, pointed out (in R.A.I.A., XXXIV, 37–38) that it is preferable not to impose this condition, because it is satisfied automatically, and is therefore redundant, except in the two end intervals, and because in the end intervals it has the effect of giving undue weight to the given values at some distance from the interval. The improved coefficients for the end intervals which result from abandoning the condition were therefore included in the set shown in Table III here as

TABLE III

PART A—TO BE USED FOR THE FIRST TWO INTERVALS

x	COEFFICIENTS OF u_x TO OBTAIN:							
	$v_{.2}$	$v_{.4}$	$v_{.6}$	$v_{.8}$	$v_{1.2}$	$v_{1.4}$	$v_{1.6}$	$v_{1.8}$
0....	$+.6667$	$+.4072$	$+.2148$	$+.0819$	$-.0404$	$-.0497$	$-.0389$	$-.0191$
1....	$+.4969$	$+.8344$	$+1.0204$	$+1.0689$	$+.8404$	$+.6229$	$+.3849$	$+.1659$
2....	$-.1426$	$-.2336$	$-.2456$	$-.1666$	$+.2344$	$+.5014$	$+.7534$	$+.9354$
3....	$-.1006$	$-.0976$	$-.0536$	$-.0126$	$-.0216$	$-.0646$	$-.1006$	$-.0906$
4....	$+.1079$	$+.1224$	$+.0884$	$+.0399$	$-.0196$	$-.0181$	$-.0041$	$+.0069$
5....	$-.0283$	$-.0328$	$-.0244$	$-.0115$	$+.0068$	$+.0081$	$+.0053$	$+.0015$

PART B—TO BE USED EXCEPT FOR THE FIRST TWO AND LAST TWO INTERVALS

x	COEFFICIENTS OF u_x TO OBTAIN:			
	$v_{n+.2}$	$v_{n+.4}$	$v_{n+.6}$	$v_{n+.8}$
$n-2$.....	$+.0117$	$+.0137$	$+.0087$	$+.0027$
$n-1$.....	$-.0921$	$-.1101$	$-.0771$	$-.0311$
n........	$+.9234$	$+.7194$	$+.4454$	$+.1854$
$n+1$.....	$+.1854$	$+.4454$	$+.7194$	$+.9234$
$n+2$.....	$-.0311$	$-.0771$	$-.1101$	$-.0921$
$n+3$.....	$+.0027$	$+.0087$	$+.0137$	$+.0117$

PART C—TO BE USED FOR THE LAST TWO INTERVALS

x	COEFFICIENTS OF u_x TO OBTAIN:							
	$v_{z-1.8}$	$v_{z-1.6}$	$v_{z-1.4}$	$v_{z-1.2}$	$v_{z-.8}$	$v_{z-.6}$	$v_{z-.4}$	$v_{z-.2}$
$z-5$...	$+.0015$	$+.0053$	$+.0081$	$+.0068$	$-.0115$	$-.0244$	$-.0328$	$-.0283$
$z-4$...	$+.0069$	$-.0041$	$-.0181$	$-.0196$	$+.0399$	$+.0884$	$+.1224$	$+.1079$
$z-3$...	$-.0906$	$-.1006$	$-.0646$	$-.0216$	$-.0126$	$-.0536$	$-.0976$	$-.1006$
$z-2$...	$+.9354$	$+.7534$	$+.5014$	$+.2344$	$-.1666$	$-.2456$	$-.2336$	$-.1426$
$z-1$...	$+.1659$	$+.3849$	$+.6229$	$+.8404$	$+1.0689$	$+1.0204$	$+.8344$	$+.4969$
z......	$-.0191$	$-.0389$	$-.0497$	$-.0404$	$+.0819$	$+.2148$	$+.4072$	$+.6667$

finally proposed by Beers in R.A.I.A., XXXIV, 59 (correcting those given earlier in R.A.I.A., XXXIII, 258).

The corresponding coefficients for ascertaining the single-age values from 5-year group totals were also stated by Beers in R.A.I.A., XXXIV, 60, and are shown in Table IV here.

TABLE IV

(Notation: $W_x = w_x + w_{x+1} + w_{x+2} + w_{x+3} + w_{x+4}$)

PART A—To Be Used for the First Two Intervals

x	COEFFICIENT OF W_x To Obtain:									
	w_0	w_1	w_2	w_3	w_4	w_5	w_6	w_7	w_8	w_9
0.....	+.3333	+.2595	+.1924	+.1329	+.0819	+.0404	+.0093	−.0108	−.0198	−.0191
5.....	−.1636	−.0780	+.0064	+.0844	+.1508	+.2000	+.2268	+.2272	+.1992	+.1468
10.....	−.0210	+.0130	+.0184	+.0054	−.0158	−.0344	−.0402	−.0248	+.0172	+.0822
15.....	+.0796	+.0100	−.0256	−.0356	−.0284	−.0128	+.0028	+.0112	−.0072	−.0084
20.....	−.0283	−.0045	+.0084	+.0129	+.0115	+.0068	+.0013	−.0028	−.0038	−.0015

PART B—To Be Used Except for the First Two
and Last Two Intervals

x	COEFFICIENTS OF W_x To Obtain:				
	w_{5n}	w_{5n+1}	w_{5n+2}	w_{5n+3}	w_{5n+4}
$5n-10$....	−.0117	−.0020	+.0050	+.0060	+.0027
$5n-5$.....	+.0804	+.0160	−.0280	−.0400	−.0284
$5n$........	+.1570	+.2200	+.2460	+.2200	+.1570
$5n+5$.....	−.0284	−.0400	−.0280	+.0160	+.0804
$5n+10$....	+.0027	+.0060	+.0050	−.0020	−.0117

PART C—To Be Used for the Last Two Intervals

x	COEFFICIENTS OF W_x To Obtain:									
	w_{z-10}	w_{z-9}	w_{z-8}	w_{z-7}	w_{z-6}	w_{z-5}	w_{z-4}	w_{z-3}	w_{z-2}	w_{z-1}
$z-25$..	−.0015	−.0038	−.0028	+.0013	+.0068	+.0115	+.0129	+.0084	−.0045	−.0283
$z-20$..	−.0084	+.0072	+.0112	+.0028	−.0128	−.0284	−.0356	−.0256	+.0100	+.0796
$z-15$..	+.0822	+.0172	−.0248	−.0402	−.0344	−.0158	+.0054	+.0184	+.0130	−.0210
$z-10$..	+.1468	+.1992	+.2272	+.2268	+.2000	+.1508	+.0844	+.0064	−.0780	−.1636
$z-5$...	−.0191	−.0198	−.0108	+.0093	+.0404	+.0819	+.1329	+.1924	+.2595	+.3333

(*ii*) When reproduction of the given values is not required, coefficients for a non-reproducing interpolation minimizing the sum of the squares of the $(j + 1)$th differences when $j = 3$, and again using six terms for subdividing an interval into five parts, have also been suggested by Beers in R.A.I.A., XXXIV, 19. The corresponding coefficients for ascertaining the single-age values from 5-year group totals are given in R.A.I.A., XXXIV, 20.

117A. These interpolation methods of pars. 115–17, which have not yet been used extensively, may be expected, under suitable conditions and with properly chosen coefficients, to produce greater smoothness in mortality tables constructed from population statistics than the tangential and osculatory formulae of pars. 99–111. In practice, however, it will of course always remain true—as De Forest, W. F. Sheppard, and others have emphasized (cf. Wolfenden, T.A.S.A., XXVI, 107 [footnote], 110 [footnote], and 112, and Jenkins, R.A.I.A., XXXIV, 47–49 and 184)—that it is important to select a set of coefficients which will be capable of dealing with the actual values of $\Delta^3 u$, or $\Delta^4 u$, or $\Delta^5 u$, . . . , by appropriate assumptions respecting the errors in u or one of its orders of differences, and the value to be chosen for j. It is equally important, in order to gauge fairly the effects of different methods, that each procedure should be tested by examining the graduated or interpolated values of that order of differences which the method aims to adjust (even though other orders of differences may be examined also). The selection of method, moreover, should be made in any particular case without attaching undue weight either to custom or to examples based on other data which may exhibit different characteristics—for the problem of graduating or interpolating population statistics, with their extensive and varied errors, is not in any sense routine.

(x) *"Interlocking" Interpolation Formulae*

118. Another type of interpolation was suggested in 1948 by Aubrey White in T.A.S.A., **XLIX**, 337, which represents a compromise between the "continuous" viewpoint of the tangential and osculatory formulae (see par. 115) on the one hand, and the "discrete" approach (*loc. cit.*) of Beers' method on the other. White remarked that the strict finite difference analogue (appropriate for the discrete approach) of equal derivatives at the points of junction (as in tangential and osculatory interpolation) would be to require the equality of a specified number of central sub-differences and mean sub-differences of adjacent curve segments at their points of junction. He thus proposed to make equal at the border point "either the first $2n + 1$ of 1, $\mu' \delta'$, δ'^2, etc., or the first $2n$ of μ', δ', $\mu' \delta'^2$, etc., depending on whether an odd or an even number of conditions are to be set," where the primed symbols indicate that the sub-interval is taken as the unit in computing differences and mean values. It is thus seen, as he explains, that "this is equivalent to equating the points in the two curves involved in these sub-differences"; the conditions consequently become that "the two curves intersect at a number of points one greater than the highest order of differences set equal, the points to center about the border

point and to be separated from each other by the given sub-interval";
and "the resulting curves will resemble strands of wire twisted together,
suggesting the term 'interlocking' for the curves, and, by extension, for
the points." An algebraic expression can be written for such an "interlocking" formula, and it is possible to think of a continuous curve segment
in each interval as for the basic ideas of tangential or osculatory interpolation; on the other hand, from the discrete point of view, the sub-
differences which enter into the derivation of the formula are actually
computed from certain discrete values of the function, and we may think
of successive groups of discrete points rather than successive curve segments. As White points out, the well-known tangential and osculatory
formulae of both the reproducing and non-reproducing types (such as
those of Karup-King, Sprague, Jenkins, etc.) are obtainable as special
cases of the appropriate "interlocking" curve.

No numerical application of these formulae has yet been published;
their practical utility, therefore, remains to be determined.

(xi) *Reproducing Subtabulation Minimizing the Sum of the Squares of All Differences of Given Order by Difference-Equation Operations*

119. It has been suggested by C. A. Spoerl (T.A.S.A., XXXVIII, 403
—see also XLIX, 300), H. Vaughan (J.I.A., LXXII, 491), and T. N. E
Greville (Boletim do Instituto Brasileiro de Atuaria, II, 7), that subtabulation (i.e., the subdivision of the intervals between given values into a
specified number of equal parts) might be regarded as an over-all operation, in which each interpolated value will depend on all the given values
and not merely on a limited number such as four or six, and the interpolated terms will have over the whole series the minimum sum of the
squares of differences of any given order. Vaughan and Greville independently have described procedures, involving the solution of a difference-equation, by which such an interpolation can be effected.* These
methods give, in the sense thus prescribed, the smoothest possible interpolation. However, the process is more laborious than the use of formulae
limited to a finite range, and in many cases it is doubtful if there would be
a great difference in the numerical results in comparison, for example,
with a reproducing minimized difference interpolation of the type described in pars. 114–16. It is unlikely, therefore, that these procedures
will ever be used extensively.

* It is interesting to note that White has shown (T.A.S.A., XLIX, 357) that certain
"interlocking" formulae, derived on altogether different assumptions, yield interpolated values identical with those produced by this approach.

(xii) Pivotal Values

120. In some of the experimental reconstructions of the English life tables which were performed by George King, as recorded in par. 99 here, it was necessary first to calculate certain preliminary quinquennial values, by ordinary interpolation formulae for the bisection of decennial groups, in order to provide a set of equally spaced (but ungraduated) quinquennial values from which the intermediate terms could be found by tangential or osculatory interpolation. King subsequently (in J.I.A., XLIII, 109) evolved a development of this procedure which has been used on numerous occasions. In that development the data (usually the deaths and populations separately) are arranged in 5-year age groups (which, in accordance with the principles of pars. 53–54, may be assumed to be correct in total); from these groups quinquennial adjusted (i.e., "graduated") values, called *pivotal* (or sometimes "guiding") values, are calculated for the central year of age of each group; the resulting pivotal values of q_x are computed therefrom; and then the intermediate values of q_x at each age are filled in from these pivotal values by tangential or osculatory interpolation.*

King obtained his pivotal values by ordinary differences. If u_x denotes the data (deaths or populations usually) for the year of age x to $x+1$, the

5-year age groups $\sum\limits_{x=n}^{x=n+4} u_x = w_n$, say, are taken for quinquennial values of

n. In the simplest practical case of determining the central value u_7 from

the three groups $\sum\limits_{0}^{4} u_x$, $\sum\limits_{5}^{9} u_x$, and $\sum\limits_{10}^{14} u_x$, which together constitute

the series $u_0 \ldots u_{14}$, we see that $u_7 = \sum\limits_{0}^{7} u_x - \sum\limits_{0}^{6} u_x = y_8 - y_7$ say,

where $y_n = \sum\limits_{0}^{n-1} u_x$ so that—using Δ for a 5-year interval—

$$\Delta y_n = y_{n+5} - y_n = \sum\limits_{0}^{n+4} u_x - \sum\limits_{0}^{n-1} u_x = \sum\limits_{n}^{n+4} u_x = w_n .$$

---

* Since the pivotal values computed by the several methods discussed in pars. 120–24 here are, as stated, graduated values, the student's understanding of the principles involved may be assisted by the explanations of the nature and objects of graduation which are given in "The Fundamental Principles of Mathematical Statistics," pp. 89–90 and 120.

But

$$y_8 = y_0 + \tfrac{8}{5}\Delta y_0 + \tfrac{24}{50}\Delta^2 y_0 - \tfrac{8}{125}\Delta^3 y_0 + \tfrac{14}{625}\Delta^4 y_0$$

and

$$y_7 = y_0 + \tfrac{7}{5}\Delta y_0 + \tfrac{14}{50}\Delta^2 y_0 - \tfrac{7}{125}\Delta^3 y_0 + \tfrac{14}{625}\Delta^4 y_0$$

whence u_7, being $y_8 - y_7 = .2\Delta y_0 + .2\Delta^2 y_0 - .008\Delta^3 y_0$

$$= .2\Delta y_5 - .008\Delta^3 y_0$$

$$= .2w_5 \ - .008\Delta^2 w_0 \tag{49}$$

$$= .216w_5 - .008(w_0 + w_{10}) \ . \tag{50}$$

This formula can also be deduced easily by the method used by E. L. De Forest and shown by H. H. Wolfenden in T.A.S.A., XXVI, 85–87. It is correct to fourth differences of y and therefore third differences of u. After King had concluded that it gave satisfactory pivotal values, it was used (in conjunction with the Karup-King third difference tangential reproducing formula of par. 101 here) in his official construction of the English Life Tables No. 7 for 1901–10 and No. 8 for 1910–12 (see the Supplement to the 75th Annual Report of the Registrar-General for England and Wales, and J.I.A., XLIX, 297), and subsequently by Sir Alfred Watson in No. 9 for 1920–22 and No. 10 for 1930–32 (Registrar-General's Decennial Supplements for 1921 and 1931, and J.I.A., LIX, 125), by L. A. Bullwinkle in the Northern Ireland Life Table for 1925–27 (Registrar-General's Review of Vital Statistics of Northern Ireland and Life Tables, 1926), and by Sir Alfred Watson in the Scottish Life Table for 1930–32 (Supplement to the 78th Annual Report of the Reigstrar-General for Scotland, and T.F.A., XVI, 67). The formula has also been adopted on many occasions in several other countries, e.g., in New Zealand (see L. S. Polden's paper already mentioned in par. 61 here), in Australia (see the paper by F. W. Barford noted in par. 127, and the Australian Life Tables 1946–1948 prepared by W. C. Balmford, Commonwealth Actuary), in Canada (see M. D. Grant's construction described in T.A.S.A., XXXV, 8), and in the United States (as stated by T. N. E. Greville in the U.S. Life Tables and Actuarial Tables, 1939–41, p. 123). These repeated instances of the use of King's formula are attributable in Britain largely to the advantages resulting from uniformity of treatment in a long series of tables, and also in all cases to its simplicity, ease of application, and often sufficiently satisfactory results. The popularity which it has thus attained, however, should not be taken as indicating either its theoretical or practical superiority over the more modern pivotal formulae described in pars. 121–23 (see also Wolfenden's comments in T.A.S.A., XXXV, 291–92).

121. Since these pivotal values are determined from the grouped data by an elementary process of graduation, it may sometimes be advisable to use a formula based upon more groups, and higher differences (where necessary), in order to obtain a wider basis for the method. When differences of the u's up to order j are retained, so that in effect $u_x = A + Bx + Cx^2 + \ldots + Jx^i$, we can use $j + 1$ groups (with the corresponding range) and still obtain a direct solution; and with 3, 5, ... symmetrical groups, as in (49) and (52) here, the formulae are the same for $j = 2$ or 3, 4 or 5, ... Thus, taking u_x as a continuous function and the origin at the centre of the range, the required value for the central year of age is

$$\int_{-\frac{1}{2}}^{+\frac{1}{2}} u_x\,dx = \int_{-\frac{1}{2}}^{+\frac{1}{2}} (A + Bx + Cx^2 + \ldots + Jx^i)\,dx = A + \frac{C}{12} + \frac{E}{80} + \ldots\,.$$

The given numerical value, w, of any group comprising t terms, in which the abscissa of the middle ordinate is a, is similarly equivalent to

$$\int_{a-\frac{t}{2}}^{a+\frac{t}{2}} (A + Bx + Cx^2 + \ldots + Jx^i)\,dx\,,$$

from which A, B, ... are immediately expressible in terms of w; and hence the above central value

$$A + \frac{C}{12} + \frac{E}{80} + \ldots\,,$$

or any other non-central value or group of values, follows at once in terms of w.* As examples, with 3 groups and $j = 2$ or 3 we get King's formula (49); with $j = 3$ and four consecutive groups of the range $u_0 \ldots u_{19}$ we find

$$u_{9\frac{1}{2}} = .1165\,(w_5 + w_{10}) - .0165\,(w_0 + w_{15})$$
$$= \tfrac{1}{10}[(w_5 - .165\Delta^2 w_0) + (w_{10} - .165\Delta^2 w_5)] \qquad (51)$$

as used in Henderson's "Mortality Laws and Statistics," pp. 75 and 94; while with five consecutive groups and $j = 4$ or 5

$$u_{12} = .221376w_{10} - .011584\,(w_5 + w_{15}) + .000896\,(w_0 + w_{20})$$
$$= .2w_{10} - .008\Delta^2 w_5 + .000896\Delta^4 w_0, \qquad (52)$$

which is the pivotal formula to fifth differences of u ($j = 5$) used by King

* As shown by E. L. De Forest—see H. H. Wolfenden's paper "On the Development of Formulae for Graduation by Linear Compounding, with Special Reference to the Work of Erastus L. De Forest," T.A.S.A., XXVI, pp. 81–121, where the derivations for several cases are given in detail.

in J.I.A., XLIII, 114, and there demonstrated in the same way as (49) here.

122.* The pivotal values in the methods of pars. 120 and 121 are all found by ordinary interpolations from groups. Since the real objective in the calculation of those values, however, is to obtain reliable points which represent the data adequately but yet remove any undue fluctuations, and also because the subsequent tangential or osculatory interpolations based thereon have a tendency to show undulations and points of inflexion (cf. par. 107 here), it has been suggested (first by J. Buchanan, with subsequent investigations by W. A. Jenkins) that the pivotal values might be determined from the quinquennial sums by osculatory instead of ordinary interpolation. The pivotal value formulae so derived are:

(*i*) From Sprague's 5th difference reproducing osculatory formula of par. 100,

$$u_{12} = .2w_{10} - .008\Delta^2 w_5 + .0064\Delta^4 w_0 \qquad (53)$$

as deduced in Jenkins' paper in T.A.S.A., XXXI, 14.

(*ii*) From Jenkins' 4th difference osculatory non-reproducing formula (described in par. 107 here),

$$u_{12} = .2w_{10} - .008\Delta^2 w_5 - .00019375\Delta^4 w_0 \qquad (54)$$

as also given by Jenkins in T.A.S.A., XXXI, 13.

(*iii*) From Jenkins' 5th difference osculatory non-reproducing formula of par. 107,

$$u_{12} = .2w_{10} - .008\Delta^2 w_5 - .0042\Delta^4 w_0 \qquad (55)$$

as suggested by Buchanan in T.F.A., XII, 128–29.

The practical effects of using these formulae for the pivotal values, and then completing the interpolations by the corresponding osculatory formula from which the pivotal expression was derived, were tested in Buchanan's and Jenkins' papers. With regard to smoothness (as would be expected), Sprague's reproducing formula as a basis for both the pivotal and subsequent calculations was improved slightly by the 4th difference non-reproducing method, which in turn was improved by the non-reproducing 5th difference process, while of course the order was reversed in respect of fit.

123. The preceding formulae are all based upon direct interpolation, without imposing any conditions upon the coefficients of the *w*'s; and they represent in each case a unique solution. If it is desired, however, to em-

* The wording of this paragraph is taken largely from "The Fundamental Principles of Mathematical Statistics," p. 130.

ploy more groups than in the preceding cases without including more orders of differences it would be necessary to restrict the coefficients in some way in order to obtain a complete solution.* The pivotal values, say v_r, in the preceding formulae are immediately expressible in the "linear compound" form

$$v_r = l_r u_r + (l_{r+1}u_{r+1} + l_{r-1}u_{r-1}) + (l_{r+2}u_{r+2} + l_{r-2}u_{r-2}) + \dots \atop + (l_{r+n}u_{r+n} + l_{r-n}u_{r-n}) \qquad (56)$$

by putting the u's for the w's; and when differences above order j are neglected so that $u_x = A + Bx + Cx^2 + \dots + Jx^j$ the general form of, say, v_0 becomes

$$\left.\begin{aligned}
v_0 = {}& A \left[l_0 + (l_1 + l_{-1}) + (l_2 + l_{-2}) + \dots + (l_n + l_{-n}) \right] \\
& + B \left[(l_1 - l_{-1}) + 2 (l_2 - l_{-2}) + \dots + n(l_n - l_{-n}) \right] \\
& + C \left[1^2 (l_1 + l_{-1}) + 2^2 (l_2 + l_{-2}) + \dots + n^2 (l_n + l_{-n}) \right] \\
& + D \left[1^3 (l_1 - l_{-1}) + 2^3 (l_2 - l_{-2}) + \dots + n^3 (l_n - l_{-n}) \right] \\
& + \dots \\
= {}& (\text{say})\ c_0 A + c_1 B + c_2 C + c_3 D + \dots .
\end{aligned}\right\} \qquad (57)$$

Consequently when $j = 0$, so that $u_x = A$, we must have $c_0 = 1$; when $j = 1$ and $u_x = A + Bx$, it is necessary and sufficient that $c_0 = 1$ and $c_1 = 0$; and generally when differences above order j are negligible the conditions are that $c_0 = 1$, $c_1 = 0$, $c_2 = 0$, $\dots c_j = 0$. These conditions cover both unsymmetrical and symmetrical cases; and for the latter, since $l_n = l_{-n}$, they reduce to $c_0 = 1$, $c_2 = 0$, $c_4 = 0$, etc., and are the same when $j = 0$ or 1, 2 or 3, 4 or 5, $\dots$ When, for example, an odd number of quinquennial groups of values are used, as in (49) and (52), (56) becomes, with the groups taken centrally,

$$v_0 = \dots r' (u_{-12} + \dots u_{-8}) + q' (u_{-7} + \dots u_{-3}) + p (u_{-2} + \dots + u_2) \atop + q (u_3 + \dots + u_7) + r (u_8 + \dots + u_{12}) + \dots \left.\right\} \qquad (58)$$

and (57) and its resulting conditions are modified similarly.

In the usual case when $j = 3$ a complete solution is obtained directly by taking three symmetrical quinquennial groups, so that $q = q'$ and

---

* The subsequent arrangement of this paragraph is taken from H. H. Wolfenden's paper mentioned in the footnote to par. 121. The terms "linear compound" and "linear compounding" were first used in actuarial literature by W. F. Sheppard, and were subsequently adopted in the paper just noted (see also "The Fundamental Principles of Mathematical Statistics," pp. 132 and 282–83, for a condensed statement of the principles underlying "graduation by linear compounding").

$r = r' = 0$ and the conditions $c_0 = 1$ and $c_2 = 0$ become $5p + 10q = 1$ and $5p + 135q = 0$, whence $p = .216$ and $q = -.008$ as in (50). With five symmetrical groups ($r = r'$ and $q = q'$), however, the conditions $c_0 = 1$ and $c_2 = 0$ can give a complete solution only when the three un-knowns p, q, and r are reduced to two; and (as pointed out in J.I.A., LI, 368) if this is done by taking $p = q$, so that the conditions become $10r + 15p = 1$ and $140p + 510r = 0$, we obtain—without, it is to be noted, any introduction of the method of least squares—Henderson's formula (origi-nally given in the First Edition of Actuarial Study No. 4, p. 22)

$$v_0 = \tfrac{1}{625} [51w'_0 + 51w'_{\pm 5} - 14w'_{\pm 10}] \tag{59}$$

where

$$w'_n = \sum_{x=n-2}^{x=n+2} u_x .$$

If, however, $p \neq q$, there are three unknowns and the two conditional equations

$$\left. \begin{array}{l} 5p + \ \ 10q + \ \ 10r = 1 \\ 5p + 135q + 510r = 0 \end{array} \right\} . \tag{60}$$

If we now assume that each u is affected by an error e of which the mean square is e^2 we may determine the "best" formula (i.e., that which will secure the greatest possible reduction of the mean square error in v, on the assumptions made), by making the mean square error of v_0, or Σl_i^2, that is, $5p^2 + 10q^2 + 10r^2$, a minimum subject to (60). From these three condi-tions, therefore, we find that

$$v_0 = \tfrac{1}{7} [.696w'_0 + .488w'_{\pm 5} - .136w'_{\pm 10}] . \tag{61}$$

This formula was first given anonymously in J.I.A., LI, 368. The main objective in determining the pivotal values is that they must represent the original data satisfactorily (and permit the eventual construction therefrom of a smooth curve); consequently it may be held that they should "fit" the data in accordance with the best available *a priori* criterion of fit; and this formula accomplishes that objective by effecting the greatest possible reduction in the mean square error of v, which on the assumptions made gives the same result as a best "fitting" according to the criterion of least squares (see "The Fundamental Principles of Mathematical Statistics," pp. 283–84 particularly, and pp. 91–97, 106–8, and 322–28 with respect to the method of least squares; and T.A.S.A., XXVI, 100–105, where on p. 105 $w_n = \sum_{x=n-2}^{x=n+2} u_x$). It has been used by

T. N. E. Greville in T.A.S.A., XLV, 227 (see also H. H. Wolfenden, T.A.S.A., XLVI, 97), and in the U.S. Life Tables and Actuarial Tables, 1939–41, p. 124, for populations and deaths of Negroes between ages 32 and 72 and "other races" at ages 32 to 87, where its graduating power and its underlying assumption of "fitting" a third degree curve by least squares were considered to be appropriate and to be preferable to King's formula (50).

Since the pivotal values, as just emphasized, should fit the data in accordance with some adequate criterion (which in (61) is taken to be that of least squares) and yet must permit the eventual construction of a smooth curve, a necessary compromise between the incompatibilities of maximum fit and smoothness* is inherent in the selection of the pivotal formula for the first step and the interpolation formula for the second. This compromise can of course be reached by using a graphic graduation to find the pivotal values (as illustrated by W. A. Jenkins in T.A.S.A., XXVIII, 206). Another proposal, made by A. R. Reid and J. B. Dow (in "Graduation by the General Formulae of Osculatory Interpolation," T.F.A., XIV, 185), was to use the flexible *b* term in (48) for the pivotal values so that the expected and actual deaths should be equal, and in the interpolations to yield maximum smoothness therefrom.†

124. (*i*) All the pivotal formulae of pars. 120–23, in accordance with the usual procedures, provide expressions for the calculation of central values. In any special case, however, a non-central formula can of course be deduced easily. For example, in constructing the 1911–15 and 1916–20

---

* It may be well to reproduce here the following remarks from "The Fundamental Principles of Mathematical Statistics," p. 120: "When the graduation is accomplished by fitting a mathematical formula it will be clear that the main criterion must be a test of goodness of *fit*, since the values derived from the graduation process will lie on a mathematical curve, and therefore will be inherently 'smooth.' If, however, some other method of graduation is employed which does not necessarily place the graduated values upon an inherently smooth curve, it will evidently be necessary to test the results for *smoothness* as well as for goodness of fit. In this connection it should be noted also that in such a graduation of irregular data it will obviously not be practicable to secure a best possible fit and greatest possible smoothness at the same time—for the ultimate interpretation of a 'best possible fit' would require the precise reproduction of the original data, without any smoothness having been attained. It is therefore necessary in such cases to settle the criteria for fit and smoothness so that the practical results may be *satisfactory*, rather than *best*, in both respects."

† Reid and Dow also illustrated the following alternative uses for the *b* term in (48): (*a*) *b* taken numerically to make the formula resemble Everett's formula closely; (*b*) the pivotal values found as in (*a*), but in the interpolations *b* taken to secure maximum smoothness; and (*c*) a double application of method (*b*). The maximum smoothness was prescribed by making $\Sigma (\Delta^3 q_x)^2$ a minimum.

New Zealand tables (see the 1921 census "Report regarding the Construction of Life Tables," and Polden's paper noted in par. 61 (*iii*) here) a non-central formula (which emerges at once by putting $n = 1$ and $x = -2$ in De Forest's general expression (7) of T.A.S.A., XXVI, 87, covering King's assumptions of par. 120 here) was used to determine the pivotal values at ages 10, 15, 20, . . . , from data in a "5–9" grouping.

(*ii*) At the two ends of the table, the pivotal values which are not reached by a symmetrical formula can be found (*a*) by the corresponding unsymmetrical formulae which can be derived easily by the methods already described, or (*b*) by finite difference extrapolations from the values already determined by the symmetrical formula. An instance of (*a*) is the $u_2 = .2w_0 - .008\Delta^2 w_0$, corresponding to King's (49) herein for the central term of the middle group, for the central term of the first of the three quinquennial groups in the series $u_0 \ldots u_{14}$, which was used in the U.S. Abridged Life Tables, 1919–20, p. 34. Examples of (*b*) may be found in J.I.A., XLIII, 119 and 134, and in the U.S. Life Tables and Actuarial Tables, 1939–41, pp. 124–25. In some cases, however, it may be preferable to complete the ends of the table by the methods discussed in pars. 127–128 here, without thus extending the series of pivotal values.

(*iii*) In King's own applications of his pivotal value method, and in nearly all other instances of its use, as noted in par. 120, the pivotal values are determined from the populations, P, and deaths, D, separately; then the corresponding pivotal values of q_x follow immediately therefrom (by the appropriate formula expressing q in terms of D and P); and finally the interpolations are made from the pivotal values of q_x so found. As a variation of this procedure, and because the data were available at each age, Sir Alfred Watson in preparing English Life Table No. 9 made an experimental construction by determining quinquennial pivotal values of q_x directly (i.e., without operating on the deaths and populations separately). It was found in that instance that the final table differed inappreciably from the results of King's method of using the separate series of deaths and populations (see also T.A.S.A., XXIX, 334; and J.I.A., LIX, 128 and 211; and T.F.A., XII, 129 and 149).

(*xiii*) Curve-fitting Methods

125. Instead of using the graphic or interpolation methods of pars. 96–124, appropriate curves can sometimes be fitted to the populations and deaths, or to functions thereof. Such curve-fitting methods necessarily produce smooth graduations (and without the undulations which may appear in the results of some of the interpolation processes), although for that reason they also generally show greater deviations from the un-

adjusted data. The uses to which the final table will be applied must therefore be considered in deciding the extent to which closeness of fit may be sacrificed for the inherent smoothness which results from the fitting of a mathematical formula (cf. J.I.A., XLVIII, 211, and XLIX, 98 and 342, and "The Fundamental Principles of Mathematical Statistics," p. 120).

(a) In a few instances where the data were available for each age, Makeham's first formula (by which μ_x, colog p_x, or m_x is represented as $\alpha + \beta c^x$, or l_x is taken correspondingly as $ks^x g^{c^x}$) has been used (see, for examples, H. L. Rietz and C. H. Forsyth, R.A.I.A., I, 9, and H. L. Trachtenberg, J.R.S.S., LXXXIII, 656). Where the data are available or reliable in age groups only, the formula could be determined from the central ordinates of each group, which would be found by deducting from the group total 1/24th of the 2nd central difference (see Sir George F. Hardy's Institute of Actuaries' Lectures on "The Theory of the Construction of Tables of Mortality," pp. 57 and 87, and Henderson's "Mortality Laws and Statistics," p. 76).

Although for many tables based on population statistics the principle of "uniform seniority," which follows from Makeham's formula and greatly facilitates the computation of joint life annuities, has not been considered to be important, it is nevertheless true in modern practice that Makehamized graduations of widely used population tables may be valuable. In the U.S. Life Tables and Actuarial Tables, 1939–41, therefore, T. N. E. Greville prepared a very satisfactory Makeham version of the table for total whites, with the uniform seniority values at ages 17 or over and adjustment factors at younger ages for joint life annuities, and also with adjusted ages for the calculation of approximate joint life annuities on lives of different sex.* A detailed account is given there of the valuable method, originally due to G. F. Hardy, by which the Makeham constants were determined so that the annuity values of the previously constructed non-Makehamized table should be reproduced as closely as possible (see also the descriptions in the references stated in "The Fundamental Principles of Mathematical Statistics," p. 122).

(b) For the reasons explained in the following par. 126, however, it is

---

* Separate Makeham graduations for males and females would have required different values of the constant c, with consequent loss of the "uniform seniority" method for lives of different sex; it was accordingly felt that it was preferable to apply Makeham's formula to the table for total whites without separation by sex, and then to deal with the calculation of joint life annuities on lives of different sex by using the Makehamized table for both sexes together on the basis of specially adjusted ages (which generally required an addition to the age for males and a deduction for females) from which the equal ages of the uniform seniority table could be taken.

usually found that Makeham's first formula must be modified by introducing additional constants. Thus Hardy showed (see his Lectures, *op. cit.*, p. 88) that for the 1901 male population of England and Wales the logarithms of the central ordinates (determined as stated in (*a*) here) of decennial age groups, or log l'_x, could be represented in the form log $l'_x = A + Bx + Cx^2 + Dc^x$ according to Makeham's second formula (by which μ_x, colog p_x, or m_x is taken as $a + \gamma x + \beta c^x$, and l_x correspondingly as $ks^x w^{x^2} g^{c^x}$). The same principle was employed in the preparation of the tables for the British National Insurance Act, 1911—log T'_x (instead of log l'_x) being represented by the form just given, and the deaths being dealt with by fitting to $\Sigma d'_x$ a basic curve of the same form together with a similar supplementary curve determined so that log $\Sigma d'$ (base) + log $\Sigma d'$ (supplementary) = log $\Sigma d'$ (final table), as shown in J.I.A., XLVII, 553.

(*c*) Makeham's first and second formulae are, of course, modifications of Gompertz's original geometrical progression $\mu_x = Bc^x$. From this $\log_e \mu_x = a + bx$ where $a = \log_e B$ and $b = \log_e c$, so that Gompertz's formula can be written in the exponential form $\mu_x = e^{a+bx}$. Three improved and more elastic expressions (*i*) $\mu_x = e^{a_0+a_1x+a_2x^2}$, (*ii*) $\mu_x = e^{a_0+a_1x+a_2x^2}(1 + hx)$, and (*iii*) $\mu_x = e^{a_0+a_1x+a_2x^2+a_3x^3+a_4x^4}$ have been suggested by H. L. Trachtenberg ("The Wider Application of the Gompertz Law of Mortality," J.R.S.S., LXXXVII, 278; see also J.I.A., LXIII, 45), with illustrative applications to the English Life Tables. By taking logarithms of each side these expressions can be fitted easily by moments or least squares (in which connection see also "The Fundamental Principles of Mathematical Statistics," p. 326, with respect to the weights to be assigned in a least squares fitting of log μ_x). The last form (*iii*), which gave the best results, provides for the two points of inflexion, which are often found in the curve of log μ_x, at ages b and c as determined from the relation

$$\frac{d^2}{dx^2} \log \mu_x = a(x - b)(x - c).$$

(*d*) Because the curves of q_x, and allied functions such as μ_x, m_x, colog p_x, and log μ_x, usually present difficulties when any attempt is made to fit a single curve over the whole span of life, numerous suggestions have been made by which further modifications of Makeham's formula, or other expressions of quite different character, might be fitted to the data over large or small ranges. For the purposes of this Study it will be sufficient to refer the reader to "The Fundamental Principles of Mathematical Statistics," pp. 79–85 and 319, where various formulae which have been proposed by Hardy, Buchanan, Lidstone, Perks, Wittstein,

Steffensen, and others are stated, with indications of their applicabilities and properties (which in some cases include modified forms of "uniform seniority").

(*e*) Type I of Pearson's system of frequency curves (for which see "The Fundamental Principles of Mathematical Statistics," pp. 65–74 and 312–19) was applied extensively by T. G. Ackland as a means of representing the age distributions of the populations of India at the census of 1911 (see J.I.A., XLVII, 315). The results on that occasion, however, were considered to be unsatisfactory—H. G. W. Meikle in his 1921 Report (noted in par. 52 here) having concluded that the rates of mortality deduced therefrom showed at some ages unjustifiable departures from those which the data really indicated (see also J.I.A., XLVII, 407). Another instance of the application of Pearson's frequency curves to population statistics occurred in the preparation of the first national life tables for Egypt from the censuses of 1917 and 1927, where M. R. El-Shanawany Effendi used the curves to effect drastic redistributions of the data which were disturbed seriously by digit selections (see J.I.A., LXVIII, 188).

(*f*) The use of curves to represent the curtate or complete expectation of life (e_x or $\overset{\circ}{e}_x$) has also received some attention, because it may be claimed that in the calculation of those functions a certain amount of graduation has been done implicitly (see J.I.A., XLI, 93), and because afterwards q_x could be computed easily therefrom (even if some further smoothing were required to reach completely satisfactory values of the basic q_x which is, of course, the primary function required). Being a gradually decreasing curve, $\log_{10} e_x = a + bx + cx^2 + dx^3 + fx^4$ was suggested by G. F. Hardy (in his Lectures, *op. cit.*, p. 79); Dr. J. Brownlee used $\overset{\circ}{e}_x = ma^x + nb^x$ with considerable success (see T.A.S.A., XXV, 154, and the references therein); the formula

$$e^{cx} = \frac{e^{a-nE}}{E},$$

where E is the complete expectation and e is the base of the Napierian logarithms, has been applied to 25 of the U.S. Life Tables, 1910 (see J.R.S.S., LXXXIV, 453); and J. F. Steffensen has experimented with the reciprocal (to produce an increasing series) in the Makeham form

$$\frac{1}{\overset{\circ}{e}_x} = A + Bc^x$$

in two papers in the Proceedings of the Fifth International Congress of Actuaries, II, 247, and Svenska Aktuarieföreningens Tidskrift, 1917.

(g) The advantages which flow from the inherent smoothness of mathematical curves can sometimes be secured effectively by the useful device of graduating data by reference to some appropriate standard table from which irregularities have already been removed. Thus it has been suggested (using primed symbols to denote the values of the standard table) that

$$\log \frac{p_x}{p'_x}$$

is a function of small values which progress slowly (see G. J. Lidstone, J.I.A., XXX, 212), or that

$$\frac{T_x}{T'_x} \text{ and } \frac{l_x}{l'_x}$$

could be used in respect of populations and deaths at age x and beyond (see Henderson's "Mortality Laws and Statistics," p. 60). For certain sections of the 1921 census of India the population data were represented satisfactorily by fitting 3rd degree parabolas, usually of the form

$$y = 1 - ax - bx^2 + cx^3, \qquad \text{to } \log \frac{T_x}{T_x}$$

(see Meikle's Report referred to in par. 52 here, and the similar principles used in Vaidyanathan's subsequent 1931 Report; and A. Henry, J.I.A., XLVII, 407). The selections of appropriate standard tables and graduating formulae in the practical application of this method give wide scope, of course, for variations in judgment and ingenuity, and the inherent smoothness of the results, as in all these curve-fitting procedures, leaves only the goodness of fit to be tested satisfactorily.

(c) OLDEST AGES; AND "JUVENILE" AGES, i.e., BETWEEN INFANTILE AND ADULT AGES

126. On pp. 78 and 82 of "The Fundamental Principles of Mathematical Statistics" diagrams are shown for the typical curves of l_x and q_x (and m_x, μ_x, and colog p_x), with the object of clarifying the nature of the problem involved in the graduation of those functions.* The typical form of the curve of q_x (and of m_x, μ_x, and colog p_x) from infancy to old age is (as there described, p. 81) "a contorted U-shaped curve, with the minimum in the neighbourhood of age 11, so that from about age 11 to the end of life the curve increases steadily (often with two minor undulations in the thirties and seventies) with its convexity towards the x-axis (cf. W. Perks, J.I.A., LXIII, 41, 45, and 55, and J. S. Elston, R.A.I.A., XII,

* These diagrams have been reproduced by M. D. Miller on p. 60a of the monograph "Elements of Graduation" previously mentioned.

88). If, then, the values up to about age 10 are dealt with separately, the remainder of the curve from the region of age 11 upwards will usually be found to change slowly at first, and at the older ages to resemble more nearly a geometrical progression—a circumstance which means that often the logarithms of the values there approximate to an arithmetical progression. The points of inflexion, however, introduce great difficulties into the problem of finding any expression which will represent mortality rates over the whole period of life." Furthermore, at the oldest ages (beyond about age 90 or 95) the data are often both inadequate and unreliable (cf. par. 41 here). In consequence, the preceding methods of section (B) for the adult ages are usually satisfactory only until about age 90 or 95 at the one end of the table, and age 11, or even 15, at the other. Beyond those ages special methods are generally required.

127. At the oldest ages, on account of the paucity and unreliability of the data, it is often found that different methods of estimating the rates of mortality produce widely differing results, so that it is frequently desirable to compare the indications given by several processes. There is considerable justification, moreover, for terminating the tables at a reasonable, even if arbitrary, age by some more or less artificial method. George King, for instance (in J.I.A., XLII, 238 and 252, and XLIII, 119), first used ordinary interpolation from a short range of preceding values with $q_\omega = 1$, where the limiting age ω was fixed arbitrarily; subsequently, however, in his constructions of the official English Life Tables Nos. 7 and 8, he employed suitable values as the basis of extrapolation without assuming $q = 1$ at any age (see also J.I.A., XLII, 287 and 290, and XLIX, 315). In connection with these finite difference methods at the oldest ages where the calculations are often based on irregularly spaced values, the Newton-Sheppard system of adjusted differences, with its avoidance of the solution of simultaneous equations (as suggested in J.I.A., LVIII, 310) was employed by F. W. Barford for the interpolations at ages 88 to 104 from $q_{85}, q_{86}, q_{87}, q_{92}$, and $q_{104} = 1$ in his construction of the Australian Life Tables A^{M33} and A^{F33} (see his paper on "Australian Population Mortality, Census of 1933," Actuarial Society of Australasia, 41st Session, 1936). In the next English Life Table No. 9, on the other hand, the indicated values of q_x began to decrease above age 100, so that King's methods were found to be unsatisfactory; but it was observed that the ratio

$$\frac{\log \left({}_{10}p_{89}\right)}{\log \left({}_{10}p_{84}\right)}$$

was approximately equal to

$$\frac{\log \left({}_{10}p_{94}\right)}{\log \left({}_{10}p_{89}\right)}$$

so that a Gompertz graduation (cf. par. 97) was adopted from age 85. Gompertz graduations were also found to be appropriate from age 87 in the English Life Table No. 10 and the concurrent Scottish Life Tables. The Life Tables (1926) for Northern Ireland, however, showed that such a method would be unsuitable, and a Makeham graduation based on p_x at ages 70, 80, and 90 was eventually employed. In the United States Life Tables, 1890, etc., Wittstein's formula (par. 125(d) here)

$$q_x = a^{-(M-x)^n} + \frac{1}{m}\, a^{-(mx)^n}$$

was used. An interesting comparison of several methods, namely, (1) constant second differences for log q_x from ages 77, 82, and 105, (2) Wittstein's formula based on those same ages, (3) Wittstein's formula using ages 67, 82, and 105, and (4) constant third differences using ages 72, 77, 82, and 105, has also been given by Henderson (T.A.S.A., XXXV, 279) for determining the values of q_x between ages 87 and 102 on the basis of M. D. Grant's Canadian data.

128. At the other end of the table, from the infantile ages 0–4 to about ages 10–15, the curve of q_x changes so rapidly that special methods are frequently necessary in order to represent it properly and at the same time to secure a smooth junction with the infantile and adult values. In Farr's method the matter was dealt with by a special adjustment to m_{12}, as mentioned in par. 97. In King's paper in J.I.A., XLIII, 124 and 135, the values were supplied by calculating a third difference from known values, and in English Tables Nos. 7 and 8 he used Lagrange's formula (see footnote to par. 52) to fourth differences, although the results were not altogether satisfactory. In English Life Table No. 9 Sir Alfred Watson preferred a third difference interpolation from four non-equidistant values, and the same method was adopted in the Northern Ireland Life Tables (1926)—the arithmetical procedures and the Newton-Sheppard system of adjusted differences being discussed further in J.I.A., LVIII, 60 and 310, and being used and illustrated also in Barford's Australian paper mentioned in par. 127 here.

A significant departure from such methods, however, was found to be necessary in Sir Alfred Watson's reports on the English Life Table No. 10 and the comparable tables for Scotland based on the census of 1931 and the deaths of 1930–32, because the abnormal variations which occurred in the birth rate during and after the war of 1914–18 had caused such irregularities in the census enumerations at ages 11 to 14, and in the deaths at each age during the three years, that interpolation based on the pivotal value of q_{12} (amongst others) was felt to be unreliable. In order to secure a close relation between the deaths and the populations from which they arose, the following procedure was therefore employed (see the references in par. 120). The deaths at age 12, say, in 1930–32 would have arisen from the births

$$(\tfrac{1}{8}\beta_1^{17}+\tfrac{3}{8}\beta_2^{17}+\tfrac{5}{8}\beta_3^{17}+\tfrac{7}{8}\beta_4^{17})+(\beta^{18}+\beta^{19})+(\tfrac{7}{8}\beta_1^{20}+\tfrac{5}{8}\beta_2^{20}+\tfrac{3}{8}\beta_3^{20}+\tfrac{1}{8}\beta_4^{20})$$

$$= A_{12} \text{ say },$$

where (in the notation of par. 91 here) β_n^{17} represents the births in the nth quarter of 1917, and β^{17} denotes the births during the whole of 1917. Also, since the census date was taken as at the end of the 4th month of 1931, the populations enumerated at ages 11, 12, and 13 would have arisen from the births

$$(\tfrac{2}{3}\beta_2^{17}+\beta_3^{17}+\beta_4^{17})+(\beta^{18}+\beta^{19})+(\beta_1^{20}+\tfrac{1}{3}\beta_2^{20}) = B_{12} \text{ say }.$$

A corrected value for m_{12} was then taken as

$$\frac{\text{Deaths aged 12 in 1930–32}}{\text{Census Populations aged 11, 12, and 13}} \times \frac{B_{12}}{A_{12}},$$

and similarly for each age from 6 to 16; and finally these values were suitably graduated.

In view of the admittedly inferior results given by King's use of Lagrange's formula in English Life Tables Nos. 7 and 8, T. G. Ackland suggested in J.I.A., XLIX, 336 (see also p. 344) that better results could be obtained by deducing q_x for each age from 7 to 10 by osculatory interpolation (on the basis of equal intervals) from q_1, the unadjusted q_6, and the pivotal values q_{11} and q_{16}, while those for ages 11 to 16 could be derived similarly from the unadjusted q_6 and the pivotal q_{11}, q_{16}, and q_{21}. Other osculatory methods may also be employed. Thus Ackland in J.I.A., XLIX, 372, illustrated the process of osculatory interpolation for unequal intervals which may be useful in some cases; J. Buchanan, in J.I.A., XLII, 385, and Trans. 6th Int. Cong. Actuaries, II, 615, suggested that a fourth degree curve could be used through three ages five years apart (such as 5, 10, and 15) "so as to have at its ends the same slope as the curves to which it is there joined"; and R. Henderson in "Mortality Laws and Statistics," p. 59, described a process which involves the determination from known ordinates of the first and second differential coefficients at ages such as 5 and 10, these differential coefficients then being used in Sprague's osculatory formula which in terms of differential coefficients

(u' and u'') may be written

$$u_{x+h} = u_x \frac{(t-h)^3(t^2+3th+6h^2)}{t^5} + u'_x \frac{h(t-h)^3(t+3h)}{t^4} + u''_x \frac{h^2(t-h)^3}{2t^3}$$

$$+u_{x+t} \frac{h^3(10t^2-15th+6h^2)}{t^5} + u'_{x+t} \frac{h^3(t-h)(4t-3h)}{t^4} + u''_{x+t} \frac{h^3(t-h)^2}{2t^3}$$

for interval x to $x + t$.

A further illustration of the necessity for special methods at the juvenile ages is the procedure devised by T. N. E. Greville in the U.S. Life Tables and Actuarial Tables, 1939–41 (pp. 126 and 136), where "the rates for ages 5 to 11 were interpolated from a special third degree curve determined so as to reproduce the calculated rates of mortality at ages 4, 7, and 12, and to have the same first derivative at age 12 as the Karup-King curve used for interpolation in the age interval 12 to 17." Writing the Karup-King formula (par. 101 here) for the age interval 7 to 12 as

$$q_{7+t} = \frac{s}{5} q_7 + \frac{s^2(s-5)}{250} \delta^2 q_7 + \frac{t}{5} q_{12} + \frac{t^2(t-5)}{250} \delta^2 q_{12}$$

where $s = 5 - t$, Greville remarked that, since reproduction of q_7 and q_{12} and equality of the derivatives at age 12 would be satisfied with any value of $\delta^2 q_7$, an artificial value ϵ for $\delta^2 q_7$ can be used so that the value of q_4 will be reproduced. The preceding formula with $t = -3$ thus gives $q_4 = 1.6q_7 + .768\epsilon - .6q_{12} - .288\delta^2 q_{12}$, whence, by substituting $\delta^2 q_{12} = q_{17} - 2q_{12} + q_7$ and solving,

$$\epsilon = \tfrac{1}{96}(125q_4 - 164q_7 + 3q_{12} + 36q_{17})$$

which was used as the artificial value of $\delta^2 q_7$ in the Karup-King formula.*

* An analogous device, for which the determination of the artificial value ϵ there required is also shown by Greville (*loc. cit.*), was used for ages 28 to 31, where a special third degree curve was found which would have the same ordinate and first derivative at age 27 as the Karup-King curve used in the age interval 22 to 27, and the same ordinate and first derivative as Jenkins' non-reproducing formula (47) of this Study which was used in the interval 32 to 37.

VIII

THE CONSTRUCTION OF ABRIDGED LIFE TABLES FROM POPULATION STATISTICS

129. When it is anticipated that a mortality experience will form the basis of extensive financial calculations it is necessary to construct a complete life table, with the consequent monetary functions, in addition to the preparation of the fundamental graduated rates of mortality, q_x, at each age. If, however, it is intended to use the data merely as a guide to the mortality it is not necessary to proceed beyond the determination of reliable values of q_x; and in comparing such rates with those of other communities or classes a life table need not be constructed, for comparisons may be effected immediately between the rates of mortality themselves. Even for such simple purposes, however, Medical Health Officers have frequently considered it essential to calculate certain life-table functions— particularly $\mathring{e}_x$; and although this is not necessary, and in some cases may even be misleading (see Section IX here), some of the short methods of procedure are valuable contributions to the general theory of life-table construction, and will therefore be considered here.

The general principle of these abridged methods is that, when the data are taken in age groups (x to $x + n$), the n-year probabilities $_np_x$ can be computed approximately—and hence the values of l_x at the corresponding age intervals follow immediately from an arbitrary radix. Then, in order

to pass to e_x, which is $$\sum_{t=1}^{t=\infty} {}_tp_x = \frac{\sum_{t=1}^{t=\infty} l_{x+t}}{l_x},$$ or to $\mathring{e}_x$, which is $$\frac{\sum_{t=0}^{t=\infty} L_{x+t}}{l_x},$$

it is only necessary to pass from these values of $_np_x$ or l_x at $n$thly intervals to the sums of $_tp_x$ or of l_{x+t} or of L_{x+t} within each interval, and thence by summation to the values of e_x or $\mathring{e}_x$ for $n$thly values of x.

130. (i) *Dr. Farr's Method*

In this method, which was introduced in connection with certain local life tables based on the 1841 census of England and Wales (Supplement 35th Registrar-General's Report), p_0 was found from the births and deaths, and m at each age from 1 to 4 from the death and census returns. For subsequent age-groups covering n years ($n = 5$ or 10) the ratio of deaths to population as in par. 97, or $_nm_x$ say, was used to give $_np_x$ by means of the assumption that

$$\left(\frac{2-{}_nm_x}{2+{}_nm_x}\right)^n = (p_x \cdot p_{x+1} \ldots p_{x+n-1}) = {}_np_x.$$

From these values of ${}_np_x$ those of l_x were then determined for ages n years apart, and thence ΣL_x and $\mathring{e}_x = \dfrac{\Sigma L_x}{l_x}$ at such ages were found on the assumption that the years of life experienced between ages x and $x+n$ were $\dfrac{n}{2}(l_x + l_{x+n})$.

This method of deriving ${}_np_x$ would be satisfactory if p_x followed a geometrical progression; but since this is not generally the case the resulting values are not very reliable. The assumption as to the years of life, also, usually overstates the true values, with the result that the final values of $\mathring{e}_x$ are considerably overstated, especially at the higher ages (see Newsholme's "Vital Statistics," 3rd Edn., pp. 282–84; and J.I.A., XLIII, 78).

131. (*ii*) *Dr. Hayward's Method*

In order to correct the overstatement which follows from taking the years of life simply as $\dfrac{n}{2}(l_x + l_{x+n})$ in Farr's method, Dr. Hayward divided the n years into k parts and calculated the years of life as

$$\frac{n}{k}\left\{\frac{l_x + l_x p^{\frac{n}{k}}}{2} + \frac{l_x p^{\frac{n}{k}} + l_x p^{\frac{2n}{k}}}{2} + \ldots + \frac{l_x p^{\frac{(k-1)n}{k}} + l_{x+n}}{2}\right\}$$

$$= \frac{n}{k}\left\{\frac{l_x + l_{x+n}}{2} + l_x p^{\frac{n}{k}}\left[\frac{1 - p^{\frac{(k-1)n}{k}}}{1 - p^{\frac{n}{k}}}\right]\right\},$$

where

$$p = \frac{2 - {}_nm_x}{2 + {}_nm_x}.$$

He found that the quinquennial groups 5–9 and 10–15 need not be subdivided, that the decennial groups 15–24 up to 65–74 should be divided into two, that the groups 75–84 and 85–94 should each be taken in four equal parts, and that for the final group at ages 95 and upwards the calculation should be made in yearly stages ($k = n$)—the value of p in this last group being found by extrapolation from the values of p for the four preceding groups (see the references to Newsholme's Vital Statistics and J.I.A., XLIII, in par. 130 here).

This method has been used by Dr. Hayward in the construction of a series of tables of $\mathring{e}_x$ for England and Wales for each decennium from 1841–

1900 (J.R.S.S., LXIV, 636, and LXVI, 366), and also by Dr. Dunlop in Scotland. The values so obtained are reasonably close to those of the extended methods, as may be seen from the comparisons in J.I.A., XLII, 280–83, which show a fairly uniform understatement (not exceeding .12) in $\mathring{e}_x$ for English Life Table No. 6.

132. (*iii*) *George King's Method*

This process, which was described by King in the Supplement to the 75th Registrar-General's Report, Part I, p. 26, and J.I.A., XLVIII, 294, is an abbreviation of his extended methods, as follows: (1) "Pivotal" values of L'_x and d'_x for quinquennial ages are first found by formula (49). (2) The quinquennial values of m_x, and thence p_x and log p_x, are then computed—the log p_x at the end of the table being supplied by constant third or fourth differences from the preceding values. (3) The quinquennial log p_x is then differenced three times, and log $_5p_x$ (= log p_x + log p_{x+1} + . . . + log p_{x+4}) is calculated therefrom by the ordinary finite difference formulae

$$\log {}_5p_a = 5 \log p_a + 2\Delta \log p_a - .4\Delta^2 \log p_a + .2\Delta^3 \log p_a \quad (62)$$

for the first value; and

$$\log {}_5p_x = 5 \log p_{x-5} + 7\Delta \log p_{x-5} + 1.6\Delta^2 \log p_{x-5} - .2\Delta^3 \log p_{x-5} \quad (63)$$

for the second and subsequent quinquennial values. (4) Then, taking a suitable radix for l_a, log l_x and hence l_x are formed quinquennially by the relation log l_{x+5} = log l_x + log $_5p_x$. (5) In order to pass now to e_x, the quinquennial l_x is differenced three times, and the sum of the values for each age in each interval, that is $\sum\limits_{t=1}^{t=5} l_{x+t}$ for quinquennial values of x, are computed by the ordinary finite difference formulae

$$\sum_{t=1}^{t=5} l_{a+t} = 5l_a + 3\Delta l_a - .4\Delta^2 l_a + .2\Delta^3 l_a \quad (64)$$

for the first value, and

$$\sum_{t=1}^{t=5} l_{x+t} = 5l_{x-5} + 8\Delta l_{x-5} + 2.6\Delta^2 l_{x-5} - .2\Delta^3 l_{x-5} \quad (65)$$

for subsequent quinquennial groups—the last values at the end of the table being filled in empirically; and from these quinquennial sums of l we immediately find e_x by summing from the bottom upwards and dividing by l_x.

This method is well adapted to machine calculations; and the routine procedure is described minutely in the U.S. Abridged Life Tables, 1919–20, and also by C. C. Grove in J.A.S.A., XVIII, 1028 (see also T.A.S.A., XXV, 145). In the U.S. Tables the formulae were applied in the corresponding extended forms which do not involve differencing—such as

$$10 \log {}_5p_a = 24 (\log p_a + \log p_{a+5}) + 10 \log p_{a+5} - 10 \log p_{a+10} + 2 \log p_{a+15}$$

for (62). Grove also suggested that the determination of the pivotal values may be omitted—although that is a matter which would have to be decided from the nature of the data in each case (see J.I.A., XLIX, 352); and he found the last few quinquennial values of q_x (and thence log p_x) at ages 97, 102, and 107 by adding to the values of q_x at preceding ages hypothetical first differences, Δq, determined by multiplying the first differences of a standard table, $\Delta q'$, by the ratio $\dfrac{q_{107} - q_{92}}{q'_{107} - q'_{92}}$.

In King's papers the abridged method was not applied at ages before 11 (or 12), for which a pivotal value is obtainable by the central formula (49). It may therefore be noted that in the U.S. Tables Miss Foudray completed the values to age 0 by determining q_0, q_1, and q_2 as in par. 92(*iii*), calculating a pivotal value at age 7 by the non-central formula of par. 124(*ii*) here, and then finding log ${}_5p_2$ by formula (62) which was modified on account of the skewness of the curve (as suggested by Henderson) by taking the coefficient of $\Delta^3 \log p_2$ as unity in accordance with known values of log ${}_5p_2$. Grove applied Henderson's method of par. 92(*ii*) to find q_x for each age from 0 to 4; and since the calculation of the pivotal values was omitted, m_7 was taken as the ratio of deaths to population for age-group 5–9, from which q_7 follows, and then q_5 and q_6 were interpolated by a hypothetical first difference based on a standard table as described above for the oldest ages.

133. (*iv*) *Method Given by Editors of J.I.A.*

In J.I.A., XLVIII, 301, the Editors of the Journal of the Institute of Actuaries suggested and illustrated the following rapid method of proceeding directly from the m's, which gave very close results: (1) Since in the life table

$$m_x = \frac{d_x}{L_x} = \frac{l_x - l_{x+1}}{\displaystyle\int_0^1 l_{x+t}\,dt},$$

let $m_x^{(\frac{1}{5})}$ denote the central death-rate per 5 years for a 5-year age group,*

---

* This notation is retained here in order to exhibit the formulae as originally given and to facilitate understanding of the numerical examples referred to in the J.I.A. It

that is, $\dfrac{5\,(l_x - l_{x+5})}{\displaystyle\int_0^5 l_{x+t}\,dt}$.   Evaluating the denominator by formula (19) of King's Institute of Actuaries Text-Book, Part II, p. 476 (or taking $a = 0$, $n = 1$, and $r = 5$ in the general form of the Euler-Maclaurin expansion given on p. 189 of Freeman's Mathematics for Actuarial Students), we get

$$m^{\left(\frac{1}{5}\right)} = \frac{5\,(1 - {}_5p_x)}{\frac{5}{2}(1 + {}_5p_x) - 2\frac{1}{12}(\mu_x - {}_5p_x \cdot \mu_{x+5})}\,.$$

Hence

$${}_5p_x = \frac{1 - \frac{1}{2}m_x^{\left(\frac{1}{5}\right)} + \frac{5}{12}\mu_x m_x^{\left(\frac{1}{5}\right)}}{1 + \frac{1}{2}m_x^{\left(\frac{1}{5}\right)} + \frac{5}{12}\mu_{x+5}m_x^{\left(\frac{1}{5}\right)}}$$

and

$$\log_e {}_5p_x = -\,m_x^{\left(\frac{1}{5}\right)}\left[1 + \tfrac{5}{12}(\mu_{x+5} - \mu_x)\right].$$

If we now assume that $\frac{1}{5}m_x^{\left(\frac{1}{5}\right)} = \mu_{x+\frac{5}{2}}$ (cf. par. 97) the expression $\frac{5}{12}(\mu_{x+5} - \mu_x)$ within the bracket becomes

$$\tfrac{1}{12}\left[m_{x+\frac{5}{2}}^{\left(\frac{1}{5}\right)} - m_{x-\frac{5}{2}}^{\left(\frac{1}{5}\right)}\right] = \tfrac{1}{24}\left[m_{x+5}^{\left(\frac{1}{5}\right)} - m_{x-5}^{\left(\frac{1}{5}\right)}\right] \text{ approximately} = \tfrac{1}{12}a_0$$

where a_0 is the usual first central difference of Woolhouse's notation; so that

$$\log_{10} {}_5p_x = -\,\kappa \cdot m_x^{\left(\frac{1}{5}\right)}\left(1 + \frac{a_0}{12}\right)$$

where κ is the modulus. (2) These values may now be graduated, if desired, or intermediate graduated quinquennial values may be obtained by interpolation.

   (3) Calculate

$$e_x^{\left(\frac{1}{5}\right)} = 5\left\{\frac{l_{x+5} + l_{x+10} + \dots}{l_x}\right\}$$

by the continuous formula

$$\log\left[\tfrac{1}{5}e_x^{\left(\frac{1}{5}\right)}\right] = \log {}_5p_x + \log\left[1 + \tfrac{1}{5}e_{x+5}^{\left(\frac{1}{5}\right)}\right].$$

   (4) Obtain

$$e_x = \frac{\displaystyle\sum_1^\infty l_{x+t}}{l_x}$$

_____

should be noted that $m_x^{\left(\frac{1}{5}\right)} = 5({}_5m_x)$. The basic relation in (1) of this paragraph is also deduced in R.A.I.A., XXXII, 34–36, in terms of ${}_nm_x$.

by Woolhouse's formula for approximate summation (see Freeman, *op. cit.*, 195, and King's Text-Book, Part II, formula (27) on p. 478) which gives

$$\frac{5}{l_x}(l_{x+5} + l_{x+10} + \ldots) + 2 + 2\frac{dl_x}{dx} = e_x^{(\frac{1}{2})} + 2 - 2\mu_x,$$

in which μ_x is taken as approximately

$$\frac{l_{x-5} - l_{x+5}}{10 l_x} = \frac{1}{10}({}_5p_{x-5}^{-1} - {}_5p_x).$$

The numerical work by this method is very convenient, as may be seen from the examples in J.I.A., XLVIII, 302–3.

134. (v) *Reed and Merrell's Method*

This method was published originally in the American Journal of Hygiene, XXX (No. 2, September, 1939), 33, and was reprinted in the U.S. Census Bureau's Vital Statistics Special Reports, IX, No. 54. It again utilizes a formula connecting ${}_5p_x$ and ${}_5m_x$, and (as shown by T. N. E. Greville's examination of its mathematical basis in R.A.I.A., XXXII, 29–43) it is in fact closely related* to Method (*iv*) here.

Denoting $l_x - l_{x+5}$ by ${}_5d_x$, and $T_x - T_{x+5}$ by ${}_5L_x$,

and since by definition ${}_5m_x$ is $\dfrac{{}_5d_x}{{}_5L_x}$,

and as also we have the relation

$$_5m_x = -\frac{1}{{}_5L_x}\left(\frac{d_5L_x}{dx}\right)$$

as for m_x and L_x, it follows that

$$_5d_x = {}_5L_x \cdot {}_5m_x = -\frac{d}{dx}({}_5L_x),$$

and the Euler-Maclaurin summation formula then gives

$$l_x = \sum_{h=0}^{\infty} {}_5d_{x+5h} = {}_5L_x\left\{\tfrac{1}{5} + \tfrac{1}{2}({}_5m_x) + \tfrac{5}{12}\left[{}_5m_x^2 - \frac{d}{dx}({}_5m_x)\right] + \ldots\right\} \quad (66)$$

since

$$-\frac{d}{dx}({}_5L_x \cdot {}_5m_x) = {}_5L_x\left[{}_5m_x^2 - \frac{d}{dx}({}_5m_x)\right].$$

Now colog ${}_5p_x = \log l_x - \log l_{x+5}$; expanding the logarithm of the expression in braces in (66), noting that $l_{x+5} = l_x - {}_5L_x \cdot {}_5m_x$, and simplifying,

---

* For this reason the method is included in this Section as Method (*v*), although actually it was published later than Methods (*vi*) and (*vii*).

we obtain (cf. also R.A.I.A., XXXII, 34–36)

$$\operatorname{colog}_e \, _5p_x = 5 \, (_5m_x) + \frac{125}{12} \, (_5m_x) \frac{d}{dx} \, (_5m_x) + \dots \qquad (67)$$

If it is further assumed (cf. pars. 97 and 133) that

$$_5m_x = \mu_{x+\frac{5}{2}} = B \, c^{x+\frac{5}{2}}$$

approximately by Gompertz's formula, it follows that $\dfrac{d}{dx} \, (_5m_x) = k \, (_5m_x)$ approximately where $k = \log_e c$. Substituting this value in (67) gives finally the basic formula of Reed and Merrell's method

$$\operatorname{colog}_e \, _5p_x = 5 \, (_5m_x) + 125 \, a \, (_5m_x)^2 \qquad \text{where} \qquad a = \frac{k}{12}. \qquad (68)$$

By fitting curves based on this explanation to 33 of Glover's 1910 life tables, they arrived at the value .008 for a, and on that basis published tables showing the values of $_nq_x$ over a wide range of $_nm_x$ for $n = 5$ and 10.

With these values an abridged life table can be constructed "in less than two hours," and the results are usually sufficiently accurate for most practical purposes (see R.A.I.A., XXXII, 38).

135. (*vi*) *E. C. Snow's Method*

This method was published, with a great number of examples, in Part II of the 75th Annual Report of the Registrar-General of England and Wales (see also J.I.A., LII, 393, and J.A.S.A., XVII, 1025). The first assumption is that in any sectional population $_np_x$ can be expressed as a function of the observed death rate $_nm_x$ (the ratio of deaths to population between ages x and $x + n$)—the constants in the assumed relation being determined from those which were found to exist for the whole of England and Wales in 1910–12 for similar values of $_nm_x$ (not necessarily for the same age group). At ages under 10, p_0 was found to be given with sufficient accuracy for the purposes in view as unity less the "infantile mortality rate" $\left(i. \, e., \, 1 - \dfrac{D_0^z}{E_0^z} \right)$ as frequently given in Medical Officers' reports (see footnote, par. 79); p_1 was expressed as $k + l \left(\dfrac{2 - m_1}{2 + m_1} \right)$; and $_3p_2$ and $_5p_5$ were calculated by the relation $_np_x = f - g_n m_x$. At ages over 10 the quadratic form $_np_x = d + c(_nm_x - e)^2$ was used with quinquennial or decennial age groups; and at the final ages above 85 the type adopted was $\log \, _np_x = a - b_n m_x$. Having found $_np_x$ from the observed $_nm_x$ by this method, the column l_x at the available age intervals then followed directly. In order now to pass to $\mathring{e}_x$, the sums of l in the corresponding intervals were assumed to be expressible similarly in terms of $_np_x$—the relations being of the form

$$\frac{N'_{\overline{xn}}}{l_x} = a + b\,(_np_x)$$

for intervals 2–5* and 5–10, while at higher ages the same form, or a constant relation, or the quadratic $d' + c'(e' \pm _np_x)^2$ was used according to the range of $_np_x$. Finally N'_x was found by summing $N'_{\overline{xn}}$, and $\overset{\circ}{e}_x$ followed at once.†

In the report previously mentioned some 280 abridged tables for different parts of England and Wales were constructed by this method. The calculations were greatly facilitated by the tabulation of the values of $_np_x$ and $_nk_x$ corresponding to $_nm_x$ and $_np_x$ respectively for usual ranges, thus providing a simple procedure by which a very accurate abridged table can be constructed "in three or four hours." The method was also used to compute quinquennial values of $\overset{\circ}{e}_x$ for Northern Ireland in 1891, 1901, and 1911 (see the Registrar-General's Review of Vital Statistics of Northern Ireland and Life Tables 1926, p. 57). Those preliminary tabulations, however, were necessarily preceded by a great amount of experimentation; and as they may not be applicable to populations of other times or places the method would hardly be applicable to other cases without considerable investigation.

136. (*vii*) *Construction by Reference to a Standard Table*

(*a*) This process was given in J.I.A., LII, 396, and is in effect a simplification of the J.I.A. method of par. 133. As in that method the relation used to give colog p from the m's by age groups is

$$\text{colog}_{10}\,_np_x = \kappa\, m_x^{\left(\frac{1}{n}\right)} \left(1 + \frac{a_0}{12}\right).$$

---

* In the description given here, N' as now prescribed by the new international notation is adopted instead of the former open-faced letter used by Snow and the actuaries of his day. For interval $1 - 2$, $\dfrac{N'_{\overline{xn}}}{l_x}$ necessarily $= 1$. Snow denoted $\dfrac{N'_{\overline{xn}}}{l_x}$ by $_nk_x$.

† In determining $\overset{\circ}{e}_0$ the usual $\dfrac{N'_x}{l_x} - \frac{1}{2}$, which at higher ages can be applied continuously in the form $\overset{\circ}{e}_x = \left(\dfrac{N'_{x+1} + l_x}{l_x}\right) - \frac{1}{2}$, was modified in the first year of age to allow for the uneven distributions of deaths therein, in accordance with the formulae for L_0 in par. 93(*ii*) here.

Denoting functions of the table under construction by dashes, and those of a standard table without dashes, it therefore follows that

$$\operatorname{colog} {}_n p'_x = \operatorname{colog} {}_n p_x \left\{ \frac{m'^{\left(\frac{1}{n}\right)}\left(1+\frac{a'_0}{12}\right)}{m^{\left(\frac{1}{n}\right)}\left(1+\frac{a_0}{12}\right)} \right\}.$$

In order now to pass from ${}_n p'_x$ so found to $\mathring{e}_x$ the relation employed was

$$\left(\tfrac{1}{2} + {}_1 p_x + \dots + {}_{t-1} p_x + \tfrac{1}{2}\, {}_t p_x\right) = \frac{t}{2}\left(1 + {}_t p_x\right) + \frac{t^2-1}{12}\left({}_t p_x \mu_{x+t} - \mu_x\right)$$

by Woolhouse's formula for approximate summation (see Freeman, *loc. cit.*, and formula (26), p. 478, of King's Text-Book), from which

$$\left(\tfrac{1}{2} + {}_1 p'_x + \dots + {}_{t-1} p'_x + \tfrac{1}{2}\, {}_t p'_x\right) = \left(\tfrac{1}{2} + {}_1 p_x + \dots + {}_{t-1} p_x + \tfrac{1}{2}\, {}_t p_x\right)$$
$$+ \frac{t}{2}\left[\left(1 + {}_t p'_x\right) - \left(1 + {}_t p_x\right)\right]$$

approximately; and from the values calculated by this formula $\mathring{e}_x$ follows by the continuous formula

$$\mathring{e}_x = \left(\tfrac{1}{2} + p_x + \dots + {}_{t-1} p_x + \tfrac{1}{2}\, {}_t p_x\right) + {}_t p_x \mathring{e}_{x+t}.$$

This method is very rapid and convenient, as may be seen from the example given in J.I.A., LII, 396.

(b) A further simplification in the method of construction by reference to a standard table has been introduced in the preparation of the abridged life tables for whites and non-whites by sex which since 1945 have been published each year for the United States by the National Office of Vital Statistics (see the United States Abridged Life Tables, 1945, by T. N. E. Greville, in Vital Statistics Special Reports, National Office of Vital Statistics, XXIII, No. 11, for a discussion of the assumptions involved, and Part I of the annual volume "Vital Statistics of the United States"). If the death rates by ages in the standard table and in the table under construction are known to be very close, it may be assumed with sufficient accuracy that

$$_n q'_x = {}_n q_x \cdot \frac{{}_n m'_x}{{}_n m_x}.$$

The l'_x values are then constructed on the basis of the figures so found, and $_nL'_x$ is calculated from the approximate relation

$$_nL'_x = {_nL_x} \cdot \frac{l'_x + l'_{x+n}}{l_x + l_{x+n}}.$$

The results are then summed to give T'_x, and $\overset{\circ}{e}_x$ follows from division by l'_x. In these abridged U.S. tables the values of q_0 employed are found by formula (18a) here (see also par. 79).

IX

METHODS OF COMPARING THE MORTALITIES
OF DIFFERENT COMMUNITIES*

137. As stated in par. 129 it is not necessary to proceed beyond the determination of reliable values of q_x or m_x at each age in order to compare the mortalities of different communities—for by that method the exact nature and extent of the differences in mortality may be observed, not only at the several age periods of life, but also as between the male and female sexes. Such comparisons at each age, however, are somewhat laborious; and a more compact method, which also has the advantage that it partially eliminates accidental errors when the ungraduated rates are employed, is therefore to compare the probability of dying over 5 (or 10) year age-periods by using $|_5 q_x$ (or $|_{10} q_x$). The use of such values, however, necessitates either the construction of a life table or the calculation of log $_n p_x$ by the short formula of pars. 133 and 136.

138. In order to employ the original data without the preliminary construction of an extended or abridged life table, therefore, several more compact measures, in the nature of index-numbers, have become widely used. Of these, the first was the *crude death rate*, which is merely the ratio of the deaths at all ages to the population at all ages. The crude rate for males may thus be written symbolically as $\dfrac{\Sigma d^m}{\Sigma P^m}$ where the Σ denotes the sum (of the male deaths d^m or of the male populations P^m) at each age (or age group). This may be written also as

$$\frac{\Sigma (P^m q^m)}{\Sigma (P^m)} \tag{69}$$

where q^m is the rate of mortality $\dfrac{d^m}{P^m}$. Similarly the crude female rate is

$$\frac{\Sigma (d^f)}{\Sigma (P^f)}, \quad \text{or} \quad \frac{\Sigma (P^f q^f)}{\Sigma (P^f)} \tag{70}$$

and the crude "persons" rate is

$$\frac{\Sigma (d^p)}{\Sigma (P^p)}, \quad \text{or} \quad \frac{\Sigma (P^p q^p)}{\Sigma (P^p)} \tag{71}$$

* This section is largely founded on H. H. Wolfenden's paper in J.R.S.S., LXXXVI, 399, "On the Methods of Comparing the Mortalities of Two or More Communities, and the Standardization of Death-Rates." The notation which was there used as being most convenient for the purposes in view is retained here.

where of course $d^p = d^m + d^f$, $P^p = P^m + P^f$, and $q^p = \dfrac{d^p}{P^p}$. This formula may also clearly be written as

$$\frac{\Sigma (d^m + d^f)}{\Sigma (P^m + P^f)}, \qquad \text{or} \qquad \frac{\Sigma (P^m q^m + P^f q^f)}{\Sigma (P^m + P^f)}. \qquad (72)$$

These two forms (71) and (72) are identical, and, of course, give the same numerical results.

These crude rates are the weighted averages of the death rates at the various ages, where the weight is taken as the population P of the particular community. Such rates are clearly unsatisfactory and misleading; for two communities with exactly the same rates of mortality at each age, but with different relative values of P, may show radically different crude death-rates, on account only of the different values of P, that is, by reason solely of the fact that the two communities have different age and sex constitutions.

Although the crude death rate is usually stated for all ages from birth, it may, of course, also be computed similarly for ages above any age x. Also, instead of being founded upon the original population data, as is usually the case, the graduated data as derived from the life table may be used; and in that case the crude death rate above age x becomes

$$\frac{d_x + d_{x+1} + \dots}{L_x + L_{x+1} + \dots} \qquad \text{or} \qquad \frac{d_x + d_{x+1} + \dots}{l_x + l_{x+1} + \dots}$$

according as the central death rate $\dfrac{d_x}{L_x}$ or the probability of dying $\dfrac{d_x}{l_x}$, as found from the life table, is used as the basis. In the first form above (sometimes referred to as the "life-table death-rate") it has attained some prominence—because, being $\dfrac{l_x}{T_x}$, it is the reciprocal of $\overset{\circ}{e}_x$. It must therefore be noted that all the above crude rates, including this "life-table death-rate" and its reciprocal $\overset{\circ}{e}_x$, are weighted averages in which the weights are derived from the data of the particular community under examination. The weights used in the crude rate (69), for example, are the original P's, and those used in the life-table death-rate $\dfrac{l_x}{T_x}$ and $\overset{\circ}{e}_x$ are the L's of the life table. The rates (69)–(72) are thus dependent on the particular original age (and sex) constitution of the community under examination, as shown by its P's—such constitution resulting from the particular birth, death, and migration rates which the community has experienced. The "life-table death-rate" and $\overset{\circ}{e}_x$ are similarly dependent on the particular age (and sex) constitution of the community as shown by the L's of the life table—those L's resulting from the particular death rates of the community under examination. In none of these cases, therefore, are the weights independent of the particular community. Consequently, if, say, the actual mortality rates in one community are double those in another, the crude rate and the life-table death-rate will not necessarily (or usually) be doubled. Comparisons of such rates may therefore frequently lead to erroneous conclusions (cf. J.R.S.S., LXXXV, "Discussion on the Value of Life-Tables in Statistical Research," pp. 544–46, 552–54, and 555; J.I.A., LII, 395; and T.A.S.A., XXXV, 281–82).

139. The foregoing defect in the crude rate as a weighted average may be remedied by the employment of a system of weights which are independent of the age and sex constitutions of the particular community. Consequently the Registrar-General of England and Wales in 1883 introduced the *standardized death rate*. The *direct* method of computing such a standardized rate is to take a standard population, and to apply to this standard population the death rates, at the various ages and sexes, of the particular community; and then, by dividing the deaths so computed by the standard population, to deduce the "standardized death rate" which would emerge if the mortality rates of the particular community were to prevail in the population of standard age and sex constitution.

The proper formulae for these standardized rates so as to maintain any fundamental relationships which may exist between q^m, q^f, and q^p are shown in the paper referred to in the footnote at the commencement of this section to be

$$
\left.
\begin{array}{l}
\text{Standardized male rate ,} \quad \dfrac{\Sigma\,(P_s^p q^m)}{\Sigma\,(P_s^p)} \\[3ex]
\text{Standardized female rate ,} \quad \dfrac{\Sigma\,(P_s^p q^f)}{\Sigma\,(P_s^p)} \\[3ex]
\text{Standardized "persons" rate ,} \quad \dfrac{\Sigma\,(P_s^m q^m + P_s^f q^f)}{\Sigma\,(P_s^m + P_s^f)}
\end{array}
\right\} \quad (73)
$$

where P_s^m, P_s^f, and P_s^p $(= P_s^m + P_s^f)$ are the standard male, female, and persons populations.

This is the system used since 1913 by the Registrar-General of England and Wales. It was also adopted in the U.S. Census Bureau's Report on "Mortality Rates, 1910–1920" and in some of the annual reports, and in the Canadian reports on Vital Statistics. These "directly standardized" rates, being absolutely independent of the age and sex distributions of the particular community, may be compared with confidence.

140. In numerical applications of this method the distributions of the

standard population obviously should be reasonable, for otherwise undue importance would be given to the death rates of the particular community at those ages where the standard population might be abnormally large. The standard which has been employed widely is that of England and Wales in 1901, because there are practical advantages for purposes of comparison in retaining the same standard as long as possible. That 1901 population has relatively few infants and old people; other standards have therefore been suggested (see T.A.S.A., XVIII, 280), of which one of the most important is that recommended by the International Statistical Institute and composed of the populations of a number of European countries in 1900 or 1901. In order to reflect the considerable change which has occurred since 1901 in the age distribution of the standard population of that date, the Registrar-General of England and Wales in 1940 introduced a *Comparative Mortality Index*, which for any year z is the ratio of the standardized rate for year z to the standardized rate for 1938 when both those rates are based on the mean of the age distributions of the years 1938 and z (see the "Registrar-General's Statistical Review of England and Wales for the Six Years 1940–1945," published in 1949 as a review for the whole six years in consequence of the disturbances due to the war).

In connection with this problem of choosing an appropriate standard population, it is essential to remember that directly standardized rates are really index-numbers which are constructed only for purposes of comparison, so that no significance is to be attached to their absolute magnitudes; the main characteristic of the standard population consequently should be that it is not unnatural or clearly abnormal. In practice it will be found that various standard populations chosen within reason have insignificant effects upon the inferences to be drawn from comparisons of directly standardized rates for different geographical areas at all ages from all causes (see, for an example, the Census Bureau's "Vital Statistics in the United States, 1900–1940," by F. E. Linder and R. D. Grove, pp. 80–81). Care, however, must of course be taken in drawing inferences from comparisons of standardized rates in respect of subdivisions of a general population, e.g., for certain causes of death or occupations, in which the age distributions of the populations exposed to risk may show peculiar characteristics sharply different from any normal general population—see Sections XI and XII here.

141. The work of calculating and applying the death rates of the particular community in the "direct" method of par. 139 is considerable if, as is usual, it has to be done for a great number of districts (see, for example, the numerical illustration in Newsholme's "Vital Statistics," p. 228). An

approximate *indirect* method has therefore been devised by the Registrar-General's office which does not necessitate the calculation and use of the death rates of the particular community at each age (or age-group). In this method an "Index Death Rate" is first calculated, being that crude death rate which would be shown by the population of the district if the mortality of the standard prevailed therein. That is, "Index Death Rate" =

$$\frac{\Sigma\,[\,(\text{Population of District}) \times (\text{Death Rate of Standard})\,]}{\text{Total Population of District}}\,.$$

A "standardizing factor," being

$$\frac{\text{Index Death Rate of Standard}}{\text{Index Death Rate of District}}$$

that is,

$$\frac{\text{Crude Death Rate of Standard}}{\substack{\text{Crude Death Rate of District which would be shown if standard}\\ \text{rates prevailed therein}}}$$

is now computed—this factor giving a measure of the extent to which the crude rate for the district is affected by variations in age distribution shown by its population as compared with the standard population. Therefore, multiplying the crude death rate of the district by this standardizing factor, a death rate for the district is found as would appear if the age distribution of the district were the same as the age distribution of the standard.

This indirect method is applied in the reports of the Registrar-General mainly in the presentation of "persons" death rates—the separate male and female rates not being given, because the persons rate may be considered to give the most comprehensive single figure for the rapid comparison of one district with another. The formula so used for the "persons" rate is

$$\underbrace{\frac{\Sigma\,(P^m q^m + P^f q^f)}{\Sigma\,(P^m + P^f)}}_{\substack{\text{Crude}\\ \text{"persons"}\\ \text{rate of}\\ \text{community}}} \times \underbrace{\frac{\Sigma\,(P_s^m q_s^m + P_s^f q_s^f)}{\Sigma\,(P_s^m + P_s^f)}}_{\substack{\text{"Persons"}\\ \text{rate of}\\ \text{standard}}} \times \underbrace{\frac{\Sigma\,(P^m + P^f)}{\Sigma\,(P^m q_s^m + P^f q_s^f)}}_{\substack{\text{Reciprocal of}\\ \text{index "persons"}\\ \text{death rate}\\ \text{of community}}}\,. \quad (74)$$

$$\underbrace{\phantom{\frac{\Sigma\,(P_s^m q_s^m + P_s^f q_s^f)}{\Sigma\,(P_s^m + P_s^f)} \times \frac{\Sigma\,(P^m + P^f)}{\Sigma\,(P^m q_s^m + P^f q_s^f)}}}_{\text{Standardizing Factor}}$$

A numerical example of its application may be found on p. 229 of Newsholme's "Vital Statistics." Its rationale and limitations, and the formulae for the separate "indirect" standardizations of the male and female rates, are deduced by H. H. Wolfenden in J.R.S.S., LXXXVI, 408–10 (see footnote at commencement of this Section).

The method is an approximation only, and is not completely independent of the age and sex distributions of the community as is the direct method; the validity of its basic assumptions should therefore be tested numerically—especially in important cases—prior to its extensive application (see Wolfenden, *op. cit.*, p. 408 and footnote). It should be noted also, as pointed out in T.A.S.A., XVIII, 279, that comparisons of indirectly standardized rates lead to the same conclusions as the method of comparing the ratios of actual to expected deaths, since formula (74) can be expressed as (Crude Rate of Standard) × [(Actual Deaths of Community) ÷ (Expected Deaths of Community by Standard)].

X

THE FORECASTING OF MORTALITY RATES

142. In par. 64 the explanation and mathematical relationships were stated by which the deaths D_x^z in the year of age x to $x+1$, which occur in the calendar year z, arise from the births of the calendar years $z - x - 1$ and $z - x$. In order now to keep this time of birth clearly in view, it will be convenient simply to add to D_x^z the symbol y to identify the time of birth, so that the D_x^z deaths will be more fully visualized by $^y D_x^z$; that is to say, $^y D_x^z$ will denote the deaths aged x last birthday (i.e., in the year of age x to $x+1$) which occur in the calendar year z and were born at time y (being in fact the calendar years $z - x - 1$ and $z - x$).

Correspondingly, $^y q_x^z$ will denote the probability of death in the year of age x to $x+1$, as observed in the calendar year z with respect to those who were born at time y (being the calendar years $z - x - 1$ and $z - x$). If, therefore, we have available the data of a long series of calendar years $n, n+1, n+2, \ldots$ (but have no data for any earlier years except with respect to the births in year $n - 1$ which are required to determine $^n q_0^n$), so that the values $^y q_x^z$ at all ages have been computed for each of those calendar years, a complete tabulation of the results could be presented in a table of the following form:

YEAR OF AGE x TO $x+1$	CALENDAR YEAR OF OBSERVATION z					
	n	$n+1$	$n+2$	$n+3$	$n+4$	$\ldots$
0	$^n q_0^n$	$^{n+1}q_0^{n+1}$	$^{n+2}q_0^{n+2}$	$^{n+3}q_0^{n+3}$	$^{n+4}q_0^{n+4}$	$\ldots$
1		$^n q_1^{n+1}$	$^{n+1}q_1^{n+2}$	$^{n+2}q_1^{n+3}$	$^{n+3}q_1^{n+4}$	$\ldots$
2			$^n q_2^{n+2}$	$^{n+1}q_2^{n+3}$	$^{n+2}q_2^{n+4}$	$\ldots$
3				$^n q_3^{n+3}$	$^{n+1}q_3^{n+4}$	$\ldots$
4					$^n q_4^{n+4}$	$\ldots$
.						$\ldots$
.						$\ldots$
.						$\ldots$

143. From this table the values of q with respect to age, year of observation, and year of birth can be followed in three ways:

(1) By taking the *rows*, the values such as $^n q_0^n$, $^{n+1}q_0^{n+1}$, $^{n+2}q_0^{n+2}$, $\ldots$, for age 0, or $^n q_1^{n+1}$, $^{n+1}q_1^{n+2}$, $^{n+2}q_1^{n+3}$, $\ldots$, for age 1, and so on, show the

189

variation for a constant age according to time (the year of observation). The births took place in different years.

(2) By taking the *columns*, the values such as $^{n+4}q_0^{n+4}$, $^{n+3}q_1^{n+4}$, $^{n+2}q_2^{n+4}$, ..., for the constant year of observation $n + 4$ show the variation according to age for a constant year of observation (time). The births again took place in different years.

(3) By taking the *diagonals*, the values $^nq_0^n$, $^nq_1^{n+1}$, $^nq_2^{n+2}$, ..., for the constant time of birth n show the variation according to age and time (year of observation). The births here took place in the same years.

Of these three procedures, method (1) gives in each row an apparently simple view of the variation of the mortality of a given age according to time; the time element, however, which is thus implicit in each value varies according to both the year of observation and the year of birth, so that each row shows in reality the manner in which the q of a particular age is influenced by the generation from which it originally arose and also by the calendar year in which the deaths occurred.

Method (2) is of course the usual process of using a fixed calendar year (or often in practice several consecutive calendar years) as the period of observation in which to determine values of q_x for the various ages; but although the time of observation is thus fixed, it will be seen that the deaths at the various ages, having been born at different times, are in fact the survivors from different generations.

Method (3), however, sets out with the people born only at time n, and follows them through successive years of age as they pass through the corresponding years of observation; and as it thus deals with the mortality history of the particular generation born at time n, it has been called the *generation* method.

144. These concepts are important when, having ascertained the values of $^vq_x^z$, we consider their applicability in some future calendar year. For, if mortality is continually changing over time, it evidently may be advisable to "forecast" the values of q_x to be anticipated in future years, before applying them to the long-range prediction of populations (cf. the remarks in par. 63(iv) here), or in other demographic or financial estimations. In order thus to forecast, for example, a value for q_{30} in some future calendar year $n + m$, it will be clear from the preceding table that we could use (i) the values of q_{30} along the row—in which case extrapolation to the right of the complete table to the year $n + m$ would predict q_{30}^{n+m} from known values of q_{30} for past calendar years which have been influenced by (a) year of observation and (b) year of birth, although no means are available for measuring the relative importance of (a) and (b). By (ii) proceeding down the columns, no extrapolation for the future

year $n + m$ can be made, since the year of observation does not vary in the column. Finally, (*iii*) following the diagonals, the unknown q_{30}^{n+m} could be predicted by extrapolation to the southeast of the table. Here extrapolation from the diagonal for time of birth n (i.e., the lowest diagonal appearing in the table) would give q_{30}^{n+30}; from the next higher diagonal for the generation born at time $n + 1$ an extrapolation would provide q_{30}^{n+31}; the next diagonal for $n + 2$ would produce q_{30}^{n+32}; and so on. A value for the specific year $n + m$, if desired, would then be determined from the series q_{30}^{n+30}, q_{30}^{n+31}, q_{30}^{n+32}, ...

145. Applications of these principles to population mortality have been considered in a number of papers. In his "Mathematical Theory of Population" (Appendix A, 1911 Census of Australia), p. 380, Knibbs advocated the construction of "fluent" life tables which would recognize the type of trend shown by method (1). In Britain, at about the same time that the problem was receiving close attention with respect to the forecasting of mortality rates for annuitants,* V. P. A. Derrick ("Observations on (1) Errors of Age in the Population Statistics of England and Wales, and (2) Changes in Mortality Indicated by the National Records," J.I.A., LVIII, 117) examined the graphs of the national mortality rates for a number of age groups over the years from 1846 to 1923, and then replotted the values by year of birth as in method (3); and since the latter were to some extent roughly parallel, the suggestion was raised that the year of birth may have an influence upon the mortality shown by its generation in future years.

Subsequently W. O. Kermack, A. G. McKendrick, and P. L. McKinlay (in two papers on "Death Rates in Great Britain and Sweden," The Lancet, 1934, 698, and The Journal of Hygiene, XXXIV, 433), again supposing that mortality is dependent on the attained age and the time of birth, assumed that mortality rates could be expressed approximately as the product of two functions related respectively to the attained age and the generation, so that $^{v}q_{x}^{z}$ could be examined in the form

---

* The principal references to be consulted on this allied subject would be: "The Mortality of Annuitants, 1900–1920," by W. P. Elderton and H. J. P. Oakley (The Institute of Actuaries); "Forecasting Mortality," by W. P. Elderton (Skandinavisk Aktuarietidskrift, 1932, 45); "Mortality Experience of Government Life Annuitants, 1900–1920," by Sir A. W. Watson and H. Weatherill (of which a résumé appears in J.I.A., LV, 144); "On the Calculation of Rates of Mortality," by A. R. Davidson and A. R. Reid (T.F.A., XI, 183); discussions of the forecasts from the British offices and British Government life annuitants' investigations of 1900–1920 to be found in J.I.A., LIII, 243, and LIV, 43; and "A New Mortality Basis for Annuities," by W. A. Jenkins and E. A. Lew (T.S.A., I, 369), which includes comments on many of the analyses considered in this Section.

$Q\,(x)\cdot R(x - t)$ where $Q(x)$ is a function of the age alone and $R(x - t)$ is a generation function based on the mortality t years before at age $x - t$.

If the ratios $\dfrac{^{v+n}q_x^{z+n}}{q_x^z}$ on this hypothesis are then computed from known values of q, the age function $Q(x)$ disappears, and the trends of the resulting ratios of the R's can be used for an arithmetical forecasting of values for future years. This method was discussed further by M. Greenwood, who commended its simplicity and its consequent possibilities as a method for short forecasts (see his "English Death Rates—Past, Present, and Future," J.R.S.S., XCIX, 674). Later E. C. Rhodes adopted a logistic (see par. 63(*iii*) here) to represent the generation function R, and applied the consequent theory with results which were in substantial agreement with those reached arithmetically by Kermack and his co-authors; Rhodes merely claimed, however, that his investigations showed the reasonableness of the hypothesis that mortality might be represented by the form $Q\,(x)\cdot R\,(x - t)$, and he specifically warned against the use of his results for extrapolation (see his paper on "Secular Changes in Death Rates," J.R.S.S., CIV, 15).

Logistic curves were also illustrated in Greenwood's paper (*loc. cit.*) as a means of representing, for several ages x, the series of $^{v}q_x^z$ values along the rows as in method (1). In another paper by H. Cramér and H. Wold ("Mortality Variations in Sweden; A Study in Graduation and Forecasting," Skandinavisk Aktuarietidskrift, 1935, 161), Makeham's formula was employed to represent, by separate fittings, both the mortality rates down the columns as in method (2), and those along the diagonals as in method (3); the series of Makeham constants so found for the "period" mortality rates of the various columns were then graduated by using logistics for log c and β and straight lines for α, and the "generation" constants derived from the diagonals were graduated similarly; and finally the "period" and "generation" values were used to give forecast values of μ_x for six decennial ages.*

These various methods have been compared by A. H. Pollard in a paper on "Methods of Forecasting Mortality Using Australian Data" in J.I.A., LXXV, 151, and comments on many of the analyses considered in this Section may be found in the paper by Jenkins and Lew previously noted.

---

* In this paper by Cramér and Wold, a valuable list of additional references on mortality forecasting is given, and the methods of fitting the Makeham and logistic curves (as epitomized in "The Fundamental Principles of Mathematical Statistics," pp. 327 and 331) are noteworthy.

XI

MORTALITY BY CAUSE OF DEATH

146. In analyzing statistical data with respect to cause of death, it will be evident that the first essential step must be the classification and grouping of the many medical terms by which the various causes are described on the death certificates, and the evolution of a practicable method for allocation into groups according to some standard pattern which will afford reasonable comparabilities and at the same time will deal effectively with the distinctions between primary and contributory causes (see par. 22). The complexities of this problem have been dealt with by the gradual development of the "International List of Causes of Death," which was originated at the First Statistical Congress in 1853 at Brussels (when Dr. William Farr and Dr. Marc d'Espine were appointed to prepare a plan for international agreement), and after several revisions was presented to the International Statistical Institute in 1893 by Dr. Jacques Bertillon. The List has since been revised about every ten years at international conferences in Paris in order to give effect to advances in medical practice and changes in terminology. It was first used by a few countries in 1893, and has now been adopted officially by almost all countries which maintain national statistical offices.

The latest revision—the sixth—which was adopted at Paris in 1948 and in the same year was recommended and published by the World Health Organization in Geneva, made an important change by enlarging the former list of causes of death into a comprehensive "International Statistical Classification of Diseases, Injuries, and Causes of Death," and thus for the first time provided a uniform basis for the classification of both mortality and morbidity statistics (see also par. 182 here). In the United States the National Office of Vital Statistics commenced to use this revision on January 1, 1949, together with the new death certificate (par. 22) which also follows the international recommendation of the World Health Assembly. The classification has 612 categories of diseases and morbid conditions, 153 categories for external causes of injury, and 189 categories covering injuries according to the nature of the lesion. An abridged "Intermediate List" of 150 causes of morbidity and mortality was also published for age and other population studies, and an "Abbreviated List" of 50 causes of death was proposed for tabulations of mortality and for the purposes of public health administration. The two-volume Manual covering this revision includes rules for classification and an alphabetical index of medical terms for coding medical records and death certifications.

These Sixth Revision lists thus now replace the several versions of the "Detailed International List," the "Abridged International List," and "The Short List of the Registrar-General" of England and Wales to which many references will be found in the literature prior to 1949. The periodical changes which have occurred in the various revisions have produced difficulties, of course, in the attempt to compute statistics which would be comparable over successive decennia; in the Registrar-General's "Statistical Review of England and Wales for the Six Years 1940–1945," for example, the Fifth Revision of 1938 had produced such disturbances that dual tabulations of deaths were made according to the new and old procedures, and conversion factors were calculated for application to the deaths and death-rates prior to 1939 in order to make them comparable to tabulations by the new classification. Special studies of the effects of changing to the new list when a revision is made have also been undertaken by the U.S. Bureau of the Census (see "Vital Statistics Rates in the United States, 1900–1940," by F. E. Linder and R. D. Grove, pp. 18–26). The conference on the Sixth Revision also recommended that deaths in 1949 or 1950 should be coded according to both the sixth and fifth revisions, with dual tabulations to indicate the character and extent of the changes.

147. One of the most difficult problems encountered in classifying deaths by cause arises from the essential statements on the death certificates with respect to "immediate" and "contributory (secondary)" causes, whence the primary cause under which each death shall be tabulated must be determined for statistical purposes. (The terms just stated are those used, with variations, on the death certificates of Great Britain, Canada, and the United States prior to the recommendations of the sixth revision conference.) The main objective is to place upon the physician the responsibility for stating the causes of death in such a manner that the primary cause can thence be determined satisfactorily and the deaths tabulated accordingly. The importance and complexity of the problem may be judged from the fact that, in countries where medical practice is most advanced, from 33% to about 70% of all death certificates show multiple causes (see H. L. Dunn, "The Evaluation of the Effect upon Mortality Statistics of the Selection of the Primary Cause of Death," J.A.S.A., XXXI, 116; the U.S. Census Bureau's Vital Statistics Special Report No. 47, Vol. V; and Linder and Grove, *op. cit.*, pp. 21–23).

It must be remembered, also, that the determination of the underlying cause amongst a number of possibly contributory causes is often a baffling problem for even an experienced physician, and that this difficulty is not lessened by the desires of registration officials to fit the ultimate decision into prescribed classes for statistical tabulations.

In Britain the primary cause for tabulation was settled by flexible rules until 1939; in 1940, however, rules were superseded by a new plan of selection based on acceptance of the certifying physician's opinion as to the underlying cause. In the United States between 1914 and 1949 the primary cause was determined from the death certificates then in use by a set of "priority tables," founded on general rules and many special decisions, which were published by the Census Bureau in several editions of the "Manual of Joint Causes of Death"—this inflexible system having the advantages of consistency and uniformity, but the weakness that it may disregard the physician's own indication as to the primary cause.

The British plan of accepting the physician's statement of the underlying cause led to its recommendation by the Sixth Revision conference and its adoption by the World Health Assembly. In accordance with those resolutions, therefore, the new 1949 United States death certificate (see par. 22) calls for (*i*) the disease or condition leading directly to death, (*ii*) antecedent causes, and (*iii*) other significant conditions. The intention of this phraseology is that the physician, as in Britain, shall thus show clearly his own determination of the underlying cause (under which the death would be tabulated statistically). The physician in this system consequently has "both a heavy responsibility and a great opportunity to make mortality statistics reflect the true frequencies of the underlying causes of death" (see the "Physicians' Handbook on Death and Birth Registration," 10th Edition, 1949, and also the 9th Edition of 1939 for the practices prior to 1949 and further comments on the advantages of the new plan).

With the cooperation of physicians in thus stating the underlying cause on the new certificate, it is anticipated that marked improvement will be seen in the reliability of the data and the facility with which they can be tabulated. Public health authorities also expect that the information thus secured will be more useful in the control and prevention of some of the initial causes.

148. In the periodical reports on vital statistics issued by government offices it is customary for practical purposes to state the death rate from any cause as the ratio of the deaths from that cause, by age groups and

sex, to the enumerated population for the area concerned, and then to institute comparisons between the rates so calculated.*

Crude rates, which do not take differing age and sex distributions into account, will of course be unsatisfactory, as explained in par. 138 (and T.A.S.A., XVIII, 275). In order to have a comprehensive method which will give a single mortality figure for each cause in each community and at the same time will be independent of the varying age and sex distributions, the process of direct standardization is frequently used (cf. the reports of the Registrar-General of England and Wales, and of the National Office of Vital Statistics—previously in the Bureau of the Census—in the United States, and J.I.A., XXXVI, 122–26).

149. Mortality tables analyzed by causes (or groups of causes) of death are sometimes constructed. Extensive tables of this kind were published by E. B. Nathan in T.F.A., X, 45, on the basis of the 1911 census of England and Wales and the deaths of 1911–12 for 20 main groups of causes. Similar calculations from the 1930 census of the United States and the deaths of that year have been made by L. I. Dublin, E. W. Kopf, and A. J. Lotka (published in part in the American Journal of Hygiene, VII, 299). Analyzed tables based on the 1940 U.S. census and the deaths of 1939–41 have been prepared jointly by the Statistical Bureau of the Metropolitan Life Insurance Company and the National Office of Vital Statistics.

The construction of such analyzed tables has been discussed by H. Wyss (in Mitteilungen der Vereinigung Schweizerischer Versicherungs-mathematiker, No. 22 [1927], 111) and M. N. Karn (Annals of Eugenics, IV, 279, and Biometrika, XXV, 91), and more fully by T. N. E. Greville

---

* For medical purposes the proportion of deaths to persons attacked by a particular disease is often used to indicate the degree of virulence, although it will give misleading results if the communities compared have dissimilar age and sex constitutions.

Another measure employed by some writers to estimate the relative magnitudes of the various causes of death is the proportion of deaths for each (or any) cause to the total deaths from all causes. This procedure, however, may be quite fallacious as a means of comparing the mortalities by cause in different communities (or even in the same community at different times), as may be seen clearly from the following illustration by Dr. Ransome: "Suppose a town of 100,000 with 2,000 annual deaths of which 500 are caused by phthisis. Here the general death-rate is 20 per 1,000; the death-rate from phthisis is 5 per 1,000 living and the deaths from phthisis form one-fourth of the total deaths. In another town having the same population the total deaths are 4,000, and therefore the death-rate is 40 per 1,000 inhabitants; the deaths from phthisis are 1,000 and therefore the death-rate from phthisis is 10 per 1,000; but the proportion of the phthisical to the total mortality is one-fourth as before. In the second town, therefore, there is by the latter test apparently no worse condition, so far as phthisis is concerned, than in the first, though matters are really twice as bad" (Newsholme's "Vital Statistics," 3rd Edn., pp. 186–87; and cf. the second footnote to par. 82 here).

in R.A.I.A., XXXVII, 283. Greville considers particularly the methods of preparing analyzed tables from data in 5-year age groups (cf. the principles stated in par. 129 here). Adopting the suggestion of Dublin, Kopf, and Lotka he proposes for n-year groups between ages x and $x + n$ the formula

$$_n d_x^i = \frac{_n D_x^i}{_n D_x} \, _n d_x \, ,$$

where D represents the actual death statistics and d the deaths in the mortality table, and i indicates the ith cause or group of causes of death.* He shows that this formula, while not strictly correct, may be expected to give very accurate results. Summing $_n d_x^i$ from age x to the end of the mortality tables gives values at corresponding intervals of l_x^i, namely, the number of survivors at age x who will eventually die from the ith cause.

150. The preparation of special mortality tables showing what the effect would be if a particular cause of death were eliminated completely has also received attention. For this purpose it is usual to assume that the various causes of death operate independently of each other. While this assumption may properly be criticized, it is not practicable to evaluate the degree of dependence between different causes of death, and the results obtained by its use are of considerable interest. As first pointed out by W. M. Makeham (J.I.A., XIII, 329, and XVIII, 317; see also H. H. Wolfenden's explanation in T.A.S.A., XLIII, 272–74), this assumption of independence gives rise to a law of composition of decremental forces under which the total force of mortality is the sum of the separate forces of mortality from the various causes of death.† It follows that the probabilities of survival must satisfy the relation

$$_n p_x = {_n p_x^{(-i)}} \, {_n p_x^{(i)}}$$

where the $(-i)$ refers to a mortality table in which all causes of death except the ith cause are operating, and the (i) refers to a table in which the ith cause alone is operating. Obviously $_n p_x^{(-i)}$ can be computed from the formula just given if the values of $_n p_x^{(i)}$ are known.

---

* This superscript i for cause of death is used here so that Greville's R.A.I.A. paper may be followed easily; it must not be confused, of course, with the superscript z which is employed throughout this Study to denote the calendar year (see par. 64).

† The theory of multiple decrement tables can be developed from the same point of view. This is brought out by Wolfenden in the reference cited, and also subsequently by C. J. Nesbitt and M. L. Van Eenam in R.A.I.A., XXVII, 202, and by W. G. Bailey and H. W. Haycocks in their recent pamphlet "Some Theoretical Aspects of Multiple Decrement Tables."

In making this computation by single years of age, Greville considered it satisfactory to assume (following a method used by Dublin and Lotka —see R.A.I.A., XXXVII, 292) that $q_x^{(i)}$ is equal to q_x^i, namely, the probability in the complete analyzed mortality table that a survivor at age x will die from the ith cause during the succeeding year. For data by 5-year age groups, however, this method was not sufficiently accurate; accordingly he developed the formula

$$\operatorname{colog}{}_n p_x^{(-i)} = \frac{{}_n D_x^{(-i)}}{{}_n D_x} \operatorname{colog}{}_n p_x$$

which has the advantage that the multiplication rule for probabilities of survival is satisfied automatically when ${}_n p_x^{(-i)}$ and ${}_n p_x^{(i)}$ are determined analogously.

In order to compute values of the expectation of life in the special mortality table from which the ith cause has been eliminated, Greville suggested calculating the required L's by the formula

$$_n L_x^{(-i)} = \frac{{}_n d_x^{(-i)}}{{}_n d_x^{-i}} {}_n L_x$$

where ${}_n d_x^{-i}$ are the deaths in the complete analyzed mortality table from all causes except the ith cause. He showed that, although the values of ${}_n L_x^{(-i)}$ are consistently overstated to a very slight extent, the resulting values of the expectation of life are not affected appreciably.

151. Reference has already been made in par. 148 to the deficiencies of crude death rates by cause as an over-all index of the relative importance of different causes of death. In public health administration it is often desirable to have an index which will indicate properly the relative importance of the different causes. Even standardized rates may be criticized on the ground that they do not reflect the greater loss to society in the death of a person in the prime of life as compared with that of an elderly person who in any case would have lived only a few years. For this reason certain measures based on "potential years of life lost" have recently been proposed. For example, one might take the deaths occurring in a certain calendar year from a given cause and multiply the deaths at each age by the expectation of life at that age. The sum of these products might be regarded as the aggregate potential years of life lost as a result of the operation of the given cause of death. Theoretically, the expectations of life used in this computation should be based on a special mortality table from which the given cause of death has been eliminated; F. G. Dickinson and E. L. Welker, however (in Bulletin 64, Bureau of Medical Economic Research of the American Medical Association, entitled "What Is the

Leading Cause of Death? Two New Measures") have concluded that for comparative purposes it is sufficiently accurate to use the expectations of life from a general mortality table.* W. Haenszel (American Journal of Public Health, XL, 17) has suggested a similar measure in which, instead of using expectations of life, the deaths at each age are simply multiplied by the difference between that age and a fixed age such as 65, 70, or 75. As compared with the index using expectations of life, this proposal has the advantage of providing a uniform standard of comparison for different countries, social classes, or time periods.

* In this paper consideration is also given to a second measure, based on temporary expectations of life to age 65 only with the object of estimating "the potential years of working life lost."

XII

OCCUPATIONAL MORTALITY

152. Since the establishment of efficient registration systems in various countries, numerous investigations have been made with the object of estimating as closely as possible the mortalities in different occupations, and especially the particular hazards in each occupational group as they may be indicated by analyses of the causes of death. For England and Wales occupational mortality studies were made by Dr. Farr from the census data of 1861 and 1871 and the deaths of 1860–61 and 1871; Dr. Ogle considered the census material of 1881 and the deaths of 1880–82; Dr. Tatham based two examinations on the censuses of 1891 and 1901 and the deaths of 1890–92 and 1900–1902 respectively; these periodical investigations were continued in the two Registrar-General's Decennial Supplements on mortality in certain occupations as indicated by the censuses of 1911 and 1921 and the deaths of 1910–12 and 1921–23 which were completed under the guidance of Dr. T. H. C. Stevenson; and the data of the 1931 census and the deaths of 1930–32 have been analyzed in the Decennial Supplement prepared under Dr. Percy Stocks (see the various official reports here noted; T.A.S.A., XXIX, 331; and P. Stocks, J.R.S.S., CI, 669). For Scotland similar analyses were published by Dr. Blair-Cunynghame and Dr. Dunlop from the censuses of 1891 and 1901, and other studies have also been made on the Continent of Europe (see T.F.A., V, 1, and J.I.A., LV, 266).

153. As already mentioned in par. 49, certain difficulties (in addition to the usual errors of age, etc., affecting all statistics of the general population) are encountered in the calculation and comparison of occupational mortality rates. These difficulties are involved mainly in (i) the methods of classifying the occupations; (ii) discrepancies between the occupational designations on the census schedules and on the death certificates; (iii) the determination of a satisfactory population at risk in each occupational group; (iv) the relation of physical fitness, environment, social-economic status, and other factors to the nature of the occupation; and (v) the method of comparing the rates of mortality of different occupations.

(i) The evolution of a method of recording and classifying occupations which will satisfy the varied requirements of governments, industrialists, sociologists, actuaries, statisticians, and others who use the resulting statistics in different forms has always been a problem of great difficulty, which has received much attention in the various census offices and else-where. In order to achieve many desired purposes the data should indicate at least (*a*) the worker's position in his industry, i.e., whether an em-ployer, an employee, or working on his own account, (*b*) his skill and intelligence, (*c*) the special services rendered or processes performed, and (*d*) the healthfulness and other important features of the occupation. However, an extremely complicated classification would be necessary to reflect all those influences in any manner which would permit of subse-quent statistical analyses, and one of the accompanying disadvantages would be that in some of the numerous subdivisions the material would be very small. The type of classification now generally adopted in prac-tice, therefore, is an occupational classification with an industrial frame-work, since many occupations mean little when they are considered apart from the industries in which they are pursued.

In Great Britain the classification prior to the 1921 census had been mainly on an industrial basis (so that a clerk in a textile company would be included in the textile industry). In 1921, however, the tabulations were made by industry and by occupation, in accordance with a resolution of the British Empire Statistical Conference that the basic principle of the industrial classification should be the "product" or "type of service," and that of the occupational classification the "process carried out" and the "material worked in," with the primary classification in the latter case according to the "material worked in" so as to avoid, for example, "the consolidation of picklers of onions and picklers of metals which might result from a primary classification by process" (cf. T.A.S.A., XXIX, 331). For the 1951 census the terms "industry" and "occupation" were defined very carefully in the "Classification of Occupations" pub-lished by the General Register Office. In the United States, similarly, the questions on the population schedule were enlarged in 1910 so that each person was required to state (1) "Trade or profession of or particular work done by this person, as spinner, salesman, laborer, etc."; (2) "Gen-eral nature of the industry, business, or establishment in which this person works, as cotton-mill, dry-goods store, farm, etc."; and (3) "Whether em-ployer, employee, or working on own account." These enquiries have been developed until in the 1950 U.S. census (in addition to questions as to being employed or unemployed, and hours of work) every person was asked (1) "What kind of work was he doing, for example, nails heels on shoes, chemistry professor, farmer, farm helper, etc."; (2) "What kind of business or industry was he working in, for example, shoe factory, state university, farm, etc."; (3) "Class of worker, i.e., for private employer, for Government, in own business, or without pay on family farm or business." In the Canadian census of 1941, the question respecting the occupation similarly asked for (1) "Trade or profession," etc.; the query with regard to the industry, however, was divided into (2) "Kind of product or service, as for example rubber shoes, drugs, etc.," and (3) "Branch of industry, as for example manufacturing, retail trade, etc."; and status was covered by a question as to (4) "Employer, own account, wage-earner, or unpaid family worker." The wording of the questions in the 1951 Canadian census was (1) "Occupation (what kind of work did this person do in this industry? For example, office clerk, sales clerk, auto mechanic, iron moulder, graduate nurse, etc.)"; (2) "Industry (what kind of business or industry is this? For example, rubber shoes manufacturing, drugs retail trade, grain farming, etc.)"; and class of worker was to be described as "wage or salary earner, employer, own account, or no pay."

By such questions it is theoretically possible to obtain the numbers in each specific elementary occupation in each industry or service group (cf. the U.S. Census Bureau's Classified Index of Occupations, and its Alphabetical Index of Occupations and Industries; in this connection note also the League of Nations' classification for the gainfully occupied population which was recommended by the Inter-American Statistical Institute for its proposed 1950 hemispheral census—see Estadística, March, 1945, p. 11). In tabulating the results of such enquiries, however, it is often difficult to follow a detailed classification by occupation in each industry (as had been attempted in Vol. IV, Occupation Statistics, of the 1910 U.S. Census), on account of ignorance or indifference on the part of the individuals enumerated and the carelessness of the enumerators. The results consequently now are often published "by grouping together all the workers in each separate occupation without regard to the different industries in which the occupation is pursued" (see Vol. IV, 1920 U.S. Census), in order to reach finally a classification for statistical purposes which shall be as nearly as possible occupational rather than industrial.

(*ii*) The discrepancies which frequently occur between the occupational designations used by the individual and the enumerator on the census schedule, and those given by relatives on the death certificate, cause much trouble in the attempt to produce reliable occupational mortality statistics from the general population. This has proved to be the case despite efforts to elicit a statement of occupation on the death certificate in conformity with the occupational groups of the census classifications (cf. par. 49 here; T.A.S.A., XIX, 136 and 140; J.I.A., LV, 267; P. Stocks, J.R.S.S., CI, 707; and H. L. Dunn, J.A.S.A., XXXV, 89).

(*iii*) In attempting to determine a satisfactory population at risk for each occupational group it must be remembered that the numbers enumerated in each occupation at a census necessarily include only those who were then so occupied. Some censuses, therefore, have asked questions of everyone with regard to the previous occupation or the occupation at the preceding census. The recent introduction of additional questions for a sample of the population, moreover, has provided opportunities for sampling queries as to kind of work, kind of business or industry, and class of worker in respect of the last job done by those who were not occupied at the date of the census (cf. par. 12).

The material so available has an important bearing on the basis to be adopted for the determination of the population at risk. Mortality rates, for example, computed only from the numbers occupied at the census date take no account of those who were formerly occupied and may have been forced to retire by reason of ill-health or disablement directly caused by the occupation; consequently they would understate the true occupational mortality in the more dangerous trades. In the occupational study based on the 1901 census of England and Wales and the deaths of 1900–1902, therefore, those reported as being "unoccupied" or "retired" were classified also according to their previous occupations, so that for each of the age-groups 25–34, 35–44, 45–54, and 55–64 (comprising the main working years of life) the mortality rates were based firstly on the "occupied," and secondly on those "occupied and retired." In the corresponding report on the 1921 census the age limits of 25 and 65 were extended to 20 and 65 because it was felt that even at age 20 the average worker has been subjected to the environment of his occupation sufficiently long that his mortality may be influenced by it. The data were also examined only for ages 35 to 65 (as well as for ages 20 to 65) in the report on the 1931 census, because to some extent objections may be raised to the inclusion of the earlier ages in attempts to assess the effects of occupation on mortality. The inclusion of the retired with the occupied is not, of course, an ideal basis, because the retired are secluded from the special hazards of their former occupations, and the statistics of the retired are not so reliable as those of the occupied; but it gives probably a more satisfactory basis between ages 20, 25, or 35 and 65 than the occupied alone, since it takes into account the mortality of those who have been forced to retire as a result of the hazards of the occupation (see Part II of the Supplement to the 65th Report, and the 1921 Decennial Supplement, of the Registrar-General of England and Wales; J.I.A., XLIII, 231; and T.A.S.A., XVIII, 269).

(*iv*) In the preceding discussion of the basis to be used for the populations at risk in each occupational group, physical fitness and environment were mentioned incidentally as being two of the most important factors which evidently must influence occupational mortality. Preliminary selection naturally induces the physically unfit to take up the less exacting occupations, and subsequent re-selections continually force those who are engaged in strenuous callings to abandon such occupations on the occurrence of some comparatively slight illness or mishap. The result is that in general the computed mortalities of the more exacting occupations will be too low, while the mortalities of those employments not requiring such complete fitness—into which those becoming unfitted for the more strenuous callings will be likely to drift—will be exaggerated.

Any attempt to measure effectively the influences of environment, such as locality, density of population, type of housing, income level, standard of living, etc., upon the mortalities of different occupations is, of course, attended by formidable difficulties because of the impossibility of disentangling the numerous and related causes. Since 1911, however, the British reports have developed an approach by classifying the occupations according to social-economic status in five broad groups, covering respectively the upper and middle classes (professional, etc.), intermediate classes, skilled workers, the partly skilled, and unskilled workers. Furthermore, in order to employ a statistical method (as far as may be practicable in so complex a problem) for measuring the social-economic influences and thus eliminating them from the general picture of occupational mortality, so that the direct effect of an occupation as a separate factor may then be isolated, the Registrar-General's 1931 Supplement (see also P. Stocks, "The Effects of Occupation and of its Accompanying Environment on Mortality," J.R.S.S., CI, 669) used in each case the wives of the occupied men as a "control group" (subject only to the social-economic influences, but not to the direct effects of the occupation), and thereby estimated the men's occupational risk by causes of death (as well as, incidentally, the influence of social-economic factors on the women).

(*v*) For comparing the rates of mortality of different occupations, the principle of direct standardization (see pars. 139–40) has been used for many years by the Registrar-General of England and Wales in the calculation of a *Comparative Mortality Figure* for each occupation. The standard population used in computing this figure is taken only from age 20 (previously 25) to 65 in order to cover approximately the effective working years, and is reduced (to facilitate comparisons on a per mille basis) so that the standard mortality rates therein would produce 1,000 deaths. It must be noted, however (in contrast with the reliability which is to be anticipated, as stated in par. 139, from standardizations of the death rates of different communities at all ages and from all causes, when no subdivisions by occupation are made), that distortions may sometimes result in comparing these standardized "comparative mortality figures" for various occupational subdivisions, because the age distributions in some occupations are sharply abnormal and are wholly different from those of any typical standard population. The Registrar-General consequently added comparisons of actual and expected deaths in the 1921 and 1931 reports (see the review in T.A.S.A., XXIX, 331, and J.I.A., LIX, 144 and discussion).

A method of standardization in which the standard population is composed arbitrarily of exactly the same number in every age group has also been suggested by Yule for dealing with comparisons of occupational mortalities (see G. U. Yule, "On Some Points Relating to Vital Statistics, More Especially Statistics of Occupational Mortality," J.R.S.S., XCVII, 1, and comments by Linder and Grove, *op. cit.*, pp. 81–83). The effect of this equal weighting is obviously the same as would be obtained by taking simply the arithmetic mean of the q's for the various age groups.

XIII

THE USE OF CENSUS AND REGISTRATION DATA IN THE COMPILATION OF STATISTICS RELATING TO MARRIAGES, BIRTHS, ORPHANHOOD, UNEMPLOYMENT, ETC.

154. The preceding pages have dealt primarily with the employment of statistics of the general population as a basis for mortality tables. Many other important enquiries in which actuaries are interested, however, may be founded on census and registration material, for such data comprise information relating to a wide range of sociological problems. In particular, actuarial estimates of the coverages and costs of social insurance and social welfare plans of many different kinds are necessarily based upon statistics of the mass of people to whom such schemes are to be applied.

The principal sections into which these further problems may be subdivided are those concerning: (1) *Marriages;* (2) *Births and Fertility;* (3) *Dependency and Orphanhood;* and (4) *Unemployment.*

(1) Marriages

155. *Rates of Marriage.*—In pars. 16–25 a brief description was given of the situation in various countries with regard to the registration of marriages and tabulations of the resulting statistics. When reliable data are available, *rates of marriage* are of course most satisfactorily examined by calculating the probability or central rate of marriage at each age or age-group—separate compilations being made for bachelors, spinsters, widowers, and widows (and divorced, where available). If a comprehensive figure is desired for the comparison of such rates for different communities and times, they may be standardized for differences in age distribution (on the principles already stated in pars. 139–41 for dealing with mortality statistics).

Such rates, however, whether by ages or standardized, are not always easy to calculate in years other than the census years, because then they may involve the estimation of the intercensal populations in each marriageable class. Crude rates, therefore, are often employed in reports on vital statistics, by taking (*a*) the ratio of the number of marriages in each marriageable class to the corresponding number of bachelors, spinsters, widowers, widows, or divorced persons, at all ages or at marriageable ages over 15 or 18, or by using (*b*) the still more composite number of marriages per 1,000 living, of all classes of the population at all ages. Such crude rates, of course, may again be misleading (cf. par. 138), although for some demographic purposes they may give a sufficiently reliable indication of the general trend of marriage rates from year to year.

156. Population statistics compiled by the U.S. Census Bureau have also been used in the construction of double decrement mortality and marriage tables for single men and single women by W. H. Grabill ("Attrition Life Tables for the Single Population," J.A.S.A., XL, 364). Marriage rates for single males under 23 and single females under 22 were based provisionally on the 1940 census data (since the marriage transcripts were deficient in number at ages under the legal age of consent, and were too numerous in the early twenties on account of misstatements of age); at higher ages provisional rates were derived from the 1940 marriage data for 23 States (as given in Vital Statistics Special Reports, Vol. 17, No. 9). Because the improved economic conditions of 1940, and marriages which had been deferred from the previous depression, had produced an exceptional number of marriages in 1940, these provisional rates were modified so that they would be consistent with the number which would have been anticipated in 1940 for the population at marriageable ages and the average annual marriage rates during 1920–1939. The mortality basis for single persons was derived at ages over 20 from the Census Bureau's "Mortality by Marital Status, 1940" (Vital Statistics Special Reports, Vol. 23, No. 2), and at younger ages from the 1939–41 U.S. Life Tables without regard to marital condition.

157. *Marital Status, and Relative Ages of Husbands and Wives.*—In connection with the calculation of probabilities or rates of marriage at each age (or age-group), it is of course often necessary to use tabulations of the proportions of the census population according to marital condition, which are obtainable readily from the schedules. Statistics of the relative ages of husbands and wives, which again can be derived from tabulations of the data recorded on the census schedules, are also frequently of value for other purposes (cf. T.A.S.A., XVIII, 266, 281, and 284; and J.I.A., LII, 37, and LVI, 182–83).

158. *Mortality According to Marital Status.*—When census data are tabulated according to marital status, rates of mortality for each such class can be computed if the death certificates similarly record the marital condition at death (as on the certificate illustrated in par. 22) and if the data thus available are tabulated. An illustration of such material is the U.S. Census Bureau's Special Report on mortality by marital status already mentioned in par. 156.

In Great Britain the mortality rates for spinsters, married women, and widows have been given in the reports of George King on the 1911 census and the deaths of 1910–12, and by Sir Alfred Watson in the corresponding 1921 and 1931 reports (see the references in par. 120 of this Study). King also constructed separate life tables for each class; Watson, however, refrained from doing so, on the ground that each marital group is subject to increments and decrements (such as the married women group being increased by spinsters marrying and decreased by husbands dying) which disturb the validity of the life table as a concept for depicting the mortality experience of a cohort of supposedly homogeneous lives.

159. *Rates of Widowhood.*—In order to calculate rates of widowhood, i.e., the proportions of married women who, in each year of age (or in each year of age by duration of marriage), are left as widows by the deaths of their husbands, it would be necessary for the death certificate of a married man to record the age of his wife (and the date of their marriage, or its duration). As these items are not stated on the death certificates, estimated rates can be prepared indirectly by assuming mortality rates for married men in conjunction with tabulations of the relative ages of husbands and wives, or an approximation can be reached in some cases by using the average (weighted) age of the husbands or more accurately from the weighted means of their mortality rates (see T.A.S.A., XVIII, 282, and J.I.A., XLV, 421).

160. A complete treatment of the character and technical utilization of the marriage statistics derivable from population data does not fall within the scope of this Study. The discussion here must therefore be limited to the indications stated in pars. 155–59. It may be emphasized, nevertheless, that various types of marriage statistics, especially when taken in conjunction with material respecting fertility, are obviously of major importance in many investigations into the sociological and economic implications of population growth or decline (such as those which recently have engaged the attention of the Royal Commission on Population in Great Britain, where anxieties had arisen with regard to the trends in fertility, size of families, and total population).

(2) Births and Fertility

161. The principal measures of basic actuarial importance in connection with statistics of births and the analysis of fertility are the birth rates according to age, sex, and marital condition of the parent, i.e., more precisely, the *probabilities or rates of issue* to persons (either married or still single) of each sex and age. In the presentation of such rates it is

desirable to distinguish between single and plural births, and to give separate tables for those which are legitimate and illegitimate.*

When birth registrations are sufficiently reliable the most satisfactory method would be to construct, from such registrations and the corresponding tabulations of parents, complete tables showing the ages of the parents at the births of their children (subdivided by number of children at a birth, and according to legitimacy), and thence to compute the probabilities or rates of issue to all the potential parents (or to all males or females) of ages and sexes corresponding to those who were tabulated as having children. A valuable discussion of the compilation of tables of this description has been given by C. H. Wickens in Appendix B, 1911 Census of Australia ("On the Materials for, and the Construction of, Tables of Natality, Issue, and Orphanhood"), where extensive data which had been available in Australia for many years past were used, and tables were included showing (1) the ratio of the legitimate births per annum to the mean number of males of the same age as the fathers, (2) the average number of children per confinement, by age of father, and also (3) the surviving legitimate children under one year of age, corresponding to males surviving out of 100,000 at age 14, and (4) the children under 15, who either have their fathers living or are orphans, corresponding to males surviving out of 100,000 at age 14.

The calculation of these issue rates by age necessitates a knowledge of the ages of parents at the births of their children. This information has been obtained for many years on the birth certificates of the United States, Canada, Australia, and some other countries, so that tabulations of the number of births according to the ages of the mothers have been available for such computations.†

* In reports on vital statistics the term "age-specific birth rate" will be encountered; it means the number of births (of both sexes) to mothers of a given age, divided by the total number of women of that age. When differentiation of the births by sex is made, the "male (or female) age-specific birth rate" is used correspondingly to describe the male (or female) births to mothers of a given age divided by the total women of that age.

† In Great Britain, however, this material was not collected at the time of the preparation of the cost estimates for the National Insurance Act of 1911; Sir George Hardy and F. B. Wyatt consequently then had recourse to certain New Zealand data as to the number of children under 5 left by deceased males, and applied thereto the mortality among the fathers and children, and the number of births, in order to work back to the probabilities of issue (see J.I.A., XLV, 421). It may also be noted that subsequently a series of select issue rates was published in J.I.A., XLVIII, 112, on the basis of the census figures of the Borough of Camberwell, showing for six selected ages at marriage of females the central issue rates at each age attained (as well as aggregate tables for husbands and wives irrespective of the age at marriage). The Population

162. In the reports which are issued annually in many countries on birth registration statistics, however, such elaborate presentations of issue rates are not necessary. An indication of the birth rates of the population from year to year may then be obtained by calculating the legitimate birth rates, by age groups, for the married women living between about ages 15 and 45, and the similar illegitimate birth rates by age groups for the unmarried women aged 15–45. Where more compact figures are required for purposes of comparison these rates may then be "directly standardized"; or if the rates by age groups cannot be ascertained, the crude legitimate and illegitimate rates for all the ages 15–45 may be calculated and then "indirectly standardized" on the principles of par. 130 (cf. Supplement to the 75th Registrar-General's Report, Part III, p. xviii, and Newsholme's "Vital Statistics," p. 86). The crude birth rate, being the ratio of the total births to the total population of both sexes at all ages, has also been used widely; but it is, of course, subject to the disturbances of varying distributions as pointed out with respect to the crude death rate in par. 138.

163. The probabilities or rates of issue according to the ages and sexes of the parents, and their further tabulation by duration of marriage, which may be required for actuarial purposes (par. 161), and the "birth rates" which are commonly used in reports on vital statistics for presentation to the public (par. 162), are often referred to in general language as measures of "fertility." Care must be exercised, however, in the use of this last term; it is employed by statisticians in many different senses, and therefore should always be carefully defined when any so-called "fertility rate" is quoted.

Since "fertility" in its general demographic aspects must always be of interest to vital statisticians and the sociologists, data were collected on the census forms at the 1910 U.S. Census and the 1911 census of England and Wales with respect to the number of years the present marriage has lasted, the number of children born alive to each married woman, and the number still living. The English data thus obtained were analyzed in Vol. XIII, Part 1, of the 1911 reports, and by Dr. T. H. C. Stevenson in J.R.S.S., LXXXIII, 407 (see also Newsholme's "Vital Statistics," p. 96, and T.A.S.A., XVIII, 283). These questions, which were expressly intended to produce "fertility" statistics, were omitted, however, from the 1920 U.S. and 1921 English censuses. In Great Britain the two new questions which were introduced in the census of 1921 (see par. 164 here) were used instead to give indications of the comparative incidence of "fer-

---

(Statistics) Act of 1938 (see par. 163 here) has now made possible the calculation of probabilities of issue to women at each age—see, for example, the Government Actuary's Report on the National Insurance Act, 1946 (Cmd. 6730).

tility" among various sections of the population in the year preceding the census (see the 1921 census report, England and Wales, on "Dependency, Orphanhood, and Fertility").

In 1946, because such data had been omitted from the censuses after 1911, the Royal Commission on Population found it necessary to conduct a special voluntary "family census" based on a 10% sample of all women who were or had been married, by asking for their ages, dates of marriage, dates of birth of their children, and the occupations of their husbands; and they recommended (since "at present in Great Britain the arrangements for the collection and analysis of fertility statistics are not adequate to modern needs") that family census questions should be included henceforth as an essential part of the decennial census in order to make possible the continuous study of family size.*

In the United States fertility questions were reinstated at the 1940 census, including queries in respect of each woman ever married as to her age at first marriage and the number of children ever born alive. On the 1950 census form the questions were asked only for each person (male or female) on the $3\frac{1}{3}\%$ sample lines, and included queries on the duration of marriage and the number of children ever born alive to each female who had ever been married.

The 1941 Canadian census asked, in respect of each woman ever married, her age at first marriage, the number of children ever born alive, and the number living on June 2, 1941 (the census date). Such questions, however, were omitted from the census of 1951.

In Great Britain the securing of more adequate material concerning fertility and marital status has also been facilitated notably by the passage in 1938, as a temporary enactment requiring periodical renewal, of the Population (Statistics) Act. This measure provides for additional but confidential enquiries (from which, however, statistical tabulations may be made) when births, stillbirths, and deaths are registered. With respect to births and stillbirths the questions cover the age of the mother, the date of the marriage, the number of children by the present husband and the number still living, and the number of children and the number

---

* The conclusions of the Royal Commission emphasized that during the last 70 years in Great Britain the salient feature of the population changes has been the fall in "the average size of the family." This phrase is used by the Commission to indicate "the number of children born per married couple"—it is thus concerned "not with the average number of persons in a household, nor even with the average number of dependent children in a family, but with the average number of live births to a marriage of 'completed fertility,' i.e., one in which the wife has passed the limit of the childbearing period, [where] in computing this average it is of course necessary to include childless marriages as well as those which are fertile." See also J.R.S.S., CXIV, 41 and 48 with respect to the technical difficulties involved in this concept.

still living by any former husband. Upon registration of a death the data
secured are (1) in the case of a male, whether he had ever been married
and whether he was married when he died; (2) in the case of a married
woman, the year and duration of her marriage, and whether she had children by her husband; and (3) the age of the surviving spouse.

(3) *Dependency and Orphanhood*

164. The actuarial problems encountered in connection with dependency at advanced ages in the general population do not as a rule involve
statistics beyond the scope of those already referred to in this Study. At
young ages, however, data are frequently required which hitherto have
seldom been obtained; a brief reference must therefore be made to the
nature of the problem thus presented.

In connection with various types of schemes for pensions to widows and
children it is often necessary to know the numbers, ages, and sexes of
children (under, say, age 16) in relation to the ages of their fathers or their
widowed mothers. Such statistics have been collected for many years in
New Zealand on the death certificates of males (see G. King, J.I.A.,
XXX, 299; J.I.A., XLV, 421; and T.A.S.A., XVIII, 284), although they
have not been—and still are not—available for other countries. For the
calculation of "family annuities" by the "collective method" material of
this type can, as an alternative, be called for on the census schedules in
respect of living families. Consequent on a realization of the general in-
adequacy of the data bearing on these matters, therefore, two new and
direct questions were inserted in the 1921 census schedule of England and
Wales, and Scotland. Those questions asked (1) in respect of each child
under 15, whether the parents were both alive, the father dead but the
mother alive, or vice versa, or both parents dead, and (2) required, in
respect of married men, widowers, and widows, a statement of the number
and ages of all living children and step-children under 16. The value of
these statistics in the calculation of "family annuities" is pointed out in
J.I.A., LII, by G. King (p. 37) and Menzler (p. 372), and is well illustrated
in the Appendix to the British Government Actuary's Report on the
Financial Provisions of the Pensions Bill, 1925 (Cmd. 2406) which is reprinted in J.I.A., LVI, 180. Such data, however, are still generally unob-
tainable from population material, notwithstanding representations by
actuaries with regard to their importance. The reason for this has been
mainly that census and registration officials have been reluctant to add
the necessary questions to the census schedules or the death certificates.

165. In the United States valuable statistics on family composition—
even though they are now somewhat out of date, and were affected by
the low birth rates of the depression period—may be found in Vol. XI,

Memorandum No. 45, of the Bureau of Research and Statistics, Social Security Board, on "The Urban Sample; Statistics of Family Composition in Selected Areas of the United States, 1934–36." The data, which covered family size and type, children, employment status, occupation, income, housing, race, nativity, and education, were gathered in 1935–36 through a house-to-house canvass by the Works Projects Administration under the National Health Survey.

The number of paternal orphans, also, has been estimated for 1940, 1945, 1950, and 1955 by T. J. Woofter (see Social Security Bulletin, October, 1945). The calculations were made by taking the number of births by age of father in each of the preceding 18 years, applying the death rates of fathers by age to determine the number of deaths among fathers, and using survival rates of children to compute the number of orphans surviving to the specified year.

(4) Unemployment

166. Original calculations of the costs of unemployment insurance plans have frequently required statistics with respect to working time lost, and the probabilities of being unemployed within a period of 12 months for n weeks or more, which can be collected on the census schedules. Data concerning employment or unemployment status at the date of the census, and the number of weeks worked during the preceding 12 months, are also of value for many other purposes.

On the 1950 U.S. census schedule, for example, each person aged 14 or over accordingly was asked whether (yes or no) he or she did any work at all last week (not counting work around the house), whether work was being sought, whether he or she had a job or business even though last week no work was done, and the number of hours worked during the last week. On the sample lines, also (cf. par. 12), persons 14 years of age and over were asked for how many weeks work had been sought, and in how many weeks was any work at all (not counting work around the house) done in 1949. On the 1941 Canadian census schedule questions with regard to unemployment were included in the form "If a wage-earner, were you at work on June 2, 1941?" and "If not, give reason," and for wage-earners only two employment enquiries were made as to the number of weeks worked and total earnings during the 12 months prior to June 2, 1941 (the census date).

The tabulated replies to such queries, of course, are subject to many inaccuracies, because they depend wholly upon the knowledge, memory, and degree of care exercised by the individual who answers the census enumerator's questions.

XIV

THE THEORY OF REPRODUCTIVITY

167. The ideas set out in the preceding sections of this Study dealing with mortality rates and the methods of stating marriage rates and birth rates, inevitably for many years have led vital statisticians and mathematicians, sociologists, economists, and others (now often comprehensively described as the "population mathematicians" and the "demographers") to seek a compact mathematical-statistical measure which might give reliable indications of the trends which result from the combined impacts of these varying rates of birth, marriage, and mortality. Obviously this must be very difficult, for the rates are highly complex and are continuously changing—sometimes quite sharply; moreover, marriage and birth rates are subject to the voluntary controls of individuals, and those controls are influenced largely by racial, religious, social, and economic forces, and by periods of peace or war. The best that can be done can only be the construction of some kind of mathematical model, based upon greatly simplified and technically manageable suppositions. Such hypothetical models must, of course, be viewed in contrast with the known but unmeasurable complexities of the rates actually involved; both in their composition and their use it must be clearly understood that at many points they substitute fanciful imagination for reality. Their practical utility is consequently open to considerable debate. Their theoretical foundations, however, must be included here because now they are encountered widely in the literature, and the techniques which they involve are interesting despite their demonstrable weaknesses.

In pars. 161–63 consideration was given to the meanings and methods of stating "probabilities or rates of issue" and "birth rates," and attention was directed to the importance of defining "fertility" in any discussion of that word. Two other general terms, namely, "reproduction" and "reproductivity," will also be encountered—frequently in a sense almost synonymous with "fertility" or "births," though again in a recent technical terminology where their precise meanings and implications must be carefully defined. The theory underlying the "measures of reproductivity" to be now examined will be followed with ease only when the special definitions of this recent terminology are thoroughly understood.

168. *The Gross Reproduction Rate.*—Let $f'_F(x)$ denote the female birth rate at age x—that is, as in the footnote to par. 161, the "female age-

specific birth rate," being the female births to mothers aged x divided by the total women aged x—and suppose that the mothers' child-bearing ages are covered by ages λ to L only. It will then be evident that the simple total $\sum\limits_{x=\lambda}^{x=L} f'_F(x)$ will give the number of daughters who would be born to each woman during the childbearing ages λ to L, so long as (*a*) the woman is not subject to the risk of mortality between ages λ to L, and (*b*) it is considered appropriate in the calculations thus to compute the daughters by using values of $f'_F(x)$ determined from a short and fixed observation period (1944, which may be called the "base period," in the example here) which ignores the mother's "generation" (cf. Section X). These conditions may be seen easily from column (2) of the table on p. 217 (taken, with slight rearrangement and amplified column headings, from A. H. Pollard's paper on "The Principles and Limitations of Fertility Indices," Actuarial Society of Australasia, 1947) which with illustrative data shows the form of calculation in 5-year groups adopted in many similar examples to be found in the writings of Kuczynski and others. The index thus computed (which was first used by Kuczynski) has become known as the *Female Gross Reproduction Rate*. It will be noted that it is independent of the actual age, sex, and marital distributions of the population (here a particular population in 1944) for which the rate is computed. Its value 1.289 (in the example) is claimed by its advocates to suggest that 1,000 women living through the child-bearing period of this generation without any loss by death would replace themselves by 1,289 women in the next generation, and consequently that the births are here more than sufficient to "maintain" the population—i.e., the population is more than "reproducing itself," and therefore is "steadily increasing."[*]

This concept, however, is obviously most unrealistic, and indeed meaningless—particularly in its supposition that the mothers are not subject to mortality. It is stated here only because it is the first step in the development of the "net" reproduction rate (par. 169), and also because it has been described as providing evidently an upper limit which the net rate would attain if mortality were to improve so greatly that it would become negligible.

The gross reproduction rate explained in this paragraph is the female rate, relating mothers and daughters. A corresponding male rate tracing

---

[*] These phrases are placed in quotes because they constitute the customary language of the proponents of these theories, and because on careful examination they reveal the objectives and practical limitations of the methods.

sons and fathers can, of course, also be computed with a similar rationale The female rate, however, has usually been employed in practice on the grounds that females actually bear the children, the range of ages λ to L is shorter for women than for men so that the calculations are easier, and the required data are more readily available for females.

For the purposes of mathematical analysis, the female and male gross reproduction rates can be stated as $\displaystyle\int_{\lambda}^{L} f_F(x)\,dx$ and $\displaystyle\int_{\alpha}^{\beta} f_M(x)\,dx$, where $f_F(x)$ and $f_M(x)$ are the instantaneous female-to-female and male-to-male birth rates, and α and β for males are the age limits corresponding to the female λ and L. Since the f's are zero for all values of x beyond these limits, the integrals can be taken as $\displaystyle\int_{0}^{\infty} f_F(x)\,dx$ and $\displaystyle\int_{0}^{\infty} f_M(x)\,dx$.

169. *The Net Reproduction Rate.*—When the mortality of mothers, which is ignored in the gross reproduction rate, is introduced, it will be clear that

$$\sum_{x=\lambda}^{x=L} \left({}_x p_0^F\right) f_F'(x) = \sum_{x=\lambda}^{x=L} \left(\frac{l_x^F}{l_0^F}\right) f_F'(x),$$

where the F in ${}_x p_0^F$ and $\dfrac{l_x^F}{l_0^F}$ indicates that those values are taken from an

appropriate female life table, will give the total number of daughters who would be born to each original female baby during her lifetime—again on assumption (*b*) of par. 168. This index, which was first used by R. Böckh in Germany and subsequently was adopted by Kuczynski and many others (including the central vital statistics offices of several countries), is called the *Female Net Reproduction Rate.* In column (5) of the example here its value 1.176 would be used to suggest that 1,000 female babies (of one generation) would in their turn, and with due allowance for their mortality prior to and during their child-bearing periods, produce 1,176 female babies (of the next generation), and consequently that the "balance of births and deaths" is more than sufficient to "maintain" the population—i.e., the population is more than "reproducing itself" and is therefore "steadily increasing."*

With the same notation as in par. 168, and writing l^M for the values from a male table in contrast with l^F for the female values, the female net reproduction rate is

$$\int_{\lambda}^{L} \left(\frac{l_x^F}{l_0^F}\right) f_F(x)\,dx,$$

* See footnote to the previous paragraph.

and the male rate is

$$\int_a^\beta \left(\frac{l_x^M}{l_0^M}\right) f_M(x)\, dx.$$

Extending the limits as before, the female rate can be written more compactly as $\int_0^\infty \varphi_F(x)\, dx$, where

$$\varphi_F(x) = \left(\frac{l_x^F}{l_0^F}\right) f_F(x)$$

ILLUSTRATIVE APPROXIMATE CALCULATION FOR FEMALES OF THE GROSS RE-
PRODUCTION RATE, NET REPRODUCTION RATE, AND INHERENT RATE OF
NATURAL INCREASE, FOR 1944, USING 5-YEAR AGE GROUPS

Age Group (1)	Female Age-Group Birth-Rate* to Mothers, in Base-Period 1944, f_F' (2)	Assumed Midpoint, x, of Age-Group (3)	$_xp_0 = \frac{l_x}{l_0}$ from Female Life Table Appropriate to Base-Period 1944 (4)	Daughters Born to Each Original Female Baby during Her Lifetime $= 5[(2)\times(4)]$ (5)†	$(5)\times(3)$ $= R_1'$ (6)†	$(5)\times(3)^2$ $= R_2'$ (7)†
−19....	.01102	17.5	.93704	.05165	.904	15.817
20–24....	.06249	22.5	.92888	.29025	6.530	146.936
25–29....	.07825	27.5	.91789	.35911	9.876	271.576
30–34....	.05948	32.5	.90527	.26921	8.749	284.356
35–39....	.03501	37.5	.89031	.15586	5.845	219.180
40–44....	.01069	42.5	.87268	.04666	1.983	84.284
45–......	.00088	47.5	.85068	.00376	.179	8.484
Total..	.25782	....	....	1.17650 $= R_0'$	34.066 $= R_1'$	1,030.633 $= R_2'$

Female Gross Reproduction Rate = 5(.25782) = 1.289.

Female Net Reproduction Rate = R_0 = 1.176.

Calculation of the Inherent Rate of Natural Increase, r, by (93): $a = R_1'/R_0' = 28.955$; $R_2'/R_0' = 876.017$; $\tfrac{1}{2}\beta = \tfrac{1}{2}(a^2 - R_2'/R_0') = -18.8125$; $\log_e R_0' = .162542$. Hence, by (93), $-18.8125r^2 + 28.955r - .162542 = 0$, from which the admissible solution‡ is $r = .00563$.

* For example, .06249 is taken as $\dfrac{\text{Births to mothers } 20\text{–}24 \text{ l.b.d.}}{\text{Female population } 20\text{–}24 \text{ l.b.d.}}$

Instead of using female birth rates to mothers as here, the total rate of male and female births to mothers is often employed in practice, with subsequent adjustment by multiplying the results by the sex ratio at birth (see R. J. Myers, T.A.S.A., XLI, 94–96 and 101, and references there cited).

† In cols. (5), (6), and (7) the figures shown follow those in Pollard's paper; as explained by their author, they have been cut down from his original extended calculations which actually were made with a greater number of decimals throughout.

‡ The two solutions of this quadratic are .00563 and 1.53456. The latter, however, is evidently inadmissible, because (a) r clearly must lie in the neighborhood of .0056 (meaning a population increase of slightly over $\tfrac{1}{2}\%$ p.a.), since .00561 is the single solution indicated by the linear relation stated in the footnote to equation (93) in the text; (b) 1.53456 is thus an extraneous solution, just as a cubic or higher extension of the approximate (93) would produce still other extraneous roots; and (c) a population increase of 153% p.a. obviously must be dismissed as being impossible on general grounds.

has been called the female "net fertility function" (being the probability, at birth, that a female child when she attains age x will, for the next generation, bear a female child). The corresponding male rate would then be $\int_0^\infty \varphi_M(x)\,dx$ where the male "net fertility function" $\varphi_M(x)$ is

$$\left(\frac{l_x^M}{l_0^M}\right) f_M(x)\,,$$

i.e., the probability, at birth, that a male child when he attains age x will then become the father of a male child. It is to be noted that the net fertility functions $\varphi_F(x)$ and $\varphi_M(x)$ involve the rates of mortality and birth explicitly, and also the marriage rate implicitly.

170. These concepts require close examination. Firstly, when computed in practice by the formula of par. 169 as in the numerical example here, they implicitly involve the assumption (b) stated in par. 168, and thus in effect use different generation values of $f'(x)$—since all the values of $f'(x)$ are ordinarily derived from a fixed period of observation (the base period) which involves different generations—to compute an index which is supposed to forecast the births of a single generation.

Secondly, the values of the birth rate $f'(x)$—which implicitly involve also the antecedent marriage rate at some earlier age in respect of legitimate births—are usually based on a particular short period of observation (here the base period 1944), and the values of the mortality function $_xp_0$ likewise are generally* taken from a life table based on some particular short period of observation appropriate to the base period; and with these values an attempt is made to estimate future births over a long span of years, on the assumption that the values will not change—regardless of the fact that they are almost certain to change appreciably. Objection to this feature of the calculations has been expressed by several critics. J. Hajnal, for instance (in Population Studies, I, 137), has remarked that "to look upon the long-term prospects of population growth following from the maintenance of the situation of a given year in terms of rates which are certain not to remain as they are is clearly an unreasonable proceeding." In an official Appendix (p. 246) to the Report of the British Royal Commission on Population the fundamental defect of the net reproduction rate is stated by W. A. B. Hopkin to lie in the fact that "it defines the demographic habits of the population in terms of the

---

* The Registrar-General of England and Wales has modified this customary procedure by using the lower forecast mortality rates to be expected in the future in order to find what he calls an "effective" reproduction rate. This modification in the comparatively unimportant mortality assumption, however, usually produces only a trivial difference in the third decimal place of the ordinary net reproduction rate.

age-specific fertility and mortality rates of a particular year or series of years; this procedure may not be seriously unsatisfactory on the side of mortality . . . but on the side of fertility it is quite inadequate . . . [because] recent experience has shown that the age-specific fertility rates of any one year, or even of several years together, may be substantially raised or lowered by factors which have nothing to do with the basic habits of the population." W. Perks (J.I.A., LXXIV, 327) observed that "the measurement of reproductivity, i.e., the extent to which the population was reproducing itself . . . [is] essentially a generation idea, and the troubles . . . arose out of attempts to measure a generation concept by means of data taken over a short period, and particularly the fertility data over a short period." Or, to put the matter in other language (paraphrasing slightly F. A. A. Menzler's similar criticism in J.I.A., LXXVI, 53), these reproduction rates purport to give a summary of the way population influences are working out at a given point of time, if all the forces then operating continue to operate unchanged in the future (and thus for laymen they seem to "dramatize the consequences of the demographic position obtaining from time to time"). As it is well known, however, that such forces—especially the marriage rate and the birth rate, both of which are actually involved in $f'(x)$—do not operate without changes which are sometimes drastic, reproduction rates so calculated can have no real value for the purpose of determining the likelihood of a population reproducing itself.

Thirdly (as in the case of the gross rate), the net reproduction rates ignore the actual age and sex distributions of the population, although the marital distribution is reflected indirectly in the values of the birth rate $f'(x)$; then, notwithstanding the fact that the actual distributions must in reality determine the population's reproductive capacities which the rates essay to measure, they calculate a theoretical number of births based on a purely hypothetical life-table population which in its distributions by sex and age (and without any regard for marital condition) has no necessary relation to the realities, whether with respect to the present or the future or any other actual population.

171. These features of the calculations must be interpreted as warnings that the net reproduction rate will not always provide any reliable indication as to whether a given population really is or is not reproducing itself. Actuaries, who are thoroughly schooled in the hypothetical nature and computational uses of the fictitious "stationary population" of the life table (see the footnote to par. 64 here), will hardly need to be warned that any attempt to compress the many varied influences of "reproductivity" into a single composite index-number like these reproduction rates

is foredoomed to the same kinds of difficulties and failures which vitiate so many of the conclusions which to laymen seem at first glance to be deducible from crude death rates, expectations of life, and the so-called "life table death-rate" based on varying age and sex distributions (cf. par. 138 here; "The Fundamental Principles of Mathematical Statistics," pp. 113–14; and F. A. A. Menzler, J.I.A., LXXVI, 53). The net reproduction rate, nevertheless, in recent years has captured the imaginations of the public, the press, and the politicians, just as the expectation of life unfortunately is still believed by many laymen to give a reliable and complete picture of the prospects of longevity for nations or even individuals. Policy with respect to future population growth and economics cannot be founded safely upon any such index-numbers which generally hide much more than they reveal. Again it may be said here (cf. Wolfenden, T.A.S.A., XXXV, 282) that perhaps some day we may succeed in disseminating outside actuarial ranks the truth about what the "life table," the "expectation of life," and now the "net reproduction rate," cannot do.

The calculation of a net reproduction rate (whether in the form already stated, or as modified in pars. 172–73 hereafter) thus obviously cannot under any circumstances replace a detailed analysis of the mortality, marriage, and birth rates by ages and durations as a means of examining the trends in marriages, the number of children per marriage, and the ultimate size of a population (see also J. Hajnal, Population Studies, I, 137, and B. Benjamin, J.I.A., LXXVI, 41).*

172. *Net Reproduction Rates for Males and Females.*—For the same reasons as those stated at the end of par. 168 for the gross rate, the net reproduction rate is usually computed for females, although the male rate is also sometimes given. The numerical values of these male and female rates, however, do not always give similar indications; R. J. Myers, for example, in his paper on "The Validity and Significance of Male Net Reproduction Rates," J.A.S.A., XXXVI, 275, shows instances of male rates greater, but female rates smaller, than unity, and points out that such differences are due to the relative proportions of the male and female populations which are, in fact, reflected indirectly in the values of $f_M'(x)$ and $f_F'(x)$ based on those populations. Such parallel constructions of

---

* An alternative statistical approach on such lines may be found in P. R. Cox's paper on "Reproductivity in Great Britain: A New Standard of Assessment," J.I.A., LXXIX, 239. The differences are there examined between the numbers of children actually observed, and those theoretically required for a model self-reproducing population computed on the basis of the various mortality and marriage elements involved (with emphasis on the duration of marriage as one of the most important factors).

male and female rates, moreover, illustrate the anomaly that there is a basic mathematical and practical conflict between the male and female rates when both are computed and compared. The theory of both rates, which are calculated by means of functions based on the life-table concept of a "stationary population," supposes that mortality and fertility remain unchanged and that there is no migration; furthermore, rates thus based theoretically on the life-table hypothesis can actually occur at their precise calculated values only in a population which has in fact attained a "stationary condition." In any given population, therefore, the exact theoretical net male or female reproduction rate would not be likely to occur at the time of its calculation—the rate then might in reality be larger or smaller; if, however, the assumed mortality and fertility persisted without migration, eventually the population would reach a stable age and sex composition in which the calculated reproduction rate would actually appear (see also par. 174). But if the male and female rates are supposed, as the calculations may indicate, to be not the same, the ultimate outcome in this eventually stable population must then be that in the course of time one sex would completely submerge the other; that is to say, in the final result different male and female reproduction rates cannot co-exist.

This anomaly between the male and female net reproduction rates, which is a major objection to their use, has been examined mathematically in several papers—particularly by P. H. Karmel (in Population Studies, I, 249, and 353, and II, 240, and a summary in J.I.A., LXXIV, 329) and A. H. Pollard ("The Measurement of Reproductivity," J.I.A., LXXIV, 288). Using the approach adopted in a long series of contributions by A. J. Lotka, and epitomized conveniently by E. C. Rhodes (in three papers on "Population Mathematics" in J.R.S.S., CIII, 61, 218, and 362), let $B_F(t)$, $B_M(t)$, and $B_T(t)$ denote female, male, and total births at time t, and $\varphi_F(x)$ and $\varphi_M(x)$ the female and male net fertility functions already defined. Then $B_F(t - x)$ represents the number of female children born at time $t - x$, and the number of female children born to them when they are aged x to $x + dx$, at time t to $t + dx$, is $B_F(t - x)\,\varphi_F(x)dx$, where necessarily $t > x > \lambda$; consequently the total female births at time t, for all ages of mothers in their child-bearing years, is given by

$$B_F(t) = \int_\lambda^L B_F(t - x)\,\varphi_F(x)\,dx. \tag{75}$$

Since $\varphi_F(x)$ is zero beyond the limits λ and L, as before, this may be written

$$B_F(t) = \int_0^\infty B_F(t - x)\,\varphi_F(x)\,dx. \tag{76}$$

Similarly,

$$B_M(t) = \int_0^\infty B_M(t-x)\, \varphi_M(x)\, dx\,. \qquad (77)$$

In his analysis of the male-female anomaly, Karmel points out that these two relations are connected by a third, namely,

$$B_M(t) = mB_F(t)\,, \qquad (78)$$

where m is the masculinity at birth—this relation being essential because its omission "would imply that the masculinity at birth would, for large t, approach 0 or ∞, i.e., either the male or female population would outstrip the other" (J.I.A., LXXIV, 330). Since the mathematical model thus representing the births is defined by the three functions $\varphi_F(x)$, $\varphi_M(x)$, and m, and the unknowns $B_F(t)$ and $B_M(t)$ are only two, the system is over-determinate. The reason for the anomaly can thus be seen.

In this situation Karmel and Pollard have discussed the several possible solutions which follow.

(*i*) The usual practice of demographers has been to use the system (76), (77), and (78), but (as remarked in par. 168 here) simply to omit (77), which certainly is not correct.

(*ii*) The total births could be expressed in the corresponding form

$$B_T(t) = \int_0^\infty B_T(t-x)\, \varphi_T(x)\, dx\,, \qquad (79)$$

where in $\varphi_T(x)$ the total birth rate, $f_T(x)$, would be based on half the total births to persons aged x since each birth would be counted twice; and from (78) and the condition $B_M(t) + B_F(t) = B_T(t)$ we should have

$$B_M(t) = \left(\frac{m}{1+m}\right) B_T(t) \qquad (80)$$

and

$$B_F(t) = \left(\frac{1}{1+m}\right) B_T(t)\,. \qquad (81)$$

This system (which was mentioned by R. R. Kuczynski in his "Fertility and Reproduction") is determinate. Karmel, however, views it (in J.I.A., LXXIV, 330–31) as unsatisfactory because $B_T(x)$ must depend on the varying sex distribution of the population.

(*iii*) A. H. Pollard (in J.I.A., LXXIV, 307–13 and 336) suggested tracing the total births by following the female children of males and the male children of females. If accordingly we here use $\psi(x)$ to denote the probability at birth that a male child will have a female at age x, and $\xi(y)$ for the probability at birth that a female child will give birth to a male at age y, the female births $B_F(t)$ would be $\int_0^\infty B_M(t-x)\,\psi(x)\,dx$ and the

male births $B_M(t)$ would be $\int_0^\infty B_F(t-y)\,\xi(y)\,dy$. Consequently

$$B_F(t) = \int_0^\infty \int_0^\infty B_F(t-x-y)\,\psi(x)\,\xi(y)\,dx\,dy \qquad (82)$$

and

$$B_M(t) = \int_0^\infty \int_0^\infty B_M(t-x-y)\,\psi(x)\,\xi(y)\,dx\,dy \qquad (83)$$

while also (as remarked by Karmel, J.I.A., LXXIV, 331)

$$B_M(t) = m(t)\,B_F(t), \qquad (84)$$

where $m(t)$ is the masculinity at birth expressed as a function of time. Here there are three unknowns and three equations, so the system is determinate. The expression $\int_0^\infty \int_0^\infty \psi(x)\,\xi(y)\,dx\,dy$ can then be used as a unique *Joint Reproduction Rate* which is independent of sex (a numerical example of its calculation being shown in J.I.A., LXXIV, 312). This solution, of course, still attacks the problem only in a formal mathematical sense, and therefore is again open to the practical objection (see J.I.A., LXXIV, 321, 325, 327, and 331) that its basic assumptions, as in the earlier formulations of the theory underlying reproduction rates, are unrealistic.

(*iv*) Criticizing equations (82)–(84) from the viewpoint that the functions $\psi(x)$ and $\xi(y)$ do not correspond to reality since males do not produce female children exclusively and vice versa, and that the masculinity $m(t)$, which in reality is almost constant, can vary peculiarly under condition (84), P. H. Karmel in J.I.A., LXXIV, 331–32 set out the equations involving directly a marriage function and birth rates to couples— instead of following the female-to-female and male-to-male births as in equations (76)–(78), or Pollard's female-to-male and male-to-female system of (82)–(84). Under the simplest conditions on this basis, $M_M(x, y)$ could represent the probability at birth that a male will be living and married at age y to a female aged x, $M_F(x, y)$ the probability at birth that a female will be living and married at age x to a male aged y, and $b(x, y)$ the rate of female births to couples aged x and y, so that

$$B_F(t) = \int_0^\infty \int_0^\infty B_F(t-x)\,M_F(x, y)\,b(x, y)\,dx\,dy \qquad (85)$$

$$B_M(t) = \int_0^\infty \int_0^\infty B_M(t-y)\,M_M(x, y)\,m\,b(x, y)\,dx\,dy \qquad (86)$$

and

$$B_M(t) = mB_F(t).$$ (87)

This system, however, is again over-determinate.

(*v*) In J.I.A., LXXIV, 332–34, Karmel therefore explored an approach (of which, incidentally, the usual method of calculating only a female rate is a special case) by recasting the nuptiality conditions. This led to more complex equations which are determinate. The method at one point takes an arbitrary average, however; and after an elaborate analysis Karmel concluded that "as yet it does not seem to be of practical utility."

173. *Reproduction Rates Based on More Refined Birth Rates.*—All the reproduction rates discussed in the preceding paragraphs have been constructed by using birth rates founded only on the ages of the mother, father, or the couple. Birth rates, however, depend largely on marriage durations as well as parents' ages, and also on order of birth, the number of children born alive to each mother, and sterility and spinsterhood. Suggestions have consequently been made with the object of improving the bases of reproduction rates by taking such factors into account.

(*i*) A net reproduction rate based on ages at and durations of marriage was proposed by C. Clark and R. E. Dyne (in the Economic Record, Australia, XXII, 23). If the ratio $_yb_r$ represents the annual female births during the base year at marriage duration r and age at marriage y^* divided by the corresponding annual marriages, and m_y is the proportion of females aged y who marry at that age, the female rate can then be written as

$$\int_0^\infty \frac{l_y^F}{l_0^F}\, m_y \left(\sum_0^\infty {}_yb_r \right) dy.$$

A numerical example and analysis of this index has been given by A. H. Pollard in J.I.A., LXXIV, 293–305. It requires tabulations of births according to the mother's age at marriage and calendar year of marriage. This information is available in Australia where the method was proposed, but is not recorded on most birth certificates such as the U.S. form shown in par. 22.

(*ii*) The dependence of birth rates and reproduction rates upon order of birth, number of children born alive, and sterility and spinsterhood has been examined by P. K. Whelpton ("Reproduction Rates Adjusted for Age, Parity, Fecundity, and Marriage," J.A.S.A., XLI, 501). Using

---

* This procedure is a development of an earlier but less satisfactory method due to P. H. Karmel (Economic Record, XX, 74, and see J.I.A., LXXIV, 292), which was based on values of b_r for marriage durations r irrespective of ages at marriage (instead of $_yb_r$ for marriage durations r and ages at marriage y as used by Clark and Dyne).

the term "parity" to mean the number of children born alive (in the sense that a zero-parity woman has had no live child, a first-parity woman has had one, etc., so that only the woman of n-parity can be exposed to the risk of bearing a child of $n + 1$ order), Whelpton illustrated the calculation of female gross and net reproduction rates, and intrinsic rates of natural increase (see par. 174 here), from birth rates which took into account parity as well as age, and also were refined further to allow for sterility and spinsterhood by assuming that 10% of women are sterile and 10% cannot marry before age 50. The numerical effects of these adjustments were not large. The investigation served, however, to direct attention again to the internal contradictions which are implied in the construction of reproduction rates from birth rates based on age alone (cf. A. J. Lotka, Annals of Mathematical Statistics, XIX, 205).

(*iii*) "Generation" reproduction rates, based on the total number of children ever born to a particular generation of women throughout their child-bearing years, have been discussed by M. Depoid ("Études Démographiques," No. 1, Statistique Général de la France) and T. J. Woofter (Human Biology, XIX, and J.A.S.A., XLIV, 509). Such rates possess the merit of replacing the assumption of unvarying mortality and fertility by the different rates appropriate in successive calendar years for a designated generation of women (between, say, ages 15 and 45); but they have the disadvantage that the calculations are extended over a long span of past years.

(*iv*) A "cohort" replacement rate has therefore been suggested and illustrated by T. J. Woofter in J.A.S.A., XLIV, 512, with the object of obtaining a measure based on data closer to the current year. He remarks, however, that the resulting rates "refer neither wholly to the present nor wholly to the complete experience of generations," and thus are still affected by the insoluble difficulties which largely vitiate all these attempts to find a single numerical reproduction index.

174. *The Inherent Rate of Natural Increase.*—Equations (76), (77), and (79), for females, males, and persons respectively can be written generally, by dropping the subscripts, as

$$B(t) = \int_0^\infty B(t - x)\, \varphi(x)\, dx. \qquad (88)$$

This fundamental equation, as will be apparent from its derivation in par. 172, does not refer explicitly to any initial state and therefore holds regardless of the origins of the population. This, of course, is both natural and proper, for evolution in nature is a continuous process starting from origins of which we have no knowledge. As will be noted later in par. 175

and formula (90), the arbitrary origins of the population are represented in the mathematical development by coefficients Q_n, so that the problem becomes determinate.

It will be evident, moreover, that the birth function, $B(t)$, although certainly continuous, will not be expressible under the assumed conditions by the same function of t at all points during its development. This may be seen, for example, from the synthesis given by E. C. Rhodes in J.R.S.S., CIII, 62 et seq., tracing the number of female births year by year which follow, on the assumptions here under consideration with λ and L delimiting the child-bearing ages, in successive generations from N female children all born at time 0.* A single function used throughout its range therefore will give only an approximate representation of $B(t)$. If, nevertheless, we assume that the same function for $B(t)$ can be substituted on both sides of (88), it can be seen that the equation will be satisfied, for all values of t, by a series of exponentials

$$B(t) = Q_1 e^{r_1 t} + Q_2 e^{r_2 t} + \ldots = \Sigma Q_n e^{r_n t} \tag{89}$$

so long as

$$\Sigma Q_n e^{r_n t} = \int_0^\infty \Sigma Q_n e^{r_n(t-x)} \varphi(x) \, dx = \Sigma Q_n e^{r_n t} \int_0^\infty e^{-r_n x} \varphi(x) \, dx,$$

that is, so long as

$$\int_0^\infty e^{-r_n x} \varphi(x) \, dx = 1$$

for each value of r_n.† Theoretically the roots $r_1, r_2, \ldots$, real or complex,

* Under those circumstances no children will be born while the original N are growing to maturity at age λ, so that then $B(t)$ is 0; between λ and 2λ the children born at time t will be $N\varphi(t)$; from 2λ to 3λ children of the second generation will also appear because some of those born after λ will have reached maturity, so that $B(t)$ will again be different; and so on. Generally, the result can be written $B(t) = N[\varphi(t) + \varphi_1(t) + \varphi_2(t) + \ldots]$. For large values of t the earlier functions of course make no contribution, and the number of functions involved is limited.

† The mathematical treatment given in this paragraph is a condensed statement of the theory as it has been evolved since about 1907 by numerous authors through many papers written in French, German, Swedish, Italian, and English. In 1909 L. Herbelot (Bulletin Trimestriel de l'Institut des Actuaires Français, XIX, 293) stated the fundamental integral equation of the type of (88) in an actuarial problem, using for its solution the method of successive differentiations—this method also being employed subsequently by Risser, Zwinggi, and Schultless in France and Switzerland. In 1908, however, P. Hertz (Mathematische Annalen, LXV, 1) and G. Herglotz (*ibid.*, LXV, 87) had given a convenient form of solution (as employed here). In 1911 this solution was therefore adopted by F. R. Sharpe and A. J. Lotka (Philosophical Magazine, XXI, 435) in an investigation of the problems of age distribution and natural increase; and thereafter numerous papers appeared on various aspects of the questions involved. Among these papers it may be noted particularly that in 1931 S. D. Wicksell (Skandinavisk

of this last equation are infinite in number; there is, however, only one positive real root (since $\int_0^\infty e^{-rx}\varphi(x)\,dx$, in which $\varphi(x)$ is by nature a positive function, decreases as r increases). The complex roots define the oscillations about the real root which gives the ultimate constant value of r. Furthermore, it can be shown (cf. Rhodes, *loc. cit.*, p. 77) that (89) tends to Qe^{rt} as t approaches ∞—that is to say, the ultimate form which the birth function $B(t)$ attains, under the assumed conditions of fixed birth and mortality rates by age, is Qe^{rt}. (The contributions to $B(t)$ given by the complex roots, and the manner in which $B(t)$ when t is large takes the form Qe^{rt} where r is the real root, can be seen from the numerical illustrations in J.R.S.S., CIII, 85, and in several of Lotka's papers.)

Starting again, as in par. 172, with $B(t-x)$ births at time $t-x$, the number who survive and are aged x to $x+dx$ at time t will be $B(t-x)_xp_0dx$. Writing $p(x, t)$ for $B(t-x)_xp_0$, and substituting the ultimate form of the birth function just established, it follows that when t is large

$$p(x, t) = Q\,e^{r(t-x)}{}_xp_0 = Q\,e^{rt}(e^{-rx}{}_xp_0).\qquad(90)$$

Also, the total population at time t, say $P(t)$, is $\int_0^\omega p(x, t)\,dx$ where ω is the limit of life; consequently from (90) when t is large

$$P(t) = Q\,e^{rt}\int_0^\omega e^{-rx}{}_xp_0dx.\qquad(91)$$

From (90) and (91) the ratio

$$\frac{p(x, t)}{P(t)},$$

Aktuarietidskrift, XIV, 125) obtained another solution (for which see J.I.A., LXXIV, 291) of the integral equation, by fitting a Type III Pearson curve to the net fertility function $\varphi(x)$, which in practice gives identical results, and that A. J. Lotka contributed largely to the development of the subject. A valuable and extensive bibliography, and comments on this history, may be found conveniently in Lotka's paper in the Annals of Mathematical Statistics, X, 1. The original sources should be consulted for detailed treatments of some of the more rigorous mathematical points which arise. The papers of E. C. Rhodes in J.R.S.S., CIII, 61, 218, and 362 provide an especially valuable summary.

An entirely different mathematical approach based on matrices and vectors has been given recently by P. H. Leslie—see his papers on "The Use of Matrices in Certain Population Mathematics" in Biometrika, XXXIII, 183 (with further notes in the same journal for 1948), and "The Distribution in Time of the Births in Successive Generations," J.R.S.S., CXI, 44. A. J. Lotka has observed (Annals of Mathematical Statistics, XIX, 204) that "the first application of the matrix method to these problems seems to be due to H. Bernardelli, 'Population Waves,' Journal of the Burma Research Society, XXXI (1941), 1." This treatment, however, need not be included here.

being the proportion of the total population at time t which is aged x to $x + dx$, is then seen to be independent of t when t is large—that is to say, the population, which is subject to unchanging mortality and birth rates, and regardless of its origins, ultimately attains a stable age distribution. This proposition was first established by Sharpe and Lotka in 1911 (Philosophical Magazine, XXI, 435—see also Proceedings of the Eighth American Scientific Congress, VIII, 299).

Writing now $\int_0^\omega e^{-rx} {}_x p_0 \, dx = \dfrac{1}{b}$ which is independent of t, (91) becomes

$$P(t) = \frac{Q\, e^{rt}}{b} .$$

In this population the rate of increase $\dfrac{1}{P} \dfrac{dP}{dt}$ is r. It therefore may be said that a population which is subject indefinitely to unchanging birth and mortality rates by age (with no immigration or emigration) would ultimately, whatever its origins may have been, settle down to a stable age distribution which increases (necessarily by an excess of births over deaths) at the inherent rate r. This is called *The Inherent Rate of Natural Increase.** It is, as will be seen from the preceding analysis, the value which satisfies the integral equation

$$\int_0^\infty e^{-rx} \varphi(x) \, dx = 1 . \tag{92}$$

The numerical solution for r in (92) cannot be effected directly. A sufficiently accurate value, however, can be obtained (see A. J. Lotka, J.A.S.A., XX, 330–32) by solving the quadratic equation

$$\tfrac{1}{2}\beta r^2 + a\, r - \log_e R_0' = 0 , \tag{93}$$

where

$$R_n' = \int_0^\infty x^n \varphi(x) \, dx , \qquad a = \frac{R_1'}{R_0'}, \qquad \text{and} \qquad \beta = a^2 - \frac{R_2'}{R_0'} . \dagger$$

* Alternative designations are the "intrinsic rate of natural increase," the "true rate of natural increase," the "ultimate rate of increase," or the "natural rate of increase."

† A closely approximate value can also be obtained from the following considerations. The net reproduction rate (here indicated by R_0'—the primes distinguishing these symbols from the R of the customary linear compounding notation used in the footnote to par. 111) is actually the ratio of the total births in two successive generations. The mean length, a say, of one generation evidently is given in the table of par. 168 by R_1'/R_0'. Since the inherent rate of natural increase, r, is an annual rate, it follows that $(1 + r)^a = R_0'$, or $R_0' = e^{ra}$, approximately (this relation also emerging from (93) by dropping the first term). In the numerical example, r thus computed approximately from $\log_e R_0'$ and a only is .00561 in comparison with .00563 obtained from (93).

In the example of par. 168 here, the value calculated by this method is shown to be .00563—that is to say, the female population is there estimated to possess an inherent rate of natural increase which, under its assumed unvarying mortality and birth rates by age and if it is left to itself and there is no migration, ultimately (i.e., when the population has attained a stable age distribution) would reach .563% p.a., being an increase of 5.63 daughters per 1,000 female population per annum.

175. At this stage it will be well to make clear the relationships between the hypothetical population represented by the mathematical model examined in par. 174, which starts from any origins whatever and ultimately reaches a stable age distribution increasing at rate r, and the hypothetical life-table population of customary actuarial practice which starts with a fixed number of births ($l_0 = N$, say) and is stationary ($r = 0$).

In the more general population increasing at rate r it has been shown in (91) that the total population, $P(t)$ at time t, is ultimately $Q e^{rt} \int_0^\omega e^{-rx} {}_x p_0 dx$. The birth rate at time t when t is large is

$$\frac{B(t)}{P(t)} = \frac{1}{\int_0^\omega e^{-rx} {}_x p_0 dx},$$

which is the b independent of time already used. The death rate is evidently $b - r$. In the life table, on the other hand, where $r = 0$ and the population is stationary so that time t may be disregarded, the total number living similarly computed is $N \int_0^\omega {}_x p_0 dx *$; the birth rate is

$$\frac{N}{N \int_0^\omega {}_x p_0 dx} = \frac{1}{\int_0^\omega {}_x p_0 dx};$$

and since the population is stationary the deaths and births are equal. Thus the life table is the particular case of the generalized population when $r = 0$.

The analogies here shown also may serve to emphasize the extent to which actuarial life-table procedures—devised for computational facility on the assumption of a stationary population for technical convenience only (cf. par. 64, footnote)—have been transplanted into the wider demographic field in attempts to deal with the very different problems of reproduction theory.

* This shows immediately, by analogy, that the Q in (91) is in fact determined by the origins of the population.

176. The inherent rate of natural increase evolved in pars. 174–75 can be modified suitably, of course, if the mathematical model employed is elaborated in accordance with the ideas discussed in pars. 172(*i*)–(*v*) and 173. Thus Pollard in J.I.A., LXXIV, 308 et seq., investigated the "joint rate of natural increase" on his basis of par. 172(*iii*), and also gave the rates on the assumptions made by Karmel and by Clark and Dyne as noted in par. 173(*i*). The rates emerging from the procedures of par. 173(*ii*) are shown in Whelpton's paper.

177. *The Replacement Index.*—All the reproduction rates and inherent rates of natural increase discussed in this Section require the use of birth rates by age (and sometimes also by durations of marriage). If those birth rates are not available (as might be the case for small groups of the population), a simple *Replacement Index* based only on the given population in age groups and a suitable life table has been suggested. The calculation is made by taking the ratio of the female children in a given age group in the actual population to the women in that population who would have been in the reproductive age period when the children were born, and dividing by the corresponding ratio from the life table. This rough method (which was suggested by W. S. Thompson, and has been analyzed by A. J. Lotka in J.A.S.A., XXXI, 273), was found by A. H. Pollard to give values which move closely parallel to the net reproduction rate (see J.I.A., LXXIV, 289, 314, and 317).

178. In pars. 170–71 the limitations surrounding the theory of reproduction rates were emphasized, and from the development shown in par. 174 it will be apparent that the same basic theory underlies both reproduction rates and the inherent rate of natural increase. The fundamental concepts of both measures, therefore, are equally vulnerable. Although the theory must, it seems, be included in this Study as an interesting application of actuarial technique demanding alert critical faculties, it is almost impossible for these rates to escape the charge that they are fatally unrealistic, and that consequently (as already observed in par. 171) their basic theories and numerical values cannot displace detailed analyses of the actual mortality, marriage, and birth rates by ages and durations in any examination of the cumulative trends in deaths, marriages, births, and the resulting population.

XV

SICKNESS DATA

179. The statistician's interest in records of sickness (or "morbidity") is a necessary consequence of his study of statistics of the previous occurrence of birth and the subsequent happening of death. The possibility of statistical analysis of the various types of sickness, however, is limited to those ailments which are sufficiently serious to require the attention of a doctor, for in other cases no record of the sickness could be obtained; and even in cases requiring medical attention it has usually been considered practicable to require official record only of those diseases which either are infectious or indicate the existence of occupational conditions which it is desirable to remedy.

180. Sickness data in respect of the general population may be collected either (1) by census methods of enumeration, or (2) by continuous registration. The first of these methods cannot be depended upon to give any reliable data with regard to durations of illnesses—for, as in the case of the attempts to collect death records on the census schedules (see par. 17, second footnote), the information usually would be obtained by enumerators without any medical background, and would be supplied to them by the persons concerned, or by third parties, who frequently would have poor memories as well as defective knowledge. A census enumeration of sickness, moreover, can give only a measure of the "prevalence" of sickness at the date of the enquiry; and although the data may of course be stated according to type of sickness, age, sex, occupation, etc., such important statistical information as the number of days of disability per person exposed can only be estimated roughly (cf. Sir Alfred Watson's remarks in J.R.S.S., XC, 467). Historical instances of the use of this census method are to be found in the questions relating to sickness which were included in the 1880 and 1890 United States census population schedules. More recently the National Health Survey of 1935–36 by the U.S. Public Health Service was conducted on lines which followed census methods.

181. The collection of sickness data by (2), continuous registration, originated in the necessity for public supervision over certain dangerous infectious diseases, such as smallpox, and has been extended to include other infectious and occupational maladies which also are preventable. The problem has been considered repeatedly by the British and American

Medical Associations, and by other bodies, since about 1855. The first experiments were of a voluntary or semi-voluntary character—Massachusetts and Michigan in the United States inaugurating plans for voluntary notification of certain diseases in 1874 and 1876 respectively, while in England local Acts providing for compulsory notification in those localities willing to do so were placed in operation in Huddersfield in 1876 and Bolton in 1877. In the United States, where such matters are under the control of each individual State, the first system which was compulsory and at the same time comprehensive seems to have been that adopted by Michigan in 1883. In England the Infectious Diseases (Notification) Act of 1889, which empowered any sanitary officer to enforce compulsory notification, was extended in 1899 and placed in operation over the entire country (see Newsholme's "Vital Statistics," pp. 123 et seq., and J. W. Trask's Supplement No. 12, U.S. Public Health Reports, 1914).

The systems thus inaugurated have been continually improved. In Britain weekly returns of the notifiable diseases reported to them have been made for many years by the local medical officers of health—these returns being tabulated and published in the Registrar-General's Quarterly Reports, and summarized and interpreted in the Annual Reports. The clearing system used in the United States was established in 1906 with the U.S. Public Health Service as the central agency, through which weekly Public Health Reports are published.

182. Since the value of the periodical returns in the United States depends largely upon uniformity of procedure and adequate enforcement by the individual States, a "Model State Law for Morbidity Reports" was approved in 1913 by the Public Health Service and a number of individual States. In addition to a list of notifiable diseases, and regulations providing that the original reports shall be made by the attending physician to the local health officer and thence to the State Department of Health, a "standard notification blank" was adopted calling for information by the physician as to (a) Name of disease, (b) Patient's name, age, sex, color, and address, (c) Occupation, (d) School attended by or place of employment of patient, (e) Number of persons, adults, and children in household, (f) Physician's opinion of probable source of infection or origin of disease, (g) If smallpox, whether mild or virulent, and number of times and dates of vaccination, and (h) If typhoid fever, scarlet fever, diphtheria, or septic sore throat, whether patient or any member of household was engaged in the production or handling of milk (see J. W. Trask, *op. cit.*, p. 45).

A standard diagnosis code for use in tabulating morbidity statistics, with the intention that it should be linked closely to the 1938 revision of the International List of Causes of Death, was also developed in the United States Public Health Service and the Bureau of the Census in 1940 (see Vital Statistics Special Reports, XII, No. 6) on the basis of a system of codification which had been published by J. Berkson in 1936 (American Journal of Public Health, XXVI, 606, and Proceedings, Staff Meeting, Mayo Clinic, XI, 396). After revision it was embodied in a Manual for Coding Causes of Illness. A further important advance has now been made by the promulgation of the 1948 revision of the International List, under its new name as the International Statistical Classification of Diseases, Injuries, and Causes of Death (see par. 146 here), by which for the first time a single list has become available for the uniform classification of morbidity as well as mortality.

183. Where notification is properly enforced in conjunction with uniform coding and tabulation, valuable statistics as to the prevalence and incidence of various types of sickness can be compiled. Rates of sickness, expressing the number of cases for each disease in each population group, may be stated by age, sex, occupation, etc., where the numbers are sufficiently large, and the corresponding "crude" rates without distinction of sex and age may also sometimes give a fair indication of the healthiness of the community (although such crude rates are, as always, subject to the limitations pointed out in par. 138). It will be seen, however, that the data are not generally available for the computation of rates of sickness according to duration.

XVI

CONCLUSION

184. This Study is concerned primarily with the methods of *compiling* the various types of population statistics which are of value to the actuary. It is thus intended to deal only incidentally with the subsequent interpretation of the statistics so prepared, and it excludes consideration of many other allied problems which are more particularly interesting to the general statistician. These further questions are treated extensively in a number of the works mentioned in this Study, and also in many additional references—both in English and other languages—which will be found in them. The student is therefore referred to those sources for any further information which he may require in subsequent research work, and particularly to the reports of the Registrar-General of England and Wales and the Bureau of the Census and the National Office of Vital Statistics in the United States, as well as the Journals of the Royal Statistical Society and the American Statistical Association, and the periodicals entitled "Population Studies" and "Population Index."

APPENDIX

SOME THEORY IN THE SAMPLING OF HUMAN POPULATIONS

By W. Edwards Deming, Ph.D.

1. *The Reasons for Sampling.*—Complete population censuses, in which appropriate questions are asked in respect of every individual, are large and ponderous; they employ many people; they are therefore costly. Much time is required to collect the information, and thence to tabulate the statistical data in vast hand and machine operations before the material is ready for release. Through the use of proper statistical techniques, a sample selection, instead of a complete count, can often be made with notable economies in effort, time, and cost, and generally with more efficient control. It must be remembered, however, that a sample does not give data advantageously for very small areas—or to put it in another way, the most economical sample for small areas is often one of 100%.

From the results of a sample survey, estimates are prepared which are expected to give approximations in varying degrees to the results that would have been obtained if a complete count had been taken with the same care and the same definitions. The degree of approximation is measured by the "standard error" of the estimate. Repetition of a sample will yield a distribution of estimates.

2. *Uses of Sample Surveys.*—Sample surveys are used in connection with population statistics mainly for the following purposes:

(1) To obtain counts and characteristics of the population without recourse to a complete census. For example, sample censuses of nine cities in the United States were taken in 1944 (see "A Chapter in Population Sampling," Bureau of the Census, 1947). A more remarkable achievement was the sample censuses of population and agriculture in Northern Rhodesia and Southern Rhodesia, without benefit of a prior complete census.

(2) To obtain additional characteristics of the population when the frame* is furnished by a concurrent complete census or registration. Examples are: (*a*) In the U.S. population census of 1940, supplementary information was obtained from a 5% sample of the inhabitants, and in the 1950 census samples of 20% and $3\frac{1}{3}\%$ were used (as described in par. 12

---

* "Frame" is explained in the section dealing with definitions. For the moment it may be regarded as a list of the population, area by area, dwelling unit by dwelling unit, or even name by name.

of this volume), thus broadening the scope of the census at little expense; and further economies were effected by tabulating much of the regular census information for a sample only. (*b*) In the Swedish extraordinary census of 1936, information was obtained by direct interrogation from a sample of names drawn from the national register. (*c*) Samples of areas are used to test the completeness of birth and death registrations (as noted by C. Chandrasekar and W. E. Deming, J.A.S.A., XLIV, 101; see also par. 46 of this volume).

(3) To obtain characteristics of the population without a concurrent census. Thus the Current Population Survey of the United States, initiated in 1939, gives monthly figures on employment and unemployment by age-groups, hours worked in agricultural and non-agricultural pursuits, and numerous other regular and occasional details. A similar example is furnished by the quarterly survey in Canada, initiated in 1945.

3. *Some of the Uses of Sampling in Connection with Censuses of Population.*—The next step is to enumerate and to discuss some of the ways in which sampling is used in connection with a complete census:

(*a*) In connection with a complete census, to ask certain questions of only a sample of the population. (Aim: to broaden the scope of the census at low cost, without proportionate increase in the burden of response or in the time required for carrying out the work.)

(*b*) To tabulate a sample of a complete census. (Aim: to hasten the results for large areas; to save time and expense in the production of some of the tables that would ordinarily be produced from the complete census; to broaden the scope of the tabulations.)

(*c*) To collect information from only a sample of areas or of other units. (Aim: to replace a complete census by a sample census; to gain speed; to decrease the cost or to provide information under conditions that render a complete census either unnecessary or impossible.)

(*d*) To control the quality of the coding, punching, and tabulating, at various stages of the processing. (Aim: to investigate the effects of such errors on the published tables; to control and to improve the quality of the finished product; to save time and money in the completion of the work.)

(*e*) To investigate the quality and the meaning of the figures obtained in a census. (Aim: in samples of areas, selected with the aid of statistical theory, to carry out studies on completeness of coverage, over- and under-enumeration, misunderstandings of the questionnaire, differences between interviewers; to test various methods of obtaining the information.)

4. *Definitions.*—The *frame* is a list (or file) of areas, farms, households, people, or of business establishments that would be covered in a complete count (a 100% sample). The sample is drawn from the frame. If the frame

fails to cover certain regions that are supposedly in the study, then both a complete count and a sample will be in error, by about the same amount, and for the same reason. A frame is the first step, for either a sample or a complete count.

Each member of the frame (each line, or each card) is a *sampling unit*. Each sampling unit must have a definite probability of being drawn into the sample; it is this requirement that produces a *probability sample*—by definition one whose standard error can be calculated.

An *estimate* is a number calculated from the results of the sample which is expected to give an approximation, with calculable sampling error, to the result that would have been obtained for the universe if the sample had been total. The procedure of calculating an estimate must be included as part of the sample-design. The degree of approximation of an estimate is measurable by its standard error.

The *standard error* of an estimate is a measure of precision. It is the standard deviation of all the possible estimates that may be formed from a specified sampling procedure. To be usable, a sampling procedure must be one for which the standard error is calculable from the results of a sample. A standard error is *not* calculated from outside comparisons (vide infra).

The *bias* of a procedure is a bias of the method, that is to say, of the definitions used, the form of questionnaire, the method of canvass (e.g., whether mail or interview), the training given to the interviewers, the procedure for selecting them, or of the formula of estimate. Bias, whether the survey be a complete count or a sample, is detectable and measurable only by comparing different methods in an approved experimental design.

The *population* of a sample-unit or of the frame is the number of people in it conforming to a prescribed characteristic. In the ordinary sense, the "population" of a city is its number of inhabitants, i.e., the number of people therein possessing the characteristic of being alive at midnight or at noon of a prescribed date. But a city or any sampling unit has also many other populations such as the number of males, the number of females, the number of children 10–14 in school, the number of employed males 20–29, the number of births or of deaths last month, etc. The symbol a_i will be used to denote the population of sampling unit i in the universe, and the subscript i will take the values $1, 2, \ldots, N$ for the sampling units into which the frame will be divided. P_i will denote the probability of a_i being drawn. (In the theory of multi-stage sampling, two indexes will be needed to form symbols such as a_{ij}).

The *sample design* is the blue-print of the procedure for drawing the sampling units into the sample and for forming the estimates.

5. *The Aim of Sample Design.*—Sample design requires the adaptation

of existing mathematical theory to the available facilities and administrative restrictions, and the development of new theory and new facilities when advantageous. The aims in modern sample design are these:

(*i*) To decide what precision is desirable in view of the probable costs and uses of the data.

(*ii*) To meet this precision by laying out efficient, workable, and foolproof mathematical procedures for (*a*) drawing the sampling units into the sample; (*b*) calculating the estimates to be made; (*c*) calculating the precisions of these estimates; (*d*) measuring any biases or differences in need of measurement.

The greater the accuracy demanded, the greater the cost of the survey. In all surveys (both complete counts and samples) uncertainties arise from many sources (interviewer bias, lack of clarity of definitions, non-response, etc.*), and it is wasteful to refine the sampling error too far in view of these other errors. Moreover, as data are needed as a basis for action, there is always a limiting precision beyond which the action would not be affected; in the planning of any survey, therefore, a certain "aimed at" precision will be specified which might be, for instance, a 1% or perhaps 3% sampling error in a population count, 10% in an inventory of wheat, 20% in a survey of housing characteristics, etc.

In the planning of a survey for the first time the "aimed at" precision can literally only be aimed at because some of the necessary constants in the appropriate formula for the sampling error will usually be known only approximately before the survey is taken. In a series of repeated surveys, however, the accumulated experience enables the cost of the surveys to be lowered and the precision to be adjusted closely to the requirements.

(*iii*) To appraise the precision that was actually obtained, after the survey is completed.

The constants in the formula for the sampling error, which were needed in the planning of the survey, may be estimated from the returns of the survey with some firmness, and with these constants the so-called "standard errors" of the estimates made from the survey can be calculated.†

Further information concerning the reliability of the survey may be gained by comparing its results with other surveys and studying any

---

* A partial list of sources of uncertainties, with comments, was published by W. E. Deming in the American Sociological Review, IX (1944), 359–69. This paper, revised, now forms Chapter 2 in his book "Some Theory of Sampling" (1950).

† For examples of appraisal see "A Chapter in Population Sampling," p. 14, and Chapters 11 and 12 in Deming's "Some Theory of Sampling."

significant differences. If any supplementary or simultaneous experiments were conducted in order to make tests of coverage and definitions, or to measure differences between interviewers, or between different versions of the questionnaire, these experiments should be summarized, and their bearing on the reliability of the results of the survey should be carefully explained.

6. *Random Variables; Random Numbers.*—A random variable is a number produced by a random operation. Empirically it is possible, with care, to simulate a random operation. The calculated distribution of a random variable is thus to be regarded as a prediction of a real distribution which may be obtained empirically under certain conditions. Satisfactory simulation of the random operation of drawing a sampling unit, giving all units equal probabilities, is realized in practice by the use of *random numbers*—for instance, L. H. C. Tippett's "Random Sampling Numbers," or R. A. Fisher and F. Yates's "Statistical Tables for Biological, Agricultural, and Medical Research." In some of the descriptions that follow it will be convenient to speak of the random operation of drawing sampling units as the drawing of chips from a bowl containing N physically similar chips, each marked to identify a one-to-one correspondence between it and a particular sampling unit of the frame to be sampled.

If the N sampling units are listed on N lines or cards in any convenient order, and numbered serially from 1 to N, the act of reading out a random number between 1 and N gives all N sampling units equal probability, and designates a particular sampling unit for the sample. The drawing of n random numbers produces a sample of n units.

The *mean* of the frame will be

$$\mu = \frac{1}{N} \sum_1^N a_i \tag{1}$$

and its *variance* will be

$$\sigma^2 = \frac{1}{N} \sum_1^N (a_i - \mu)^2. \tag{2}$$

Some of the a_i values may be equal. Let them then be grouped into M different classes which fall at

$$z_1, z_2, z_3, \ldots, z_M$$

with proportions

$$p_1, p_2, p_3, \ldots, p_M.$$

In this case

$$\mu = \sum_1^M p_i z_i \tag{3}$$

and

$$\sigma^2 = \sum_1^M p_i \, (z_i - \mu)^2$$

$$= \sum_1^M p_i z_i^2 - \mu^2. \tag{4}$$

The square root of the variance of a universe is its *standard deviation*, denoted by σ.

A useful measure of a distribution of which the mean is not near 0 is the *coefficient of variation*, γ, defined as the standard deviation of the universe measured in units of the mean, so that

$$\gamma = \frac{\sigma}{\mu}. \tag{5}$$

Let a sample of n units be drawn by a random operation, and let the n values of a_i be recorded *in the order drawn*. Any one sample will appear as

$$x_1, x_2, \ldots, x_n.$$

Then—to give a number of examples—the following functions of the sample are all random variables—

$$x_1; \qquad x_2; \qquad x_n; \qquad x_1 + 2, \qquad \text{for instance;}$$

$$\frac{1}{n}(x_1 + x_2 + \ldots + x_n) = \bar{x}; \qquad \frac{1}{n}(x_1^2 + x_2^2 + \ldots + x_n^2);$$

the median; the range; the maximum; the minimum.

Upon restoring the drawings, either one at a time as drawn, or after the whole sample is drawn, a new sample and a new set of random variables may be produced. The functions listed above will vary from sample to sample in a random manner; this is why they are random variables.

7. *Fundamental Theorems.*—Mathematical manipulations of the P-values of the chips in the bowl will lead to the distributions of random variables such as those already listed. Thus,* the mean of the distribution of $\bar{x}$

---

* It is presumed that the student understands the use of the operator E which in the theory of sampling denotes a mathematical average. The operator is commutative:

$$E(x+y) = Ex + Ey; \qquad E \sum_1^n x_i = \sum_1^n Ex_i.$$

will be

$$E\bar{x} = E\frac{1}{n}\sum_{1}^{n} x_i$$

$$= \frac{1}{n}\sum_{1}^{n} Ex_i$$

$$= \frac{1}{n}\left[\sum_{1}^{N} P_i a_i + \text{similar expressions to } n \text{ terms}\right]$$

$$= \sum_{1}^{N} P_i a_i. \tag{6}$$

If all the P_i are equal to $1/N$, i.e., if all N have the same probability of being drawn, this reduces to

$$E\bar{x} = \frac{1}{N}\sum_{1}^{N} a_i = \frac{A}{N} = \mu, \tag{7}$$

A being defined as $\sum_{1}^{N} a_i$, the total population of all sampling units constituting the frame, and μ being defined as the mean population per unit. We thus see that $\bar{x}$ is an *unbiased* estimate of μ when all of the N have the same probability of being drawn.

The variance of the distribution of $\bar{x}$, on the theory that the drawings are made without replacements, will be

$$\sigma_{\bar{x}}^2 = E(\bar{x} - E\bar{x})^2$$

$$= E\left[\sum_{1}^{n} x_i\right]^2 - \mu^2$$

$$= \frac{N-n}{N-1}\frac{\sigma^2}{n}. \tag{8}$$

The derivation of (8) is given, for instance, in Deming's "Some Theory of Sampling," p. 101. It is to be remembered that if every chip has the same chance of being drawn, and $P(r)$ denotes the probability of getting exactly r black chips,

$$P(r) = \binom{n}{r} q^{n-r}p^r \qquad \text{if the chips are drawn with replacement} \tag{9}$$

or

$$P(r) = \frac{\binom{Nq}{n-r}\binom{Np}{r}}{\binom{N}{n}} \quad \text{if the chips are drawn without replacement} \tag{10}$$

where $$\binom{n}{r} = \frac{n!}{r!\,(n-r)!}\,,$$

the number of possible combinations of n items taken r at a time.

Then it can be shown easily that, whether the drawings are made with or without replacement,

$$Er = \Sigma r P(r) = np \tag{11}$$

and that

$$\sigma_r^2 = \Sigma r^2 P(r) - (Er)^2$$

$$= npq \text{ with replacement} \tag{12}$$

or $$\frac{N-n}{N-1}\,npq \text{ without replacement}. \tag{12a}$$

The formulae for drawings with replacements are, of course, based on the supposition that the proportion black remains constant so that the "point binomial" (the Bernoulli series) applies. When the drawings are made without replacements, however, so that the proportion black does not remain constant, the hypergeometric series provides the basis as in (10). See Wolfenden's "Fundamental Principles of Mathematical Statistics," pp. 12–13, 27, and 65–66, and Deming's "Some Theory of Sampling," p. 121, for the proof of (12a) without replacement.

The factor $(N-n)/(N-1)$ in (8) is called the *finite multiplier* because it arises from the finite size of N. It is 0 if $n = N$, in which case the sample is complete, and there is no error in $\bar{x}$ at all; it is 1 if $n = 1$, and approaches 1 as $N \to \infty$. It is often written in the approximate form $1 - n/N$. Clearly, if the sample is small, for example if $n/N = 5\%$, expansion of the frame to double, treble, or 10 times its present size N will have little effect on the variance of $\bar{x}$. Thus it will be realized that a sample of 1,000 families drawn from a city containing 20,000 families is only insignificantly more reliable than a sample of 1,000 families from the entire 45,000,000 families of the United States. The important measure of the size of a sample is its absolute size, n, not its percentage of N.

It follows that a survey designed to give regional data for 9 geographic regions is almost 9 times as expensive as a survey designed to give data only for the country as a whole. Demands for local data must thus be considered not only with regard to the need for such data, but with regard to costs.

The square root $\sigma_{\bar{x}}$ of the variance $\sigma_{\bar{x}}^2$ of $\bar{x}$ is known as the *standard error* of the estimate $\bar{x}$. More precisely it is the standard error of the particular *sampling procedure* by which $\bar{x}$ is produced. The standard error is an important measure of the variability of an estimate because 3 standard errors measured each side of the mean of any ordinary distribution will contain practically all of the distribution; hence a sampling error is practically never observed outside the range $Ex \pm 3\sigma_x$, where Ex is the mean of the distribution of the random variable x, and σ_x is the standard error of the estimating procedure. The range $Ex \pm 2\sigma_x$ contains about 95% of the distribution of x. (See Wolfenden's "Fundamental Principles of Mathematical Statistics," p. 20.)

Suppose that a random variable X be defined as

$$X = N\bar{x} .$$ (13)

Then

$$EX = N\mu = A .$$ (14)

Thus X is an *unbiased estimate* of the total population A of the frame.

Since the mean square error (variance) of a multiple, when c is a constant, is given by the relation (see Wolfenden, *op. cit.*, p. 23)

$$\sigma^2_{cx} = c^2 \sigma^2_x$$ (15)

it follows from (8) that

$$\sigma^2_{\bar{x}} = \frac{N-n}{N-1} \frac{N^2\sigma^2}{n} .$$ (16)

Again adopting the convenience of the coefficient of variation, we may divide (8) by μ^2 and (16) by $(N\mu)^2$ and obtain

$$C_X = C_{\bar{x}} = \sqrt{\frac{N-n}{N-1}} \frac{\gamma}{\sqrt{n}}$$

$$\doteq \left(1 - \frac{n}{2N}\right) \frac{\gamma}{\sqrt{n}} \text{ when } \frac{n}{N} \text{ is small}$$ (17)

where C_X and $C_{\bar{x}}$ denote the coefficients of variation of this procedure for estimating X and $\bar{x}$, and γ is the coefficient of variation σ/μ of the frame. This is a very useful and convenient form for the variances of the estimates.

Samples drawn with proper precaution with random numbers will be found to give results in close conformity with these equations.

A case of great practical importance is the frame of 2 cells, which is useful when the sampling units can be classed as black and white, or vacant and not vacant, or passed and rejected, etc. In this case we shall assume that

$$Nq \text{ are labeled } a_i = 0$$

$$Np \text{ are labeled } a_i = 1 .$$

The mean of this frame is

$$\mu = p ,$$ (18)

and its variance is

$$\sigma^2 = pq \qquad (19)$$

as may be derived directly from (3) and (4).

Let a sample of n be drawn from a 2-celled frame, and let r be the number of black chips in the sample. Each black chip is to count 1, and each white chip 0. Then the symbol which was $\bar{x}$ is now r/n and we shall let

$$\hat{p} = \frac{r}{n}. \qquad (20)$$

It follows from (7) and (8) that if all the chips have equal probabilities,

$$E\hat{p} = p \qquad (21)$$

and that

$$\sigma^2_{\hat{p}} = \frac{N-n}{N-1} \frac{pq}{n}. \qquad (22)$$

Thus $\hat{p}$ or r/n is an unbiased estimate of p, and the variance $\sigma^2_{\hat{p}}$ of this estimate has the value just written.

8. *Single-Stage Sampling.*—The expressions just derived are those for single-stage sampling, in which each of the N sampling units has the same probability as another of being drawn. A frequently occurring application is the sampling of cases from a file of cards, or of dwelling units, farms, etc., from a list or map. Sometimes the frame (i.e., file, map, list, etc.) will already be in existence; in other cases it must be made or brought up to date. In sampling a small city for a count of the population and estimation of the number of people and families having particular characteristics, a complete listing of dwelling units over the entire city might be the initial step, to be followed by interviews at the n dwelling units falling into the sample, which can easily be drawn from the listing.

Suppose, for instance, that γ in (17) has the value 0.7 for the number of people per dwelling unit in some particular city in which a sample of dwelling units are to be interviewed with the aim of estimating the population of the city and the sizes of various classes thereof. Suppose that this is to be a survey of great precision, in which the standard error of the estimated number of inhabitants is to be 1%. Then C_x in (17) is to be .01. If $N = 50,000$ dwelling units, the arithmetic shows that the size of sample should be about 4,900 dwelling units, or about 1 dwelling unit in 10. To attain a standard error of 2%, a sample of only about 1,200 dwelling units would suffice. N here is so large that it has little effect; the sample sizes would be about the same for a city of a million dwelling units.

9. *Systematic or Patterned Sampling.*—In the sampling of human populations some people have used a "systematic or patterned" selection in

place of *n* random drawings. For a 1 in 10 systematic selection (a "decimating" sample) the procedure would be to start with a random number between 1 and 10, and to take this and every 10th dwelling unit thereafter from the list of dwelling units. Straight systematic selections are now being replaced gradually by modifications like the Tukey plan (infra).

If the listing of the *N* dwelling units were randomized to start with, a systematic selection of *n* units from the list would possess no special characteristics to distinguish it from a sample consisting of *n* independent random selections in which a random number is read out for each unit as it is drawn into the sample. However, in the process of listing, a lister will start at one corner of an area and proceed in a systematic manner up and down the streets, roads, and corridors until the job is finished: if he does not make a systematic coverage, he will soon be lost and will list some units twice and others not at all. A map showing small areas numbered in serpentine fashion within a country, county, or city is, in effect, a systematic list. A field or forest is a systematic list of rows, bands, or lines, numbered serially east to west or north to south. Successive units in most frames show some sort of serial correlation. The character of a systematic sample thus arises from the systematic layout of the frame, and not alone from the sampling.

The variance of an estimate formed from a systematic selection* will for some materials be much smaller, and for other materials much larger, than the variance of an estimate formed from a sample in which all *n* units thereof were drawn separately at random, i.e., an "independent random sample." In the sampling of human populations, however, the systematic and independent random procedures usually give about the same variances.†

In the sampling of manufactured articles and equipment, intervals of 5, 10, and multiples thereof should be avoided in a systematic selection because of the possibility of periodicities that may play havoc with the equations for the variance. The strength of modern sampling lies in computable standard errors, and a method must not be used for which the equations for variance are no longer at least approximately applicable. In case of doubt, a systematic or patterned selection should be avoided.

To preserve the advantages of geographic stratification which a

---

* The formulae for the variance of systematic sampling, which are very complicated, have been derived recently by W. G. and L. Madow ("On the Theory of Systematic Sampling, I," Ann. Math. Stat., XV, 1–24).

† See J. G. Osborne, "On the Precision of Estimates from Systematic versus Random Samples," Science, XCIV, 584–85, and "Sampling Errors of Systematic and Random Surveys of Cover-Type Areas," J.A.S.A., XXXVII, 256–64.

systematic selection gives, it is simple to divide the frame into $\frac{1}{2}n$ successive equal or approximately equal groups, and then to take two random selections from each group. This is always a safe method, and is only slightly more difficult to administer than a systematic selection straight through the frame. The Tukey plan (vide infra, par. 10) preserves both the simplicity of a patterned selection and the validity and the simplicity of the formulae for random selections.

The statistician must balance the various advantages and disadvantages against each other. Considerable knowledge regarding the statistical characteristics of a material is necessary before one can be sure of prescribing a highly efficient procedure. It is much more important, and fortunately much simpler, to prescribe a procedure that is statistically valid—i.e., one that is unbiased, or nearly so, and whose standard error is computable from the sample itself.

10. *The Appraisal of Precision.*—In the planning of a survey it may have been assumed, for example, on the basis of experience or from a pilot study that γ in (17) for a particular characteristic is about 0.7. After the sample of dwelling units has been interviewed it is possible to estimate γ very closely, and hence to estimate the standard errors of X and $\bar{x}$ very closely also. Thus, whether γ is near 0.7 or not, the standard errors of the results will in the end be known, and a corrected value of γ will be obtained for more economic planning of the next survey of similar nature.

As γ may be expected to vary from one city to another, the value obtained for one city should not be used in another except as an approximation. In practice we should take whatever values of γ were encountered in previous experience with similar materials and by speculation raise or lower such values depending on known sociological conditions. Thus, in a city where there is much doubling of families, or a tendency toward large families, γ may well be 25% higher than in some other city; such conditions would call for a 50% bigger sample to meet the same precision. Often in the planning stage it is advisable to take a preliminary sample on a small scale to get a good estimate of γ and to try out the questionnaire and instructions, and to provide necessary practical experience.

(*a*) Once the interviewing is completed, an estimate of γ may be made by drawing at random a subsample n' of the returns and performing calculations thereon to correspond with the following equations:*

$$\sigma^2 \text{ (estimated)} = \frac{N-1}{N} \frac{1}{n'-1} \sum_{1}^{n'} (x_i - \bar{x}')^2, \qquad (23)$$

* See Deming's "Some Theory of Sampling," p. 333.

where

$$\bar{x}' = \frac{1}{n'} \sum_{1}^{n'} x_i \tag{24}$$

and x_i is the population on the ith return drawn into the subsample $(i = 1, 2, \ldots, n')$. In practice $(N - 1)/N$ may often be replaced by unity. The number n' should be in the neighborhood of 100. σ, once estimated, is then used in (8) or (17) to appraise the precision actually attained. It is to be observed that this appraisal is made from the sample itself. The design of the sample must therefore be followed rigidly in the field, for otherwise such calculations may be misleading.

(*b*) Another way is to plan the sample as 10 systematic or patterned subsamples with 10 random starts, and to compute the results from each. This is the Tukey plan (see Deming, *op. cit.*). The variability between the 10 subsamples gives measures of the standard errors of the results. Let $X^{(1)}, \ldots, X^{(10)}$ be the 10 estimates of the population having some particular characteristic, and let

$$X = \tfrac{1}{10} [X^{(1)} + X^{(2)} + \ldots + X^{(10)}] \, ;$$

then

$$\text{Estimated } \sigma_x^2 = \tfrac{1}{10} \cdot \tfrac{1}{9} \sum_{1}^{10} \left[X^{(i)} - X \right]^2 . \tag{25}$$

The sampling and tabulation plans may be so laid out that the identity of the 10 subsamples is maintained, and estimates of the variances of the chief characteristics are obtained automatically, with their precisions.

Before prescribing the Tukey plan, one should make sure that there will not be any serious loss in efficiency from the use of wide strata, and that the cost of tabulating the 10 subsamples will not be too great.

(*c*) If a systematic sample was not laid out in independent subsamples, the variance of any estimate X may still be approximated. Imagine loops to be thrown around successive pairs of dwelling units in the sample. These loops form hidden strata in the frame, created by the systematic procedure of listing and sampling. The two dwelling units of a pair have been drawn from one of these hidden strata. Each pair thus gives a slight over-estimate of σ^2 for the stratum whence they were drawn. In practice one may form n' hidden strata. The equation for estimating the average σ^2 is then (see Deming, *op. cit.*, p. 333)

$$\text{Estimated Average } \sigma^2 = \frac{1}{2n'} \sum_{1}^{n'} R_i^2 , \tag{26}$$

where R_i is the range between the two values of population constituting the ith pair of returns ($i = 1, 2, \ldots, n'$). Although this device gives an over-estimate of σ^2, it is in practice extremely helpful where no provision was made beforehand for an unbiased estimate of the standard error. n' should usually be between 50 and 100. The work should of course be so laid out that variances of several characteristics are obtained at once.

It should be remembered that the calculation of a standard error (commonly called the "sampling" error) gives a measure only of the precision of the sampling, and not of the biases inherent in the definitions, in the errors of response and non-response, in the procedures of interviewing, the hiring and training of the interviewers, failure to cover the sample areas completely or to go beyond bounds, plus other sources of error. Measurement of the non-sampling errors is important and requires supplementary samples especially designed for the purpose. The presentation of the results of a survey should contain measures both of the precision (standard errors) of the figures of chief interest and of the non-sampling errors as well if any experiments have been included to measure these errors. In regard to the non-sampling errors, the presentation of the results should at least include a copy of the questionnaire, information regarding the amount of non-response, and any special difficulties encountered in procuring the information or following the instructions. Such information is essential in the proper use of the results.

11. *Two-Stage Sampling.*—The cost of a sample census taken in one stage may be represented approximately by the equation

$$k_s = k_1 N + k_2 n + tn , \tag{27}$$

where k_s is the total cost, k_1 the average cost of listing a dwelling unit, k_2 the average cost of interviewing the people in a dwelling unit, and t is the average cost of processing and tabulating the schedule or schedules from a dwelling unit. The cost of a complete count would be

$$k_c = k_3 N + tN , \tag{28}$$

where k_3 is the cost of interviewing the people in a dwelling unit when the coverage is complete. Obviously the relation between k_2 and k_3 will depend on how thin the sample is: if the sample is 100%, k_2 and k_3 are equal; if the sample is thin, such as 1:20, k_3 will perhaps treble k_2 because of the increased amount of travel between interviews. It might be, for example, that a rough relation is

$$k_2 = k_3 \left\{ 1 + \frac{N}{10n} \right\} \tag{29}$$

which will serve for speculation. The ratio $N:n$ will be computed from (12) or (17), whereupon the last equation or any other approximate relation between k_2 and k_3 will show that the costs k_s and k_c for sample and complete count become equal for small cities. Naturally the complete count would be preferred in cities of this size and below, as the complete count does not require a sample design and it gives full details of the population by small areas within the city.

On the other hand, as the size of the city increases, the cost $k_1 N$ for listing alone runs far ahead of the actual cost $(k_2 + t)n$ of interviewing and tabulating the sample; hence for very large cities, most of the total cost would be spent for listing. This is uneconomical, and a better way can be found.

One solution lies in 2-stage sampling. The city is first divided into M *primary units* or districts. A sample of m of these districts is drawn at random, and dwelling units are listed in these m districts only. These dwelling units form *secondary units* within the primary units. A sample of dwelling units is drawn from the lists, and these dwelling units furnish the information. The advantage of such a plan lies in the fact that no listing need be performed in the $M - m$ districts not drawn into the sample.

In the sampling of a city, a block or a combination of blocks forms an excellent primary unit. The secondary units may be single dwelling units as used in the above illustration, or they may be small areas or "clusters" of 2, 3, or 6 consecutive dwelling units drawn from a map. In the sampling of a region or of the whole country, the county or a combination of counties forms an excellent primary unit, within which there will be secondary units, and usually tertiary and still smaller units.

In 2-stage sampling, the estimate of A, the total population having a specified characteristic, will be

$$ X = \frac{M}{m} \sum_{i=1}^{m} \frac{N_i}{n_i} \sum_{j=1}^{n_i} x_{ij}, \qquad (30) $$

where

M is the total number of primary units (to be spoken of as districts)

m is the number of these districts drawn into the sample

N_i is the number of dwelling units listed in the ith district ($i = 1, 2, \dots, m$)

n_i is the number of dwelling units drawn into the sample from this district

x_{ij} is the population in the jth dwelling unit of this district ($j = 1, 2, \dots, n_i$)

If all M districts are drawn with equal probabilities, and if all N_i dwelling units in the ith district are drawn with equal probabilities, then it follows that

$$EX = A .\qquad(31)$$

That is, X is an unbiased estimate of A. In practice, N_i/n_i is often the same for all districts for ease in tabulation, in which case

$$X = \frac{M\,\bar{N}}{m} \times \text{(the total population of the sample)}\qquad(32)$$

wherein $\bar{N}/\bar{n}$ is written for the constant value of N_i/n_i.

The variance of the estimate X will be*

$$\sigma_{X}^2 = \left(\frac{M}{m}\right)^2 \left\{ \frac{M-m}{M-1}\, m\,\sigma_e^2 + \frac{m}{M} \sum_{1}^{M} \left(\frac{N_i}{n_i}\right)^2 \frac{N_i - n_i}{N_i - 1}\, n_i \sigma_i^2 \right\}\qquad(33)$$

where

σ_e^2 is the variance between the M districts

σ_i^2 is the variance between dwelling units within the ith district.

Mathematically defined,

$$\sigma_e^2 = \frac{1}{M} \sum_{i=1}^{M} (A_i - \bar{A})^2\qquad(34)$$

$$\sigma_i^2 = \frac{1}{N_i} \sum_{j=1}^{N_i} (a_{ij} - \bar{a}_i)^2 ,\qquad(35)$$

where

$A_i = $ the population of the ith district

$$\bar{A} = \frac{1}{M} \sum_{i=1}^{M} A_i\qquad(36)$$

$a_{ij} = $ the population of the jth dwelling unit in the ith district

$(j = 1, 2, \ldots, N_i; i = 1, 2, \ldots, M)$

$$\bar{a}_i = \frac{1}{N_i} \sum_{i=1}^{N_i} a_{ij}\qquad(37)$$

The first term of (33) arises from the fact that the districts will in practice not all have the same populations. The second term arises from the fact that the dwelling units within any district will likewise not all

---

*A derivation of this equation is given in "A Chapter in Population Sampling" (Bureau of the Census, 1947), and in Deming's "Some Theory of Sampling," Chapter 6.

contain the same populations. The statistician will try to adjust the boundaries of the districts so that they have roughly the same number of people or dwelling units so as to minimize the variances for the chief characteristics that are to be studied. In particular, large units must be broken up or set aside for separate sampling.

By raising or lowering m and n_i, the variance of X can be governed. There are many combinations of m and n_i which will produce a desired variance in X. Different combinations will incur different costs, however, and one of the chief problems of sample design is to find what combination of m and n_i will be most economical.

As an illustration, we may think of a simplified situation in which the districts all contain the same number $\overline{N}$ of dwelling units, and in which the σ_i are all closely equal to σ_w. By setting

$$\sigma_e = \overline{N} \sigma_b \tag{38}$$

(32) reduces to

$$C_X^2 = \frac{M-m}{M-1} \frac{\sigma_b^2}{m} + \frac{\overline{N}-\overline{n}}{\overline{N}-1} \frac{\sigma_w^2}{m\overline{n}}, \tag{39}$$

in which $\overline{n}$ represents the number of dwelling units to be drawn from each district, and C_X is the coefficient of variation of the estimate X. If the districts are small and already listed, and not too far apart, little overhead cost is incurred in bringing a new district into the sample, and the total cost will be closely expressible as

$$k = k_2 m \overline{n}, \tag{40}$$

wherein k_2 is the average cost of conducting an interview in one dwelling unit. Now obviously, as $m\overline{n}$ occurs in the denominator of the last term of (39), this term is constant regardless of how m and $\overline{n}$ are adjusted, provided that the total number of interviews ($m\overline{n}$) and hence the total cost (k) are held constant. The first term, however, decreases as m is increased. It follows, then, that under the assumptions made here the best allocation of effort is to take one interview per district, and to draw as many districts into the sample as funds will permit.

If the districts are so large that each one when brought into the sample entails an appreciable overhead cost k_2 of listing and supervision, then the cost-function will be more like

$$k = k_1 m + k_2 m \overline{n}. \tag{41}$$

It can be shown that the variance of X is a minimum for a given allowable cost k when*

$$\frac{\overline{N}}{\overline{n}} = \sqrt{\frac{k_2}{k_1}} \sqrt{\left(\frac{\sigma_b}{\sigma_w}\right)^2 - \frac{1}{\overline{N}}} \doteq \frac{\sigma_b}{\sigma_w} \sqrt{\frac{k_2}{k_1}}. \tag{42}$$

This is the sampling interval to apply when drawing the sample of dwelling units for each district brought into the sample. It is to be noted that m and σ_X do not occur in this equation; hence $\overline{n}$ is independent of m and σ_X. Moreover, the variances and costs are not involved separately, but only in ratios. In practice, $\sigma_b : \sigma_w$ is rarely as low as 1, but is often as high as 2, and may be 3 or 4 or higher.

If the total cost k is fixed, the number of districts to be brought into the sample will be found by solving (41) for m.

If, on the other hand, the variance of X is prescribed, say at 2% or some other level, m is to be found from (39), and the total cost k may then be predicted by (41).

By these methods—even though the assumptions underlying this development are idealized—advance estimates of σ_X and of the total cost k may be satisfactorily adjusted *in advance* to the requirements and the budget. Without such mathematical guidance, it is easy to spend several times as much money as necessary for the information obtained.

The preceding equations are applicable in a wide variety of problems. Aside from the sampling of human populations they are used in the sampling of farms, business establishments, and industrial products.

The theory for the precision of a sample taken in two stages requires a lengthy discussion of the expected values of the variances between districts and between dwelling units, and cannot be included here.† The actual procedure should, however, revert to a single stage, for ease in appraising the precision.

Cost-functions other than those used in (27), (28), (29), (40), and (41) will occasionally be found useful for special circumstances.‡

Extension of sampling designs to three or more stages involves no new difficulty, but will not be included here.

12. *Calibration Samples.*—A very important use of sampling is to calibrate a previous set of measurements. Suppose that the M districts had

---

* Eq. 42 was derived by Shewhart and by Tippett, both in 1931. Its importance, however, only became obvious after 1942 through the work of Morris H. Hansen and William N. Hurwitz in the Bureau of the Census.

† Much more general discussions will be found in "A Chapter in Population Sampling," and in Chapter 7 of Deming's book already cited.

‡ See P. C. Mahalanobis, "On Large-Scale Sample-Surveys," Phil. Trans. Royal Soc., CCXXXI B (1943), 329. Also, Hansen, Hurwitz, and Madow's "Sample Survey Methods and Theory."

populations $B_i (i = 1, 2, \ldots, M)$ at an earlier date, and now have un-known populations A_i. Suppose, too, that A_i and B_i are highly correlated; then it will suffice to measure a sample of districts, and from this sample to estimate satisfactorily what results would be obtained if all the M districts were measured afresh. The true calibration factor connecting the two sets of measurements would be

$$\phi = \frac{\displaystyle\sum_1^M A_i}{\displaystyle\sum_1^M B_i}, \tag{43}$$

but it is of course unknown.

Let a sample of m districts be drawn and let the populations A_i and B_i therefor be listed as

$$X_1, X_2, \ldots, X_m$$
$$Y_1, Y_2, \ldots, Y_m.$$

Then from this sample one may form an estimate f of ϕ by writing

$$f = \frac{\displaystyle\sum_1^m X_i}{\displaystyle\sum_1^m Y_i}. \tag{44}$$

The variance of this estimate may be written*

$$C_f^2 = \frac{M-m}{M-1}\frac{V^2}{m}, \tag{45}$$

where

$$V^2 = \frac{1}{M}\sum_1^M \left(\frac{X_i - \phi Y_i}{\bar{A}}\right)^2 \tag{46}$$

$$\bar{A} = \frac{1}{M}\sum_1^M A_i. \tag{47}$$

In practice V must be estimated from the sample of m districts; an approximate but usually very satisfactory formula may then be obtained by writing

$$C_f^2 = \frac{M-m}{M}\frac{1}{m(m-1)}\sum_1^m \left(\frac{X_i - f Y_i}{\bar{X}}\right)^2. \tag{48}$$

* A proof is on p. 172 of Deming's book.

Once f is computed from (44), the total population of all M districts today is estimated as

$$X = Bf ,\qquad(49)$$

where

$$B = \sum_1^M B_i \qquad(50)$$

or the total population as it was when the previous measurements were made. As B is a constant, and not a random variable of this sample, it follows that

$$C_X = C_f .\qquad(51)$$

Any error in B constitutes a bias and not a sampling error.

A small sample of perhaps 20 or 50 districts will often give high precision in the estimates X or f.

This equation is much used in population sampling wherein Y_i may represent a population as determined by a census-taker some time ago, and X_i is a redetermination made by a sample. If the old and new measurements are highly correlated, V is small and C_f may be small even though m is small. It is noteworthy that the old and new measurements may be stated in different units.

Another use of a calibration is found when a cheap and perhaps biased method is used on all M districts, and a sample of m of them is re-measured by a more elaborate method. The equations apply in fact wherever a district drawn at random possesses two numbers, X_i and Y_i.

13. *Stratified Sampling.*—Often, for the same cost, much greater precision (smaller variance) in X or $\bar{x}$ can be obtained by dividing the universe into strata so that the sampling units are as nearly as possible alike within strata, and as different as possible between strata. Each stratum may be thought of as a separate bowl. The gain in precision is often disappointing; on the other hand, it is often striking. Stratification should be used only when it brings more information per dollar. Some simple theory will provide a basis for the best procedure. Each survey requires separate consideration. Given a certain allowable total cost, the total sample n may be allocated in various ways amongst the several strata. The problem to be solved is to find the procedure which delivers most information (smallest σ_X) per unit cost.

An outline of the theory of stratified sampling will now be given.

(*a*) Let there be M classes, which will be designated by subscripts. The estimated total population will be

$$X = \sum_1^M N_i \bar{x}_i ,\qquad(52)$$

and from (16) it may be seen by summation that

$$\sigma^2_X = \sum_1^M \frac{N_i - n_i}{N_i - 1} \frac{N_i^2 \sigma_i^2}{n_i}. \tag{53}$$

The total cost of the survey will be

$$k = \sum_1^M k_i n_i, \tag{54}$$

where k_i is the cost of an interview or a questionnaire in Class i. It can be shown that σ_X is made a minimum when the sampling interval in the ith class is

$$\frac{N_i}{n_i} = \frac{G \sqrt{k_i}}{\sigma_i}, \tag{55}$$

where G is a proportionality constant. This equation says that n_i should not only be proportional to N_i (the number of units in Class i) but also proportional to σ_i and inversely proportional to the square root of the unit cost, k_i. Strictly, (55) should contain the factor $\sqrt{(N_i - 1)/N_i}$ which is here assumed to be unity. It is said to give *optimum allocation*.

In practice it must not be assumed that this allocation is always preferable. It will always give smaller variance in X than any other allocation; but the questions to be considered are how much smaller it will be, and whether the gain is worth the extra cost of separate allocations and tabulations by strata. A further disadvantage of optimum allocation is that each characteristic to be estimated has its own σ_i and its own specific value of N_i/n_i. Any particular value of N_i/n_i may be good for one characteristic, but not for the others.

(*b*) For such reasons, and because it yields most of the possible benefits of stratification, the most widely used allocation is *proportionate allocation* by which

$$\frac{N_i}{n_i} = \frac{N}{n} = G' \tag{56}$$

is a constant for all classes.

One may always estimate, in advance, the difference in precision to be expected from the three different systems: no stratification, proportionate allocation, optimum allocation. See, for example, Chapter 6 in Deming's "Some Theory of Sampling."

(*c*) Still another possible procedure is to use no stratification at all, in which case (16) applies, or (25) or (26) if systematic sampling is used.

In any practical problem it is necessary to compare all three allocations by computing the expected variances in X, and the costs. Some previous experience is necessary in order to provide data for estimating the σ_i which enter into the calculations, and for estimating the expected costs; but with careful effort, excellent efficiency can be built into the planning of a survey. Equations showing the advantages of one type of allocation over another are to be found in advanced treatises in sampling, to which references have been given. In particular, students who wish to proceed beyond the elements of the theory presented in this Appendix should consult the U.S. Census Bureau's "Chapter in Population Sampling," F. Yates's "Sampling Methods for Censuses and Surveys," W. E. Deming's "Some Theory of Sampling," Hansen, Hurwitz, and Madow's "Sample Survey Methods and Theory," and W. G. Cochran's "Sampling Techniques."

[PRINTED IN U·S·A]